COUNTDOWN
THE ULTIMATE CHALLENGE

GRANADA

Countdown is the creation of Armond Jammot;
It is a Yorkshire Television production

This edition first published in Great Britain in 2005
by Granada Media, an imprint of Andre Deutsch Ltd
20 Mortimer Street
London W1T 3JW

In association with Granada Media Group

Text and photographs copyright © Granada Media Group Ltd, 2005

First published as *Countdown Bumper Puzzle Book* in 2002 and
Countdown Bumper Puzzle Book 2 in 2003 by Granada Media

The right of Michael Wylie and Damian Eadie to be identified as the authors of
this work has been asserted by them in accordance with the Copyright, Designs
and Patents Act 1988.

A catalogue record of this book is available from the British Library

ISBN 0 233 00157 3

1 3 5 7 9 10 8 6 4 2

Typeset by E-Type, Liverpool
Printed and bound in the UK

Contents

Foreword

by Richard Whiteley

Hello and welcome to this monster book of *Countdown* brain-teasers. What a delight! Here are pages and pages of words and number games for you to indulge in to your heart's content.

This is a good old-fashioned puzzle book. Just like the television programme, there are no gimmicks or gizmos here – we're a computer free zone! All the games have been painstakingly worked out by Michael Wylie and Damian Eadie. Both (of course) are producers of *Countdown* and both former finalists – Michael way back in 1983, where he lost to Joyce Cansfield in Series 1, and Damian, a positive new boy, who triumphed in the final of Series 28 over Wayne Kelly in 1994.

People often call *Countdown* a quiz show but, in the strictest sense, it is not. There are no questions, merely a set of problems which require solutions. I like to call it a parlour game, in the great tradition of the programmes which were on the wireless when I was a child. Do you remember *Twenty Questions?* You had to guess an object with the help of just three clues – animal, vegetable or mineral. Or how about *Have a Go*, in which Wilfred Pickles and Mabel interviewed people in village halls all over the country? These programmes ran for years and millions tuned in.

The same can be said of television. We got a television set in 1952 (well before the Coronation which made us very posh!) and one of my earliest recollections is of tuning into *What's My Line*. A panel of four had to guess someone's job, helped only by a simple mime act. The programme ran for years in Britain and it is still broadcast in many places all over the world. All of these programmes – all based on simple concepts – have stood the test of time. And so, I think, has *Countdown*. It retains its original look (a look we thought was trendy in 1982 but now seems positively retro) and that is the beauty of it. We won't change anything just for the sake of it. We believe that is why many millions find the programme so addictive. And because we will never run out of words or numbers – there is no reason why *Countdown* shouldn't continue to run and run.

When we started out in November 1982, as the first programme on Channel 4's opening night, we had been given a five-week run. Who would have believed then that we would go on to clock up over 18 years and 3,000 programmes? In 2001 we are still going strong, with over 3.5 million viewers each day and a contract from Channel 4 until mid-2004!

For so many of us – young and old – *Countdown* in the afternoon has established itself as a fixed point in our daily timetable. It's an all too brief but reliable period in which to forget the hurly burly outside and exercise our brains. For every Granny and Granddad watching there is a grandson and granddaughter, which means we are constantly replenishing our audience as the years go on. And now that we have *Countdown* in a book, there's no need to wait until 3.15 for a daily fix!

Good luck. I warn you, these puzzles require some application and dedication. They're fun but not for the fainthearted. And if you do well and think you could have a bash at the real thing, well, who knows, we might meet up in the *Countdown* studio.

All the best,
Richard Whiteley

The rules of the game

In the programme, *Countdown* consists of 15 rounds – 11 letters games, 3 numbers games and a conundrum.

Letters games

- A contestant selects 9 letters from two piles of face-down cards (1 containing consonants, the other vowels).
- Each selection of 9 letters must contain either 3, 4 or 5 vowels, with the remainder being consonants. When the last letter has been selected, the clock is started and both contestants have 30 seconds to make the longest word they can from the letters available.
- Each letter may be used only once and only the longest word scores.
- Scoring: 1 point per letter, except for a 9-letter word – which earns 18 points.

Numbers games

- One contestant selects 6 numbers from 24 that are available. There are 4 rows to select from, the top row contains the numbers 25, 50, 75, 100; the other three rows contain the numbers 1–10 twice.
- A random 3-digit target from 100–999 is set and both contestants have 30 seconds to achieve this target, using only the four basic disciplines of addition, subtraction, multiplication and division. (No powers, fractions or decimals etc.)
- Contestants may use any or all of the numbers but may use each number only once.
- Scoring the target exactly earns 10 points. Within 5 earns 7 points and within 10 gets 5 points. Any more than 10 away from the target fails to score.

Conundrums

- A board revolves to reveal a jumbled-up 9-letter word. The contestants have to guess this 9-letter word within 30 seconds. The round is on the buzzer, and the first contestant to answer correctly gets 10 points. If a contestant gives an incorrect answer then they are excluded from any further attempts at answering and the remainder of the time is given to their opponent.

How to use this book

Letters Games

Try and make the longest word you can by using the letters in the given selection. Each letter may only be used once and you should allow yourself just 30 seconds to play each round, but if you want to take longer then please yourself. You score 1 point per letter used but you get 18 points for a 9-letter word.

Proper nouns, hyphenated words and words with capital letters are not allowed. The answers are at the back of the book, and all words given are to be found in *Countdown*'s word bible – The New Oxford Dictionary of English.

Numbers Games

You are given 6 numbers to work with that are your tools to help you reach the given target. Use any or all of the numbers but only use each number once. Only addition, multiplication, subtraction and division are allowed and you must stick to whole numbers only at all stages of your calculations – no fractions !!

Conundrum

Find the hidden 9-letter word from the letters given. A correct answer scores 10 points. As a rule of thumb, we never use 8-letter plurals as conundrums – so words like TROMBONES will never appear. All conundrums should have only one answer – but if you happen to spot a legitimate alternative then it's 10 points to you – and a rotten egg to Michael Wylie!

Hints and tips for playing the *Countdown* games

Letters games

There is no quick guide to success when it comes to finding long words. Firstly, you must know of the word – otherwise you'll never find it in the first place, so nobody is ever going to find the longest in every single round.

For example, in a selection of A A I I R H K T S, most people would struggle to get any further than shark. However, there is a 9-letter word, TARAHIKIS (fish), but unless you know of it, you are never going to find it.

However, you can increase your chances of success by looking for typical word endings that are commonplace in the English language.

Words ending in –iest, –er, –ing, –ted, etc, can often be found in selections; and trying to find words constructed like this is always a good place to start. Likewise, words starting with over–, out–, re– are often tucked away in there too.

Also, depending upon the letters in the selection, it can often be fruitful to pair together letters that have natural partners and see what can be made. For example, C + K, C + H, P + L etc.

Another tip is to always look out for double letters that can go together. Pairing together o's, e's, d's, l's, etc can yield some king-sized words. Remember that the letter 'S' is a valuable bonus that can help to make plurals, which means longer words.

Lastly, the best advice of all is that you enjoy tackling the puzzles and try to beat your own personal targets. So if your highest word ever is a 7, strive for the 8 and then aim to repeat it. Once you think you have what it takes, write to us for an application form and then wait and see what happens.

Conundrums

Most people are of the opinion that you either see them straight away or you don't get them at all. This is not really the best way to look at a conundrum. If you can't see it in 2 seconds flat, then spend the next 28 reworking the selection to see if something comes up.

Look for the endings, look for conundrums that are made up of two smaller words, e.g. CHEWLATER. You might find the word wheel then realise that the letters trac are left, making cart. Then, hey presto, you have CARTWHEEL

LETTER GAME 1

| G | E | B | O | L | S | K | A | C |

LETTER GAME 2

| O | N | D | E | L | I | N | D | A |

LETTER GAME 3

| A | L | L | E | R | U | P | I | S |

LETTER GAME 4

| A | G | F | D | E | R | U | S | A |

NUMBER GAME 1

| 25 | 6 | 8 | 3 | 7 | 7 | **860** |

NUMBER GAME 2

| 50 | 8 | 9 | 2 | 2 | 4 | **916** |

CONUNDRUM

| B | L | A | I | R | D | A | M | E |

LETTER GAME 1

A	A	E	R	B	T	S	C	I

LETTER GAME 2

D	U	N	L	O	E	D	A	I

LETTER GAME 3

A	T	H	I	N	O	S	E	L

LETTER GAME 4

G	T	E	N	W	E	O	A	T

NUMBER GAME 1

75	100	6	3	4	2	764

NUMBER GAME 2

100	5	10	9	1	1	469

CONUNDRUM

F	I	D	O	F	R	I	T	E

LETTER GAME 1

A	A	E	T	I	R	N	J	K

LETTER GAME 2

L	I	B	E	K	S	O	H	J

LETTER GAME 3

G	E	S	U	T	A	P	D	A

LETTER GAME 4

S	S	E	E	D	I	R	C	L

NUMBER GAME 1

75	25	50	3	7	5	914

NUMBER GAME 2

6	4	3	9	9	10	833

CONUNDRUM

S	I	G	M	A	S	N	A	G

LETTER GAME 1

D	I	N	P	P	E	I	W	A

LETTER GAME 2

B	R	R	G	A	U	E	H	M

LETTER GAME 3

G	I	S	S	E	R	A	L	L

LETTER GAME 4

C	H	E	T	A	C	O	S	E

NUMBER GAME 1

50	25	100	75	8	6	486

NUMBER GAME 2

25	2	4	4	5	3	615

CONUNDRUM

L	I	O	N	V	I	S	I	T

LETTER GAME 1

A	N	T	I	D	O	T	E	S

LETTER GAME 2

C	A	N	I	C	A	T	E	V

LETTER GAME 3

H	E	R	C	A	R	S	O	E

LETTER GAME 4

A	A	D	V	R	E	Y	G	L

NUMBER GAME 1

50	8	10	3	10	7	291

NUMBER GAME 2

50	75	6	5	6	7	522

CONUNDRUM

T	E	D	C	A	R	T	E	R

LETTER GAME 1

A	D	E	E	N	K	H	R	T

LETTER GAME 2

G	A	T	R	I	N	U	S	E

LETTER GAME 3

C	L	I	N	U	A	Z	E	V

LETTER GAME 4

A	E	P	T	C	O	J	S	K

NUMBER GAME 1

25	2	9	8	4	3	877

NUMBER GAME 2

100	25	50	8	5	6	347

CONUNDRUM

G	I	A	N	T	L	I	N	E

15

LETTER GAME 1

A	A	B	C	R	E	M	D	T

LETTER GAME 2

D	E	W	L	T	O	A	P	L

LETTER GAME 3

S	U	S	I	T	R	A	C	Y

LETTER GAME 4

B	E	U	N	T	O	M	U	R

NUMBER GAME 1

75	9	6	9	8	3	777

NUMBER GAME 2

2	5	6	10	3	2	474

CONUNDRUM

L	E	G	M	A	N	T	E	N

LETTER GAME 1

K	E	N	A	G	W	I	N	O

LETTER GAME 2

L	E	B	E	T	A	G	A	L

LETTER GAME 3

M	U	S	T	I	E	M	Y	O

LETTER GAME 4

C	A	G	K	B	L	U	O	T

NUMBER GAME 1

25	9	4	1	3	1	655

NUMBER GAME 2

100	8	7	10	2	2	338

CONUNDRUM

F	U	N	D	U	N	D	O	E

LETTER GAME 1

U	P	U	N	L	O	R	A	P

LETTER GAME 2

B	O	B	W	E	I	R	L	A

LETTER GAME 3

P	E	S	C	Y	C	A	T	I

LETTER GAME 4

D	R	I	C	A	V	C	E	A

NUMBER GAME 1

50	100	5	8	8	4	759

NUMBER GAME 2

75	25	1	10	7	6	924

CONUNDRUM

W	A	S	H	D	I	N	G	O

LETTER GAME 1

D	Y	S	E	T	L	I	A	L

LETTER GAME 2

M	N	M	T	E	R	O	A	E

LETTER GAME 3

T	R	Y	A	D	O	I	N	E

LETTER GAME 4

R	D	E	M	T	A	P	E	H

NUMBER GAME 1

25	8	5	3	2	3	339

NUMBER GAME 2

100	9	10	9	7	10	216

CONUNDRUM

S	T	R	A	P	T	O	R	N

LETTER GAME 1

S	T	I	N	E	K	A	L	P

LETTER GAME 2

P	O	N	D	E	W	B	O	T

LETTER GAME 3

C	K	E	E	T	D	P	I	A

LETTER GAME 4

C	R	A	N	T	O	S	U	B

NUMBER GAME 1

7	3	8	8	9	4	888

NUMBER GAME 2

50	75	100	25	5	5	740

CONUNDRUM

N	E	E	D	S	F	O	O	T

LETTER GAME 1

A	A	D	R	R	E	H	W	I

LETTER GAME 2

H	E	R	M	P	A	S	I	F

LETTER GAME 3

Y	E	L	V	I	G	O	L	N

LETTER GAME 4

B	A	D	D	A	Y	R	I	R

NUMBER GAME 1

25	50	4	8	10	8	**173**

NUMBER GAME 2

100	9	1	2	3	4	**671**

CONUNDRUM

D	I	R	G	E	L	A	N	D

LETTER GAME 1

Z	C	D	E	N	A	A	K	F

LETTER GAME 2

K	E	G	I	N	T	R	A	C

LETTER GAME 3

Y	E	T	B	I	O	L	K	R

LETTER GAME 4

N	Z	I	E	M	W	A	O	D

NUMBER GAME 1

75	6	10	3	3	8	856

NUMBER GAME 2

50	75	100	9	7	6	461

CONUNDRUM

I	T	S	A	L	O	O	N	I

LETTER GAME 1

S	H	I	D	E	O	L	P	G

LETTER GAME 2

R	E	D	V	I	L	E	D	A

LETTER GAME 3

P	L	D	L	W	E	I	O	U

LETTER GAME 4

M	L	I	B	A	N	E	T	P

NUMBER GAME 1

100	25	6	6	2	1	378

NUMBER GAME 2

25	4	10	7	1	9	883

CONUNDRUM

B	L	U	E	P	A	T	E	R

LETTER GAME 1

D	T	R	U	N	E	L	A	E

LETTER GAME 2

G	N	E	P	T	R	I	A	D

LETTER GAME 3

M	I	L	A	C	A	Y	T	U

LETTER GAME 4

F	U	G	N	T	H	I	B	O

NUMBER GAME 1

75	100	4	2	2	5	662

NUMBER GAME 2

25	100	75	3	2	4	823

CONUNDRUM

R	I	F	L	E	D	E	C	K

LETTER GAME 1

A	R	O	I	T	A	D	R	Y

LETTER GAME 2

N	E	X	I	S	C	P	E	R

LETTER GAME 3

C	U	S	P	N	E	A	E	G

LETTER GAME 4

A	S	C	I	L	E	M	F	I

NUMBER GAME 1

50	75	6	8	1	2	557

NUMBER GAME 2

25	3	5	6	7	1	991

CONUNDRUM

G	I	A	N	T	T	O	O	T

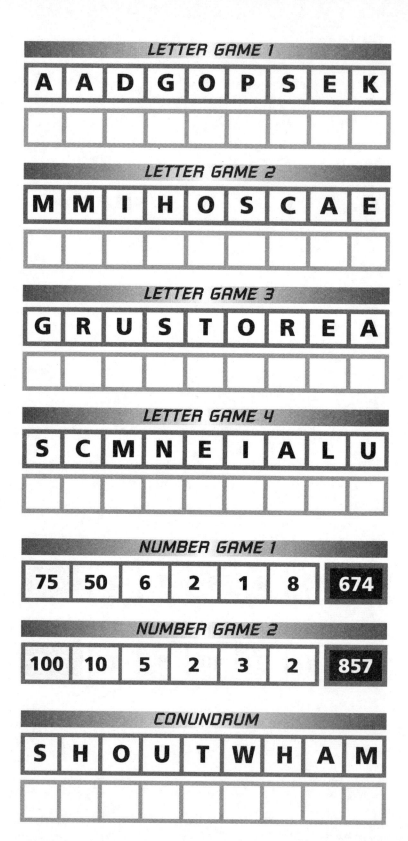

LETTER GAME 1

A	A	D	G	O	P	S	E	K

LETTER GAME 2

M	M	I	H	O	S	C	A	E

LETTER GAME 3

G	R	U	S	T	O	R	E	A

LETTER GAME 4

S	C	M	N	E	I	A	L	U

NUMBER GAME 1

75	50	6	2	1	8	674

NUMBER GAME 2

100	10	5	2	3	2	857

CONUNDRUM

S	H	O	U	T	W	H	A	M

LETTER GAME 1

B	R	R	O	T	A	A	D	D

LETTER GAME 2

G	E	L	I	N	I	D	Y	O

LETTER GAME 3

D	R	G	M	E	I	T	A	E

LETTER GAME 4

G	I	R	S	E	V	A	T	H

NUMBER GAME 1

3	7	4	4	9	9	**536**

NUMBER GAME 2

25	1	2	10	9	2	**779**

CONUNDRUM

A	F	R	E	E	L	I	F	T

LETTER GAME 1

R	O	S	E	I	M	W	O	R

LETTER GAME 2

E	B	I	J	R	A	L	K	A

LETTER GAME 3

D	E	R	B	O	W	A	R	I

LETTER GAME 4

L	L	B	E	I	A	S	T	O

NUMBER GAME 1

50	4	3	7	1	5	963

NUMBER GAME 2

100	75	25	50	7	10	618

CONUNDRUM

B	E	R	L	I	N	M	U	G

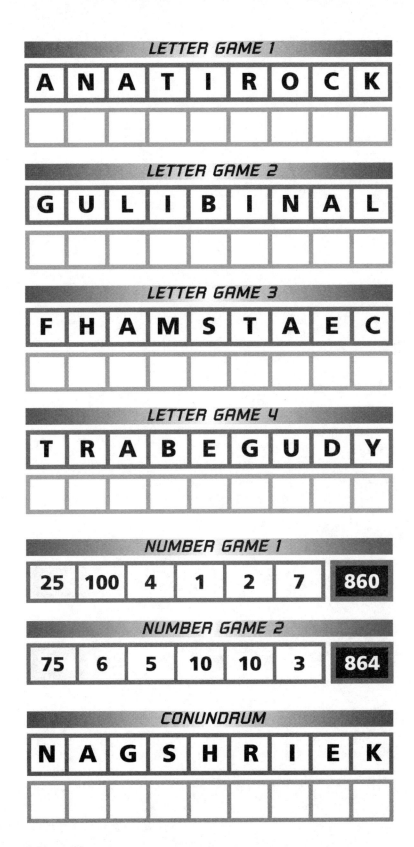

LETTER GAME 1

A	N	A	T	I	R	O	C	K

LETTER GAME 2

G	U	L	I	B	I	N	A	L

LETTER GAME 3

F	H	A	M	S	T	A	E	C

LETTER GAME 4

T	R	A	B	E	G	U	D	Y

NUMBER GAME 1

25	100	4	1	2	7	860

NUMBER GAME 2

75	6	5	10	10	3	864

CONUNDRUM

N	A	G	S	H	R	I	E	K

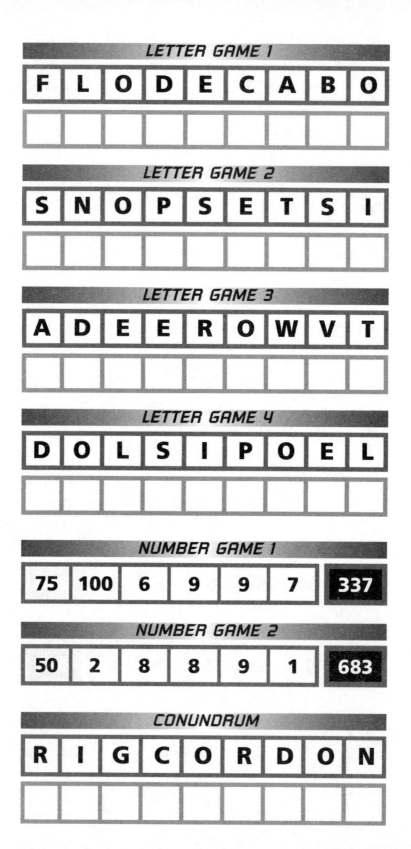

ROUND 21

LETTER GAME 1

F	L	O	D	E	C	A	B	O

LETTER GAME 2

S	N	O	P	S	E	T	S	I

LETTER GAME 3

A	D	E	E	R	O	W	V	T

LETTER GAME 4

D	O	L	S	I	P	O	E	L

NUMBER GAME 1

75	100	6	9	9	7	**337**

NUMBER GAME 2

50	2	8	8	9	1	**683**

CONUNDRUM

R	I	G	C	O	R	D	O	N

LETTER GAME 1

A	R	B	C	I	U	B	Y	A

LETTER GAME 2

A	A	S	E	T	B	D	A	R

LETTER GAME 3

G	U	N	Y	S	O	T	E	I

LETTER GAME 4

A	I	P	L	L	N	O	T	B

NUMBER GAME 1

25	50	100	5	4	8	916

NUMBER GAME 2

75	4	2	2	1	6	573

CONUNDRUM

N	I	C	K	T	E	S	S	A

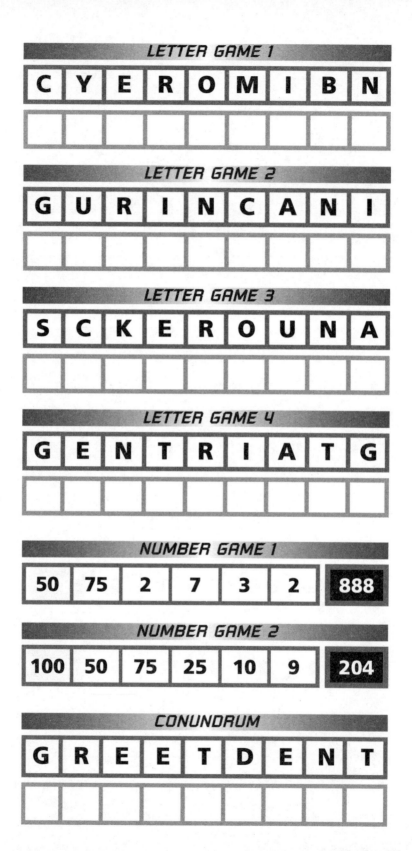

LETTER GAME 1

C	Y	E	R	O	M	I	B	N

LETTER GAME 2

G	U	R	I	N	C	A	N	I

LETTER GAME 3

S	C	K	E	R	O	U	N	A

LETTER GAME 4

G	E	N	T	R	I	A	T	G

NUMBER GAME 1

50	75	2	7	3	2	888

NUMBER GAME 2

100	50	75	25	10	9	204

CONUNDRUM

G	R	E	E	T	D	E	N	T

LETTER GAME 1

L	E	R	E	K	C	A	M	I

LETTER GAME 2

M	I	D	H	E	A	S	F	O

LETTER GAME 3

C	O	W	L	A	S	R	K	E

LETTER GAME 4

M	O	N	O	D	E	A	L	P

NUMBER GAME 1

25	1	3	5	1	6	776

NUMBER GAME 2

3	10	7	4	4	5	635

CONUNDRUM

P	E	R	R	Y	B	A	R	S

LETTER GAME 1

J	U	D	E	L	T	A	N	S

LETTER GAME 2

G	E	N	V	E	A	S	C	Y

LETTER GAME 3

A	B	E	C	I	L	A	N	T

LETTER GAME 4

G	I	N	J	E	A	S	L	T

NUMBER GAME 1

75	25	4	4	7	2	966

NUMBER GAME 2

8	5	5	7	2	1	642

CONUNDRUM

D	I	V	O	T	M	E	A	T

LETTER GAME 1

A	E	F	L	P	R	Y	E	S

LETTER GAME 2

C	C	A	R	I	O	N	T	I

LETTER GAME 3

C	L	O	B	I	S	E	A	N

LETTER GAME 4

A	D	I	I	O	N	S	B	E

NUMBER GAME 1

100	10	9	10	1	7	**741**

NUMBER GAME 2

50	8	6	9	1	2	**656**

CONUNDRUM

P	I	N	C	H	G	E	A	R

LETTER GAME 1

T	H	O	R	E	B	R	U	A

LETTER GAME 2

T	S	I	N	E	R	G	A	V

LETTER GAME 3

S	E	P	X	D	I	A	Z	C

LETTER GAME 4

A	B	E	L	I	Z	E	S	D

NUMBER GAME 1

25	50	100	75	1	9	522

NUMBER GAME 2

75	6	5	8	3	1	999

CONUNDRUM

N	I	E	C	E	T	I	F	F

LETTER GAME 1

D	O	L	O	V	I	A	N	T

LETTER GAME 2

A	D	E	E	G	H	R	A	X

LETTER GAME 3

S	T	E	A	S	I	T	E	Z

LETTER GAME 4

A	R	G	T	R	A	N	O	E

NUMBER GAME 1

25	50	2	5	5	10	723

NUMBER GAME 2

100	9	10	5	3	3	648

CONUNDRUM

S	O	L	A	R	B	A	T	S

LETTER GAME 1

Q	N	U	T	E	E	O	L	H

LETTER GAME 2

Z	I	D	C	O	H	I	S	E

LETTER GAME 3

E	N	I	E	V	A	T	L	N

LETTER GAME 4

D	E	T	I	P	O	N	A	C

NUMBER GAME 1

50	2	4	9	9	7	865

NUMBER GAME 2

75	50	100	10	4	6	787

CONUNDRUM

G	O	N	K	Y	M	I	N	E

LETTER GAME 1

A	R	T	R	I	P	O	T	E

LETTER GAME 2

A	A	G	E	M	I	N	Z	D

LETTER GAME 3

T	O	E	L	I	S	T	T	H

LETTER GAME 4

C	H	O	B	R	I	E	S	T

NUMBER GAME 1

100	8	5	1	4	9	234

NUMBER GAME 2

25	4	3	2	1	1	431

CONUNDRUM

A	M	A	D	N	U	D	G	E

LETTER GAME 1

C	R	E	N	S	U	W	A	A

LETTER GAME 2

B	R	E	D	A	W	T	E	I

LETTER GAME 3

L	I	V	E	N	S	J	A	Y

LETTER GAME 4

A	P	E	T	E	R	R	A	Y

NUMBER GAME 1

50	100	8	4	9	4	677

NUMBER GAME 2

75	5	8	4	8	3	945

CONUNDRUM

P	I	E	R	C	E	N	O	T

LETTER GAME 1

D	E	L	I	B	U	M	C	N

LETTER GAME 2

C	I	D	L	A	R	H	E	T

LETTER GAME 3

D	E	N	U	T	N	A	W	G

LETTER GAME 4

C	L	E	S	A	B	E	G	D

NUMBER GAME 1

100	7	6	1	2	7	880

NUMBER GAME 2

25	75	100	6	5	9	724

CONUNDRUM

A	S	E	M	I	S	P	I	V

LETTER GAME 1

A	N	R	W	S	T	O	R	E

LETTER GAME 2

A	C	D	E	I	M	P	N	O

LETTER GAME 3

T	I	V	E	P	A	T	A	C

LETTER GAME 4

H	P	E	N	T	A	L	E	D

NUMBER GAME 1

8	3	9	9	7	8	906

NUMBER GAME 2

50	4	4	7	5	5	639

CONUNDRUM

D	E	N	T	R	E	I	G	N

LETTER GAME 1

ROUND 34

H	S	N	I	D	E	B	A	W

LETTER GAME 2

D	E	R	E	S	O	T	V	E

LETTER GAME 3

T	E	F	L	F	A	S	T	U

LETTER GAME 4

W	L	L	E	E	R	F	A	I

NUMBER GAME 1

25	2	10	10	4	6	574

NUMBER GAME 2

75	100	5	3	3	7	955

CONUNDRUM

S	A	N	D	I	D	E	L	L

LETTER GAME 1

P	R	O	N	O	I	C	S	O

LETTER GAME 2

F	R	E	I	B	A	S	E	C

LETTER GAME 3

M	E	X	I	L	O	B	A	S

LETTER GAME 4

M	M	A	R	C	D	O	A	E

NUMBER GAME 1

100	75	50	25	8	8	620

NUMBER GAME 2

25	2	10	3	9	4	785

CONUNDRUM

A	S	U	G	A	R	S	A	P

LETTER GAME 1

X	C	L	W	A	T	H	O	E

LETTER GAME 2

D	E	H	I	W	A	R	V	C

LETTER GAME 3

B	P	O	U	F	M	I	Z	Y

LETTER GAME 4

A	T	I	C	E	M	E	T	D

NUMBER GAME 1

50	25	10	9	9	2	814

NUMBER GAME 2

75	100	50	6	9	9	249

CONUNDRUM

M	O	O	W	H	E	E	L	S

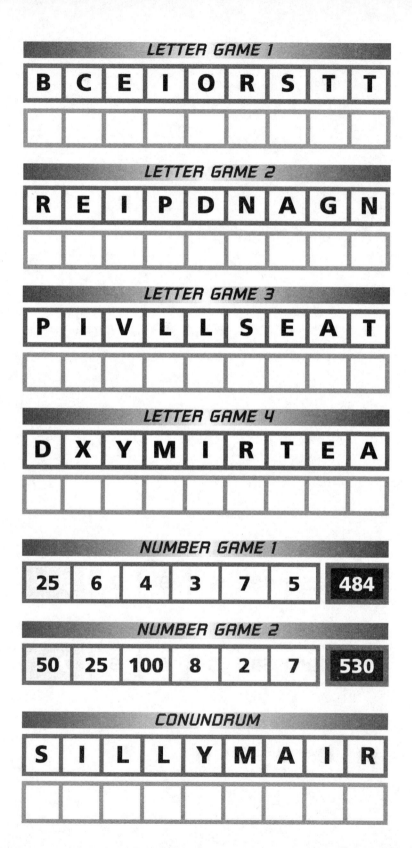

LETTER GAME 1

B	C	E	I	O	R	S	T	T

LETTER GAME 2

R	E	I	P	D	N	A	G	N

LETTER GAME 3

P	I	V	L	L	S	E	A	T

LETTER GAME 4

D	X	Y	M	I	R	T	E	A

NUMBER GAME 1

25	6	4	3	7	5	484

NUMBER GAME 2

50	25	100	8	2	7	530

CONUNDRUM

S	I	L	L	Y	M	A	I	R

LETTER GAME 1

L	N	S	E	R	I	C	E	A

LETTER GAME 2

D	R	U	S	T	O	P	E	G

LETTER GAME 3

S	T	E	X	A	L	Y	H	E

LETTER GAME 4

D	H	K	I	S	E	A	N	R

NUMBER GAME 1

6	8	10	1	9	2	516

NUMBER GAME 2

75	100	25	3	4	9	702

CONUNDRUM

P	U	L	L	E	T	M	I	X

LETTER GAME 1

T	R	I	N	B	S	A	P	E

LETTER GAME 2

C	P	L	U	L	E	U	K	E

LETTER GAME 3

S	M	I	V	W	P	R	E	A

LETTER GAME 4

N	N	A	D	K	I	G	E	W

NUMBER GAME 1

75	100	2	2	4	5	859

NUMBER GAME 2

50	25	75	100	3	6	427

CONUNDRUM

G	I	V	E	N	R	I	C	E

LETTER GAME 1

H	B	K	S	A	C	A	I	C

LETTER GAME 2

A	N	S	N	S	T	E	S	I

LETTER GAME 3

S	U	R	I	P	D	E	A	T

LETTER GAME 4

G	R	E	B	I	T	A	N	N

NUMBER GAME 1

50	9	9	6	3	4	**731**

NUMBER GAME 2

25	6	10	3	2	2	**990**

CONUNDRUM

T	O	Y	R	I	P	P	E	R

LETTER GAME 1

| A | E | E | K | V | O | R | M | D |

LETTER GAME 2

| P | T | C | R | E | E | D | I | H |

LETTER GAME 3

| B | L | R | C | W | E | A | L | S |

LETTER GAME 4

| C | I | T | K | S | O | T | S | E |

NUMBER GAME 1

| 50 | 5 | 7 | 9 | 3 | 4 | **870** |

NUMBER GAME 2

| 25 | 50 | 100 | 6 | 9 | 2 | **393** |

CONUNDRUM

| W | A | N | D | A | S | B | I | T |

LETTER GAME 1

F	E	R	I	C	A	S	E	E

LETTER GAME 2

M	A	T	U	T	I	E	L	G

LETTER GAME 3

I	L	I	S	T	E	R	A	C

LETTER GAME 4

S	E	R	T	O	L	A	M	E

NUMBER GAME 1

9	6	4	4	5	5	**721**

NUMBER GAME 2

5	6	7	1	2	3	**840**

CONUNDRUM

L	E	E	B	R	O	P	H	Y

ROUND 42

LETTER GAME 1

L	A	V	I	G	E	R	L	O

LETTER GAME 2

F	R	E	D	B	A	T	E	S

LETTER GAME 3

T	H	U	C	N	L	Y	O	U

LETTER GAME 4

A	D	N	N	C	I	H	R	E

NUMBER GAME 1

25	8	9	3	2	3	654

NUMBER GAME 2

100	75	8	9	10	7	369

CONUNDRUM

A	S	O	U	R	B	O	I	L

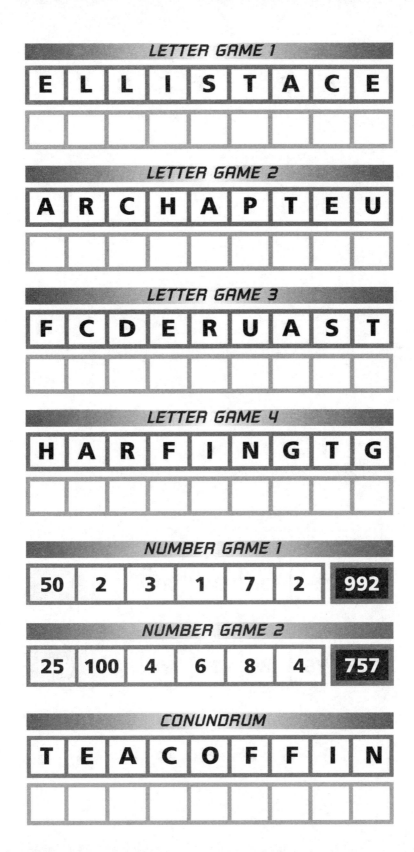

LETTER GAME 1

| E | L | L | I | S | T | A | C | E |

LETTER GAME 2

| A | R | C | H | A | P | T | E | U |

LETTER GAME 3

| F | C | D | E | R | U | A | S | T |

LETTER GAME 4

| H | A | R | F | I | N | G | T | G |

NUMBER GAME 1

| 50 | 2 | 3 | 1 | 7 | 2 | **992** |

NUMBER GAME 2

| 25 | 100 | 4 | 6 | 8 | 4 | **757** |

CONUNDRUM

| T | E | A | C | O | F | F | I | N |

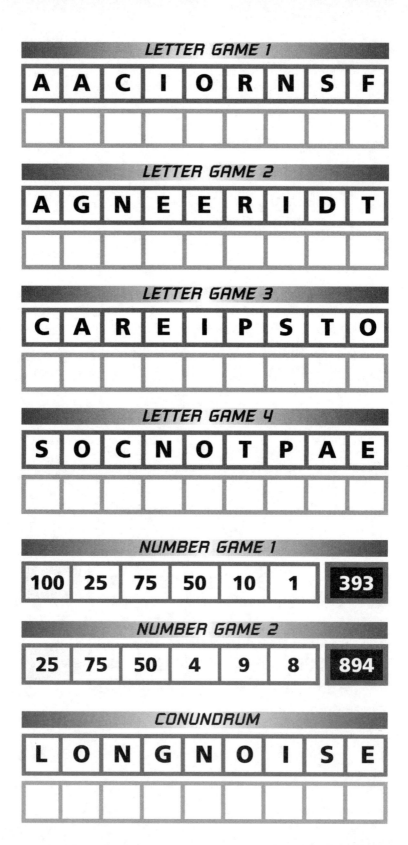

ROUND 45

LETTER GAME 1

A	A	C	I	O	R	N	S	F

LETTER GAME 2

A	G	N	E	E	R	I	D	T

LETTER GAME 3

C	A	R	E	I	P	S	T	O

LETTER GAME 4

S	O	C	N	O	T	P	A	E

NUMBER GAME 1

100	25	75	50	10	1	393

NUMBER GAME 2

25	75	50	4	9	8	894

CONUNDRUM

L	O	N	G	N	O	I	S	E

LETTER GAME 1

O	O	M	R	J	E	A	B	T

LETTER GAME 2

C	H	M	O	D	E	A	T	S

LETTER GAME 3

R	H	D	I	G	A	N	C	E

LETTER GAME 4

G	U	F	I	L	O	T	S	O

NUMBER GAME 1

50	7	3	2	8	4	924

NUMBER GAME 2

50	75	9	8	10	4	529

CONUNDRUM

V	I	E	W	A	B	A	R	N

LETTER GAME 1

E	N	B	E	R	I	D	L	A

LETTER GAME 2

E	E	D	O	N	Y	W	H	A

LETTER GAME 3

S	F	Y	L	U	M	E	I	H

LETTER GAME 4

F	R	E	D	B	E	C	A	A

NUMBER GAME 1

100	1	6	5	1	7	837

NUMBER GAME 2

25	9	2	2	4	4	671

CONUNDRUM

F	E	E	T	C	R	I	M	P

LETTER GAME 1

U	T	E	R	I	S	Y	T	A

LETTER GAME 2

S	B	A	Y	T	I	B	O	G

LETTER GAME 3

C	R	I	P	V	O	E	R	E

LETTER GAME 4

P	E	R	I	S	O	U	G	Y

NUMBER GAME 1

25	1	5	6	4	1	783

NUMBER GAME 2

50	100	7	8	5	10	624

CONUNDRUM

G	R	E	A	T	M	I	N	K

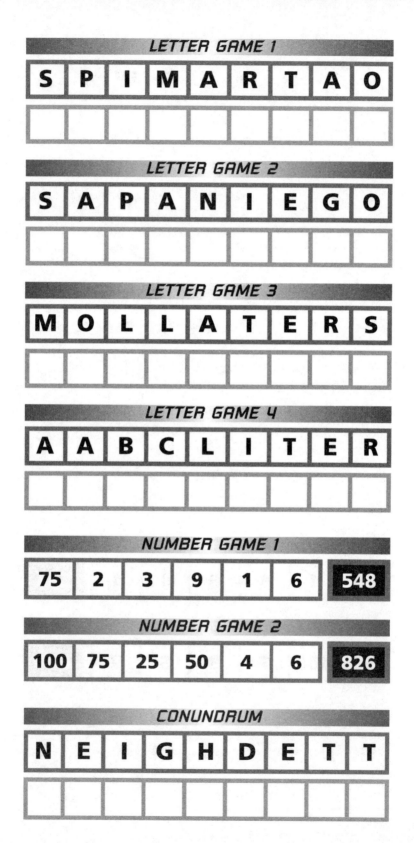

LETTER GAME 1

S	P	I	M	A	R	T	A	O

LETTER GAME 2

S	A	P	A	N	I	E	G	O

LETTER GAME 3

M	O	L	L	A	T	E	R	S

LETTER GAME 4

A	A	B	C	L	I	T	E	R

NUMBER GAME 1

75	2	3	9	1	6	548

NUMBER GAME 2

100	75	25	50	4	6	826

CONUNDRUM

N	E	I	G	H	D	E	T	T

LETTER GAME 1

| B | U | D | O | N | E | W | S | T |

LETTER GAME 2

| T | O | L | E | Z | A | R | Y | E |

LETTER GAME 3

| B | R | E | D | H | E | A | S | A |

LETTER GAME 4

| W | I | T | R | E | L | L | A | S |

NUMBER GAME 1

| 50 | 5 | 8 | 9 | 1 | 2 | 633 |

NUMBER GAME 2

| 25 | 100 | 7 | 9 | 8 | 7 | 444 |

CONUNDRUM

| C | R | O | O | L | C | E | L | T |

LETTER GAME 1

T	R	E	D	E	I	T	Y	X

LETTER GAME 2

C	L	I	M	O	R	A	T	A

LETTER GAME 3

T	O	R	K	I	P	A	N	W

LETTER GAME 4

L	U	C	H	E	Q	S	Y	I

NUMBER GAME 1

25	4	7	10	1	8	555

NUMBER GAME 2

6	7	8	9	10	5	744

CONUNDRUM

S	P	L	I	C	E	D	A	D

LETTER GAME 1

H	O	F	R	L	A	D	Y	O

LETTER GAME 2

A	G	C	I	L	A	R	T	E

LETTER GAME 3

F	Y	P	T	E	C	E	A	R

LETTER GAME 4

T	H	O	W	E	R	A	L	E

NUMBER GAME 1

25	50	75	100	8	3	687

NUMBER GAME 2

25	4	7	8	5	9	876

CONUNDRUM

P	E	R	T	P	R	O	U	D

LETTER GAME 1

S	O	P	P	T	M	A	L	U

LETTER GAME 2

K	N	I	M	E	W	E	R	A

LETTER GAME 3

M	O	S	S	R	G	E	A	T

LETTER GAME 4

H	I	N	D	A	R	C	A	T

NUMBER GAME 1

100	5	4	10	2	3	931

NUMBER GAME 2

50	25	75	3	1	2	693

CONUNDRUM

I	N	T	E	R	G	O	L	I

LETTER GAME 1

D	E	R	P	I	N	A	G	S

LETTER GAME 2

P	L	A	I	S	H	O	T	A

LETTER GAME 3

H	U	R	P	I	D	M	T	E

LETTER GAME 4

K	C	E	E	R	A	T	A	R

NUMBER GAME 1

75	50	5	9	2	2	988

NUMBER GAME 2

50	8	8	4	5	6	772

CONUNDRUM

M	O	T	H	L	I	C	K	S

LETTER GAME 1

S	R	E	A	M	T	B	E	W

LETTER GAME 2

C	I	F	C	E	I	P	S	T

LETTER GAME 3

L	A	R	N	A	B	C	E	T

LETTER GAME 4

S	A	W	A	L	I	D	E	S

NUMBER GAME 1

100	75	25	6	4	9	840

NUMBER GAME 2

25	7	3	4	1	2	366

CONUNDRUM

N	I	M	B	L	G	E	R	T

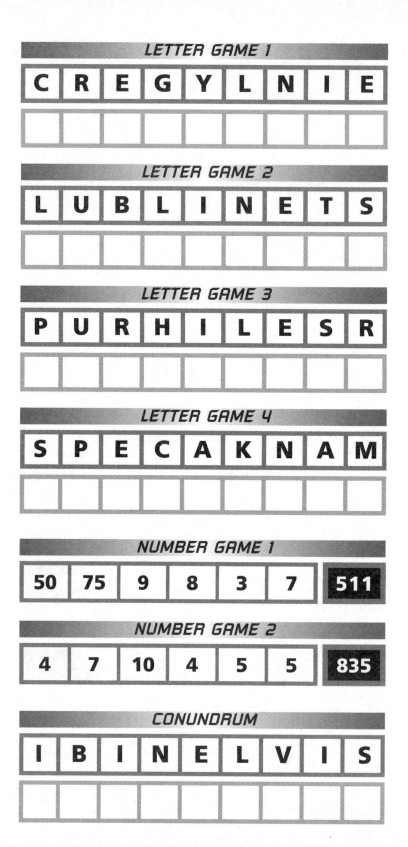

LETTER GAME 1

C	R	E	G	Y	L	N	I	E

LETTER GAME 2

L	U	B	L	I	N	E	T	S

LETTER GAME 3

P	U	R	H	I	L	E	S	R

LETTER GAME 4

S	P	E	C	A	K	N	A	M

NUMBER GAME 1

50	75	9	8	3	7	511

NUMBER GAME 2

4	7	10	4	5	5	835

CONUNDRUM

I	B	I	N	E	L	V	I	S

LETTER GAME 1

M	I	L	I	T	E	F	X	E

LETTER GAME 2

T	T	N	M	E	T	R	A	E

LETTER GAME 3

L	I	M	U	S	T	A	T	E

LETTER GAME 4

W	O	M	T	E	R	L	O	S

NUMBER GAME 1

75	4	8	9	10	9	929

NUMBER GAME 2

25	75	100	3	7	8	743

CONUNDRUM

D	I	E	S	E	L	R	O	D

LETTER GAME 1

R	O	P	E	R	A	W	S	H

LETTER GAME 2

D	E	T	R	O	V	E	X	A

LETTER GAME 3

S	H	U	W	E	R	O	A	E

LETTER GAME 4

P	N	C	H	R	O	E	D	A

NUMBER GAME 1

25	6	2	3	2	4	854

NUMBER GAME 2

25	100	50	75	10	10	306

CONUNDRUM

S	I	M	I	A	N	T	O	Y

LETTER GAME 1

C	O	R	O	T	A	M	D	E

LETTER GAME 2

C	O	N	P	U	S	O	K	C

LETTER GAME 3

Z	E	C	T	I	R	U	E	A

LETTER GAME 4

L	I	N	P	L	O	T	A	B

NUMBER GAME 1

75	8	4	5	10	8	933

NUMBER GAME 2

100	50	7	9	8	9	521

CONUNDRUM

I	R	A	N	D	I	N	G	O

LETTER GAME 1

P	E	R	S	T	I	R	N	A

LETTER GAME 2

U	M	O	S	E	T	A	L	P

LETTER GAME 3

S	U	U	L	T	R	E	V	I

LETTER GAME 4

X	I	D	E	F	O	Y	T	C

NUMBER GAME 1

25	5	8	10	5	3	414

NUMBER GAME 2

2	7	10	3	4	4	672

CONUNDRUM

H	I	T	A	B	B	E	S	S

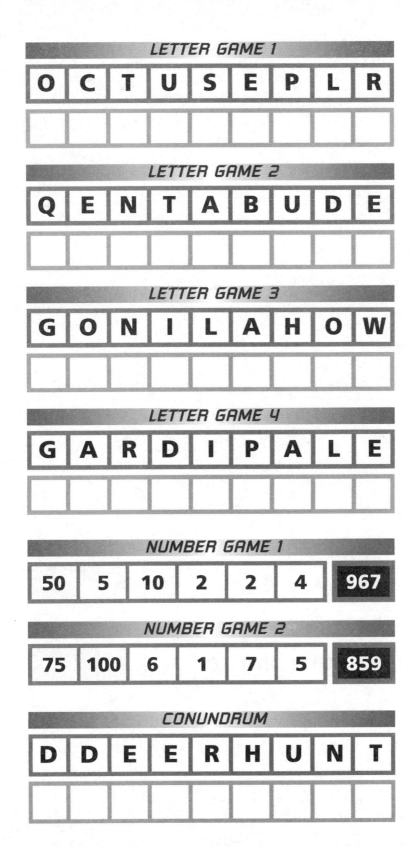

LETTER GAME 1

O	C	T	U	S	E	P	L	R

LETTER GAME 2

Q	E	N	T	A	B	U	D	E

LETTER GAME 3

G	O	N	I	L	A	H	O	W

LETTER GAME 4

G	A	R	D	I	P	A	L	E

NUMBER GAME 1

50	5	10	2	2	4	967

NUMBER GAME 2

75	100	6	1	7	5	859

CONUNDRUM

D	D	E	E	R	H	U	N	T

LETTER GAME 1

G	U	R	Y	V	E	O	A	F

LETTER GAME 2

D	R	O	B	E	L	I	A	P

LETTER GAME 3

R	O	E	L	I	S	T	E	T

LETTER GAME 4

R	E	M	O	R	B	O	S	T

NUMBER GAME 1

50	3	4	2	9	9	999

NUMBER GAME 2

25	100	75	50	6	8	222

CONUNDRUM

R	O	C	S	W	R	E	C	K

LETTER GAME 1

F	O	T	E	K	A	C	B	S

LETTER GAME 2

S	Q	U	E	R	P	A	T	D

LETTER GAME 3

D	A	M	E	R	T	A	S	N

LETTER GAME 4

P	H	E	R	I	M	O	N	K

NUMBER GAME 1

100	75	5	3	7	7	**616**

NUMBER GAME 2

25	2	3	4	1	4	**619**

CONUNDRUM

G	I	N	P	O	T	T	I	E

LETTER GAME 1

Q	I	B	E	U	T	S	R	O

LETTER GAME 2

I	V	E	L	I	M	O	C	A

LETTER GAME 3

B	E	N	I	S	R	A	C	K

LETTER GAME 4

M	O	N	G	I	L	A	F	P

NUMBER GAME 1

50	10	5	4	3	7	876

NUMBER GAME 2

8	5	3	1	4	2	522

CONUNDRUM

T	E	A	B	R	E	A	T	H

LETTER GAME 1

F	W	O	N	A	L	L	S	E

LETTER GAME 2

G	R	L	A	B	E	P	O	E

LETTER GAME 3

A	T	T	C	E	N	R	O	I

LETTER GAME 4

W	E	L	I	N	G	T	O	N

NUMBER GAME 1

75	100	50	6	3	9	781

NUMBER GAME 2

100	10	9	1	2	2	933

CONUNDRUM

G	R	A	N	D	P	I	E	S

LETTER GAME 1

S	O	N	O	C	A	M	P	E

LETTER GAME 2

H	I	G	N	O	L	R	A	W

LETTER GAME 3

K	O	R	E	S	O	N	O	L

LETTER GAME 4

G	U	N	I	L	T	O	V	A

NUMBER GAME 1

50	75	4	6	5	3	802

NUMBER GAME 2

25	8	2	3	10	7	645

CONUNDRUM

S	I	M	M	E	R	S	E	E

LETTER GAME 1

O	R	N	O	D	E	T	A	S

LETTER GAME 2

L	I	R	G	A	N	S	N	O

LETTER GAME 3

T	E	R	I	N	C	A	Y	T

LETTER GAME 4

S	T	A	L	I	Y	O	R	T

NUMBER GAME 1

100	50	75	25	4	10	**283**

NUMBER GAME 2

75	2	4	3	1	2	**960**

CONUNDRUM

S	U	P	E	R	D	E	A	D

LETTER GAME 1

S	O	D	E	P	L	A	E	B

LETTER GAME 2

H	O	M	O	D	E	C	S	I

LETTER GAME 3

S	P	U	I	N	B	E	S	M

LETTER GAME 4

M	E	R	N	U	A	S	E	Y

NUMBER GAME 1

25	3	9	6	5	6	611

NUMBER GAME 2

50	25	10	4	8	3	319

CONUNDRUM

C	A	S	E	D	T	H	I	S

LETTER GAME 1

S	I	N	C	U	A	S	E	R

LETTER GAME 2

D	R	N	E	W	A	N	D	E

LETTER GAME 3

T	E	D	I	S	P	U	C	A

LETTER GAME 4

L	U	T	O	M	A	D	E	Q

NUMBER GAME 1

10	7	9	7	8	10	621

NUMBER GAME 2

25	50	9	4	3	2	998

CONUNDRUM

S	U	P	E	R	D	O	O	N

LETTER GAME 1

| A | A | C | E | P | U | L | S | T |

LETTER GAME 2

| O | K | A | P | E | B | O | E | X |

LETTER GAME 3

| G | E | N | O | D | I | S | M | O |

LETTER GAME 4

| F | I | D | N | E | L | I | M | E |

NUMBER GAME 1

| 100 | 2 | 2 | 5 | 1 | 10 | **784** |

NUMBER GAME 2

| 25 | 10 | 7 | 9 | 9 | 2 | **931** |

CONUNDRUM

| G | R | E | A | T | P | I | N | T |

LETTER GAME 1

B	R	I	N	T	E	A	H	E

LETTER GAME 2

B	L	U	N	I	M	A	T	H

LETTER GAME 3

R	R	R	I	S	B	T	E	A

LETTER GAME 4

O	L	D	E	D	B	A	T	P

NUMBER GAME 1

25	75	100	1	3	1	**882**

NUMBER GAME 2

75	50	100	6	2	9	**421**

CONUNDRUM

L	O	C	A	L	D	A	T	E

LETTER GAME 1

| L | E | S | P | I | A | N | E | C |

LETTER GAME 2

| I | N | G | A | H | I | T | Y | N |

LETTER GAME 3

| P | H | O | M | I | N | C | A | W |

LETTER GAME 4

| H | O | P | I | N | E | R | W | S |

NUMBER GAME 1

| 75 | 8 | 6 | 10 | 2 | 4 | **999** |

NUMBER GAME 2

| 50 | 10 | 9 | 2 | 3 | 1 | **706** |

CONUNDRUM

| B | L | E | E | D | T | A | N | K |

LETTER GAME 1

Z	A	I	D	L	V	R	O	S

LETTER GAME 2

D	E	N	H	O	M	A	T	E

LETTER GAME 3

W	I	N	E	V	A	R	B	A

LETTER GAME 4

T	I	A	L	P	O	C	S	W

NUMBER GAME 1

8	3	10	7	6	1	909

NUMBER GAME 2

50	100	4	3	1	8	634

CONUNDRUM

I	N	T	O	M	A	N	I	A

LETTER GAME 1

T	H	U	P	O	N	S	E	E

LETTER GAME 2

F	C	L	U	N	K	F	I	A

LETTER GAME 3

H	O	M	O	B	R	A	T	W

LETTER GAME 4

B	U	D	R	A	N	I	S	E

NUMBER GAME 1

25	50	75	10	10	9	377

NUMBER GAME 2

25	7	9	9	4	3	858

CONUNDRUM

I	B	I	T	E	H	A	N	D

LETTER GAME 1

L	A	T	E	S	E	L	K	O

LETTER GAME 2

Y	T	H	I	M	A	N	G	E

LETTER GAME 3

M	T	R	E	I	C	O	S	I

LETTER GAME 4

Y	T	N	O	B	E	A	D	E

NUMBER GAME 1

25	100	6	4	5	2	880

NUMBER GAME 2

75	2	10	10	5	7	468

CONUNDRUM

S	U	G	A	R	I	C	O	N

85

LETTER GAME 1

H	V	C	O	N	A	I	S	E

LETTER GAME 2

A	C	D	E	E	I	L	U	T

LETTER GAME 3

C	I	R	E	N	S	T	I	Y

LETTER GAME 4

M	R	U	O	S	I	N	G	O

NUMBER GAME 1

50	100	4	5	4	5	**685**

NUMBER GAME 2

75	5	1	7	3	5	**666**

CONUNDRUM

S	T	R	A	Y	M	O	O	N

LETTER GAME 1

D	E	R	N	I	H	A	L	P

LETTER GAME 2

L	E	R	U	O	T	E	L	G

LETTER GAME 3

K	O	L	D	W	E	G	E	N

LETTER GAME 4

S	H	E	R	I	T	O	S	E

NUMBER GAME 1

100	75	8	3	5	9	441

NUMBER GAME 2

25	1	7	4	2	3	830

CONUNDRUM

N	E	C	K	B	I	N	G	O

LETTER GAME 1

C	A	N	V	O	B	I	E	C

LETTER GAME 2

T	H	O	M	A	S	T	E	Y

LETTER GAME 3

F	E	N	S	T	A	B	E	A

LETTER GAME 4

Z	E	P	I	T	M	O	I	C

NUMBER GAME 1

100	2	4	8	6	2	777

NUMBER GAME 2

7	9	10	5	10	7	842

CONUNDRUM

M	A	R	I	E	S	W	O	E

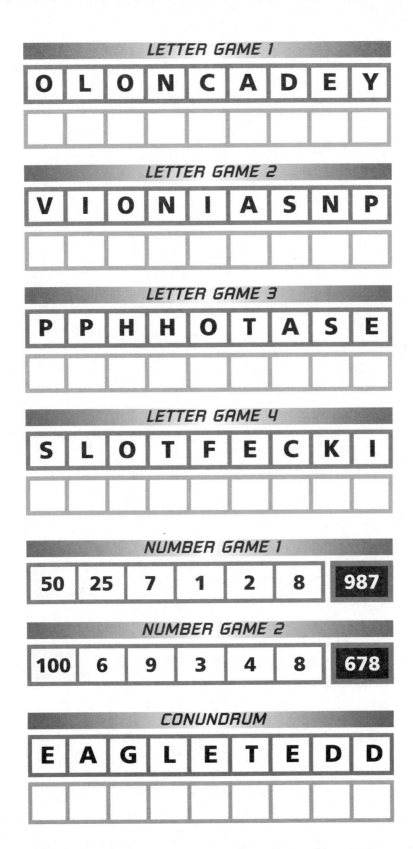

LETTER GAME 1

O	L	O	N	C	A	D	E	Y

LETTER GAME 2

V	I	O	N	I	A	S	N	P

LETTER GAME 3

P	P	H	H	O	T	A	S	E

LETTER GAME 4

S	L	O	T	F	E	C	K	I

NUMBER GAME 1

50	25	7	1	2	8	987

NUMBER GAME 2

100	6	9	3	4	8	678

CONUNDRUM

E	A	G	L	E	T	E	D	D

LETTER GAME 1

| G | O | M | I | N | S | I | J | A |

LETTER GAME 2

| I | N | D | U | R | B | E | S | T |

LETTER GAME 3

| C | H | E | B | L | E | A | M | Z |

LETTER GAME 4

| A | L | C | H | T | I | N | E | O |

NUMBER GAME 1

| 50 | 75 | 100 | 25 | 3 | 3 | 530 |

NUMBER GAME 2

| 100 | 50 | 25 | 7 | 5 | 4 | 333 |

CONUNDRUM

| J | O | E | L | Y | B | E | A | N |

LETTER GAME 1

T	T	E	E	P	P	I	S	L

LETTER GAME 2

S	T	H	I	R	K	C	E	A

LETTER GAME 3

M	O	U	N	I	S	L	E	I

LETTER GAME 4

A	B	S	D	P	R	E	D	E

NUMBER GAME 1

75	25	3	3	5	7	659

NUMBER GAME 2

25	7	7	6	5	9	342

CONUNDRUM

U	N	I	S	O	R	T	I	N

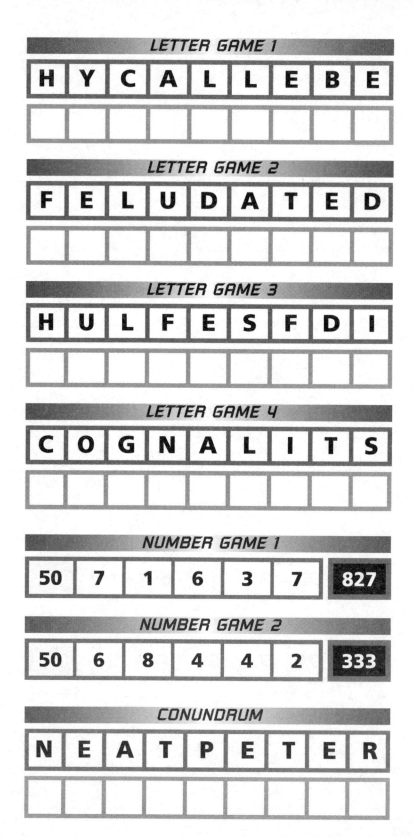

LETTER GAME 1

H	Y	C	A	L	L	E	B	E

LETTER GAME 2

F	E	L	U	D	A	T	E	D

LETTER GAME 3

H	U	L	F	E	S	F	D	I

LETTER GAME 4

C	O	G	N	A	L	I	T	S

NUMBER GAME 1

50	7	1	6	3	7	827

NUMBER GAME 2

50	6	8	4	4	2	333

CONUNDRUM

N	E	A	T	P	E	T	E	R

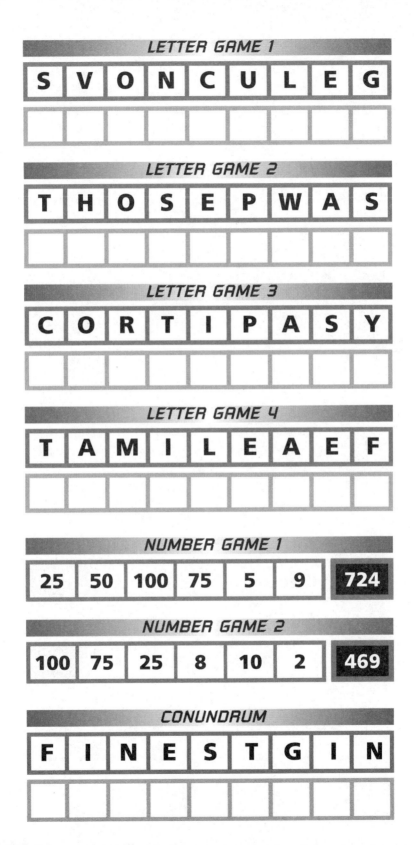

LETTER GAME 1

S	V	O	N	C	U	L	E	G

LETTER GAME 2

T	H	O	S	E	P	W	A	S

LETTER GAME 3

C	O	R	T	I	P	A	S	Y

LETTER GAME 4

T	A	M	I	L	E	A	E	F

NUMBER GAME 1

25	50	100	75	5	9	724

NUMBER GAME 2

100	75	25	8	10	2	469

CONUNDRUM

F	I	N	E	S	T	G	I	N

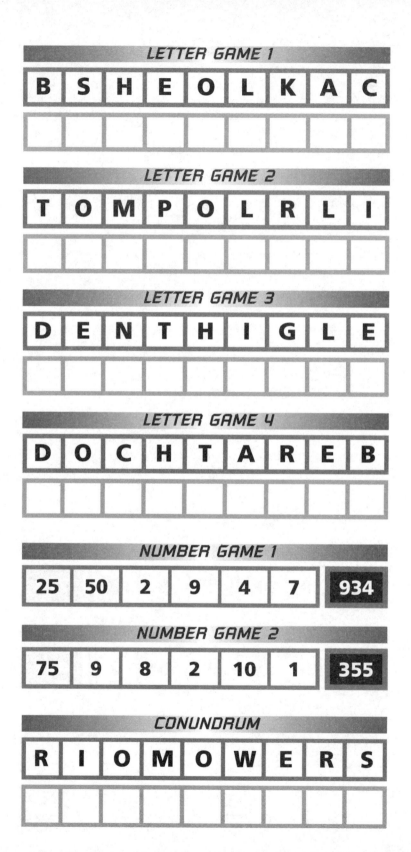

LETTER GAME 1

B	S	H	E	O	L	K	A	C

LETTER GAME 2

T	O	M	P	O	L	R	L	I

LETTER GAME 3

D	E	N	T	H	I	G	L	E

LETTER GAME 4

D	O	C	H	T	A	R	E	B

NUMBER GAME 1

25	50	2	9	4	7	934

NUMBER GAME 2

75	9	8	2	10	1	355

CONUNDRUM

R	I	O	M	O	W	E	R	S

LETTER GAME 1

W	E	B	B	O	A	T	R	P

LETTER GAME 2

R	I	N	T	E	L	E	J	H

LETTER GAME 3

C	I	N	N	O	M	G	O	D

LETTER GAME 4

T	E	N	B	E	A	U	N	P

NUMBER GAME 1

7	5	3	8	8	2	708

NUMBER GAME 2

25	1	3	5	1	7	444

CONUNDRUM

G	I	N	G	E	R	T	U	T

LETTER GAME 1

| H | I | R | R | E | D | I | P | S |

LETTER GAME 2

| W | A | I | K | E | R | T | N | R |

LETTER GAME 3

| S | C | T | E | L | M | A | S | A |

LETTER GAME 4

| S | T | E | M | N | A | T | E | T |

NUMBER GAME 1

| 100 | 25 | 2 | 8 | 10 | 8 | **749** |

NUMBER GAME 2

| 25 | 3 | 1 | 6 | 9 | 8 | **722** |

CONUNDRUM

| T | O | N | E | D | C | I | C | E |

LETTER GAME 1

F	E	I	O	L	D	I	L	P

LETTER GAME 2

G	R	I	B	S	A	M	R	E

LETTER GAME 3

D	O	N	S	A	B	E	N	I

LETTER GAME 4

T	H	I	S	T	E	R	I	S

NUMBER GAME 1

100	6	7	7	8	8	376

NUMBER GAME 2

75	6	8	3	2	8	993

CONUNDRUM

L	Y	R	I	C	A	L	D	O

LETTER GAME 1

| V | I | R | E | C | A | K | M | T |

LETTER GAME 2

| E | X | P | I | N | C | E | L | R |

LETTER GAME 3

| S | H | A | I | N | E | R | V | O |

LETTER GAME 4

| C | L | U | N | I | P | A | B | Q |

NUMBER GAME 1

| 75 | 100 | 8 | 9 | 7 | 5 | 242 |

NUMBER GAME 2

| 25 | 2 | 3 | 3 | 1 | 1 | 648 |

CONUNDRUM

| G | R | A | P | H | I | B | O | Y |

LETTER GAME 1

S	P	U	Q	I	T	E	C	K

LETTER GAME 2

H	O	S	R	M	A	C	K	E

LETTER GAME 3

M	O	N	D	E	L	A	E	T

LETTER GAME 4

S	H	O	R	P	Y	A	D	I

NUMBER GAME 1

100	50	25	7	6	1	823

NUMBER GAME 2

9	3	10	10	7	5	854

CONUNDRUM

S	P	E	R	S	I	L	A	D

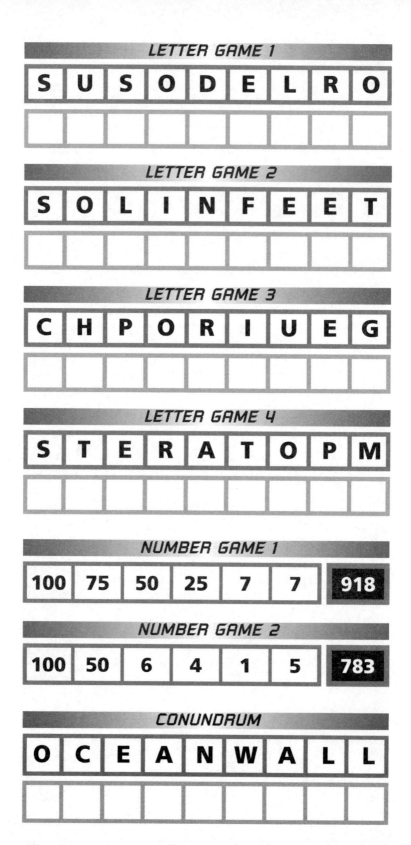

LETTER GAME 1

S	U	S	O	D	E	L	R	O

LETTER GAME 2

S	O	L	I	N	F	E	E	T

LETTER GAME 3

C	H	P	O	R	I	U	E	G

LETTER GAME 4

S	T	E	R	A	T	O	P	M

NUMBER GAME 1

100	75	50	25	7	7	918

NUMBER GAME 2

100	50	6	4	1	5	783

CONUNDRUM

O	C	E	A	N	W	A	L	L

LETTER GAME 1

W	R	I	D	E	B	L	E	T

LETTER GAME 2

L	W	E	G	I	N	C	A	R

LETTER GAME 3

L	U	R	I	C	A	S	T	O

LETTER GAME 4

C	L	O	M	I	B	S	H	A

NUMBER GAME 1

75	9	9	1	2	1	**732**

NUMBER GAME 2

25	3	4	8	10	10	**615**

CONUNDRUM

C	R	I	M	A	T	I	O	N

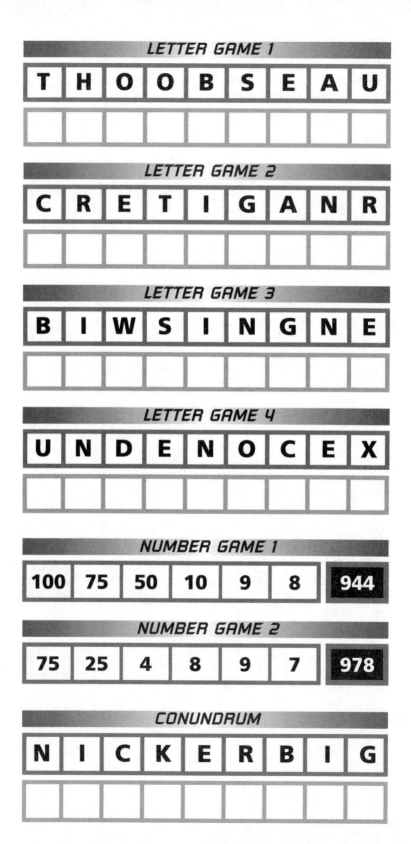

LETTER GAME 1

T	H	O	O	B	S	E	A	U

LETTER GAME 2

C	R	E	T	I	G	A	N	R

LETTER GAME 3

B	I	W	S	I	N	G	N	E

LETTER GAME 4

U	N	D	E	N	O	C	E	X

NUMBER GAME 1

100	75	50	10	9	8	944

NUMBER GAME 2

75	25	4	8	9	7	978

CONUNDRUM

N	I	C	K	E	R	B	I	G

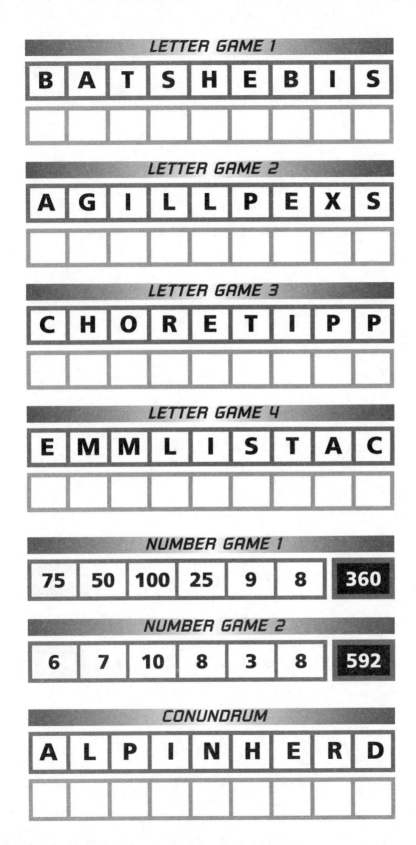

LETTER GAME 1

B	A	T	S	H	E	B	I	S

LETTER GAME 2

A	G	I	L	L	P	E	X	S

LETTER GAME 3

C	H	O	R	E	T	I	P	P

LETTER GAME 4

E	M	M	L	I	S	T	A	C

NUMBER GAME 1

75	50	100	25	9	8	**360**

NUMBER GAME 2

6	7	10	8	3	8	**592**

CONUNDRUM

A	L	P	I	N	H	E	R	D

LETTER GAME 1

F	O	O	R	G	I	N	P	W

LETTER GAME 2

S	A	R	B	E	I	S	R	E

LETTER GAME 3

S	T	U	R	N	I	M	E	O

LETTER GAME 4

H	U	B	C	L	O	U	S	E

NUMBER GAME 1

25	9	7	2	10	1	585

NUMBER GAME 2

100	3	6	2	2	1	555

CONUNDRUM

C	L	I	F	F	D	U	T	I

LETTER GAME 1

A	N	R	A	T	T	E	R	D

LETTER GAME 2

A	L	M	E	N	T	I	U	C

LETTER GAME 3

T	R	O	M	A	E	G	E	S

LETTER GAME 4

Y	I	N	T	O	R	S	I	E

NUMBER GAME 1

75	50	25	5	4	4	**637**

NUMBER GAME 2

50	75	4	4	8	2	**547**

CONUNDRUM

R	A	P	R	A	P	H	A	G

LETTER GAME 1

N	U	M	T	I	C	P	A	E

LETTER GAME 2

N	N	H	O	P	R	L	A	E

LETTER GAME 3

G	U	R	N	D	A	H	E	A

LETTER GAME 4

T	H	E	I	R	G	A	W	N

NUMBER GAME 1

50	6	5	7	9	4	679

NUMBER GAME 2

100	7	5	3	9	6	237

CONUNDRUM

N	O	S	E	S	H	R	U	G

LETTER GAME 1

A	R	C	U	S	T	E	A	C

LETTER GAME 2

M	U	T	I	Q	E	E	S	U

LETTER GAME 3

Y	A	C	I	L	L	B	N	U

LETTER GAME 4

E	E	N	B	I	R	G	D	A

NUMBER GAME 1

6	3	8	8	3	7	941

NUMBER GAME 2

50	8	7	2	1	4	689

CONUNDRUM

S	O	N	I	C	L	U	N	I

ROUND 99

LETTER GAME 1

| D | I | J | A | N | C | E | U | R |

LETTER GAME 2

| A | R | T | E | N | G | E | E | H |

LETTER GAME 3

| C | E | T | O | L | L | A | D | A |

LETTER GAME 4

| Q | U | E | B | I | Z | E | T | P |

NUMBER GAME 1

| 50 | 75 | 5 | 3 | 4 | 4 | 726 |

NUMBER GAME 2

| 75 | 4 | 6 | 6 | 5 | 3 | 849 |

CONUNDRUM

| N | I | C | K | S | Q | U | A | D |

LETTER GAME 1

F	I	L	D	O	M	A	N	D

LETTER GAME 2

G	U	S	T	I	P	E	D	O

LETTER GAME 3

D	E	T	E	N	C	I	C	O

LETTER GAME 4

A	A	B	G	E	L	I	R	C

NUMBER GAME 1

75	50	25	8	2	3	**927**

NUMBER GAME 2

50	100	25	75	4	4	**693**

CONUNDRUM

B	U	N	D	U	T	O	E	D

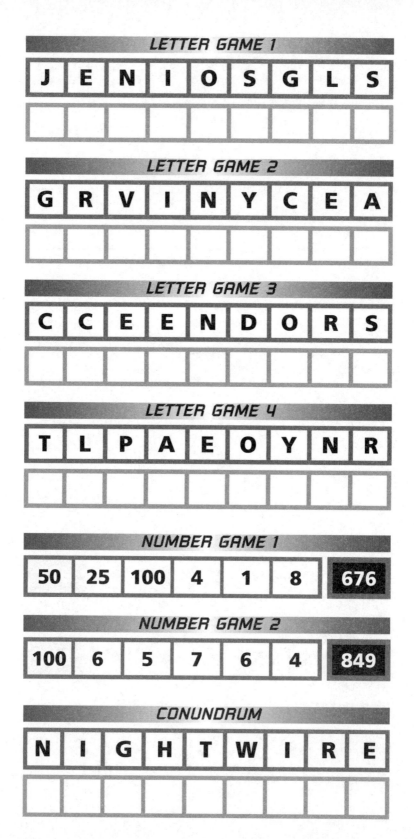

LETTER GAME 1

J	E	N	I	O	S	G	L	S

LETTER GAME 2

G	R	V	I	N	Y	C	E	A

LETTER GAME 3

C	C	E	E	N	D	O	R	S

LETTER GAME 4

T	L	P	A	E	O	Y	N	R

NUMBER GAME 1

50	25	100	4	1	8	676

NUMBER GAME 2

100	6	5	7	6	4	849

CONUNDRUM

N	I	G	H	T	W	I	R	E

LETTER GAME 1

A	D	E	I	L	M	T	T	U

LETTER GAME 2

O	O	T	H	P	A	S	T	E

LETTER GAME 3

H	A	G	N	I	B	E	D	E

LETTER GAME 4

E	H	I	O	P	S	U	R	V

NUMBER GAME 1

7	6	10	2	2	1	524

NUMBER GAME 2

50	7	2	8	9	1	875

CONUNDRUM

R	E	D	S	I	P	P	E	R

LETTER GAME 1

A	B	E	I	J	N	O	R	W

LETTER GAME 2

N	T	Z	O	A	I	P	R	E

LETTER GAME 3

A	C	E	F	L	O	N	R	Y

LETTER GAME 4

B	O	J	E	D	G	A	N	A

NUMBER GAME 1

50	6	1	3	5	4	**876**

NUMBER GAME 2

75	7	5	1	1	3	**666**

CONUNDRUM

S	U	P	E	R	C	H	A	D

LETTER GAME 1

X	A	T	G	A	L	H	E	W

LETTER GAME 2

L	R	M	E	O	T	N	I	V

LETTER GAME 3

O	I	S	N	V	A	D	E	H

LETTER GAME 4

T	A	N	O	V	U	G	T	E

NUMBER GAME 1

50	7	3	6	9	5	988

NUMBER GAME 2

4	9	8	8	2	1	650

CONUNDRUM

N	E	V	E	R	W	I	T	I

LETTER GAME 1

P	O	R	A	C	E	T	O	V

LETTER GAME 2

R	A	I	R	E	B	L	Y	Z

LETTER GAME 3

Z	D	P	I	O	M	T	E	H

LETTER GAME 4

U	P	T	H	E	N	O	S	E

NUMBER GAME 1

25	3	7	10	5	6	624

NUMBER GAME 2

100	75	3	3	4	6	849

CONUNDRUM

M	A	L	E	T	U	N	I	C

LETTER GAME 1

A	E	M	P	R	O	S	T	U

LETTER GAME 2

N	D	E	A	M	L	I	C	E

LETTER GAME 3

T	E	I	N	D	L	Q	U	O

LETTER GAME 4

D	T	I	N	O	M	A	N	E

NUMBER GAME 1

100	8	1	7	9	5	329

NUMBER GAME 2

25	7	4	1	7	4	465

CONUNDRUM

L	A	B	N	U	T	T	E	R

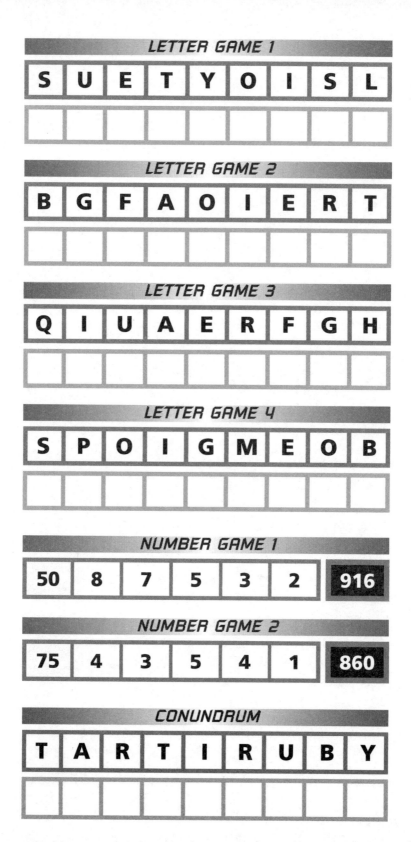

LETTER GAME 1

S	U	E	T	Y	O	I	S	L

LETTER GAME 2

B	G	F	A	O	I	E	R	T

LETTER GAME 3

Q	I	U	A	E	R	F	G	H

LETTER GAME 4

S	P	O	I	G	M	E	O	B

NUMBER GAME 1

50	8	7	5	3	2	916

NUMBER GAME 2

75	4	3	5	4	1	860

CONUNDRUM

T	A	R	T	I	R	U	B	Y

LETTER GAME 1

L	X	P	E	A	E	F	H	M

LETTER GAME 2

L	R	G	O	E	O	S	N	C

LETTER GAME 3

R	C	T	M	A	I	E	G	D

LETTER GAME 4

S	N	W	O	I	A	T	P	U

NUMBER GAME 1

25	9	10	8	2	2	781

NUMBER GAME 2

25	4	3	3	1	2	923

CONUNDRUM

M	I	N	E	R	B	U	N	G

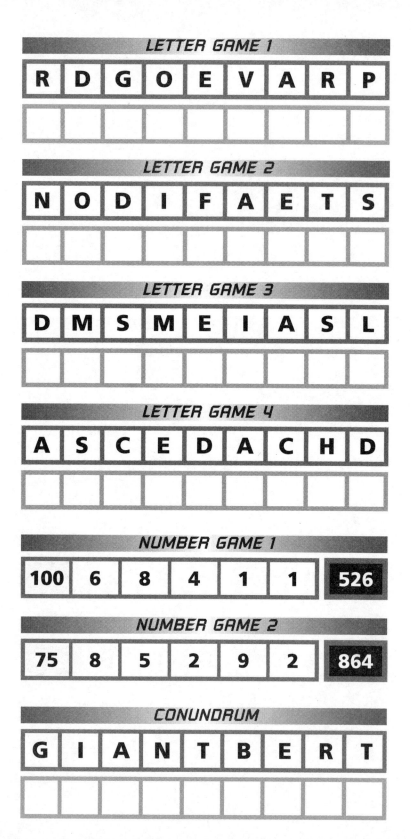

LETTER GAME 1

R	D	G	O	E	V	A	R	P

LETTER GAME 2

N	O	D	I	F	A	E	T	S

LETTER GAME 3

D	M	S	M	E	I	A	S	L

LETTER GAME 4

A	S	C	E	D	A	C	H	D

NUMBER GAME 1

100	6	8	4	1	1	526

NUMBER GAME 2

75	8	5	2	9	2	864

CONUNDRUM

G	I	A	N	T	B	E	R	T

LETTER GAME 1

G	U	T	T	A	P	O	E	R

LETTER GAME 2

N	I	S	D	A	N	V	E	H

LETTER GAME 3

I	M	U	V	N	E	C	A	R

LETTER GAME 4

A	T	H	E	R	T	O	N	S

NUMBER GAME 1

10	2	6	7	5	1	842

NUMBER GAME 2

9	6	3	8	2	9	586

CONUNDRUM

P	A	S	T	E	I	G	H	T

LETTER GAME 1

M	A	T	Y	V	O	L	N	E

LETTER GAME 2

N	E	S	O	L	C	G	E	Z

LETTER GAME 3

A	T	G	R	A	E	K	X	U

LETTER GAME 4

W	O	I	T	H	R	S	E	E

NUMBER GAME 1

75	4	6	8	5	5	795

NUMBER GAME 2

100	10	9	8	2	7	468

CONUNDRUM

I	C	E	S	I	N	N	E	R

LETTER GAME 1

N	H	T	E	I	J	R	E	A

LETTER GAME 2

O	L	C	X	S	E	A	O	V

LETTER GAME 3

C	L	O	E	T	D	I	P	E

LETTER GAME 4

M	T	C	N	I	E	O	A	I

NUMBER GAME 1

50	25	6	6	4	4	820

NUMBER GAME 2

25	2	5	6	5	3	311

CONUNDRUM

S	I	N	N	E	R	D	O	G

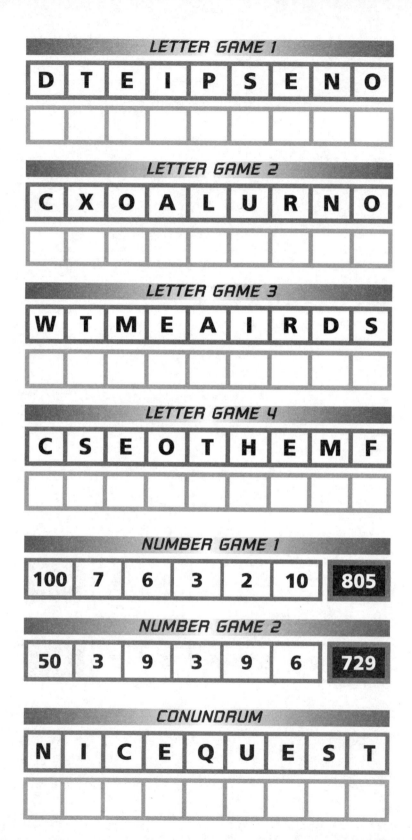

LETTER GAME 1

D	T	E	I	P	S	E	N	O

LETTER GAME 2

C	X	O	A	L	U	R	N	O

LETTER GAME 3

W	T	M	E	A	I	R	D	S

LETTER GAME 4

C	S	E	O	T	H	E	M	F

NUMBER GAME 1

100	7	6	3	2	10	805

NUMBER GAME 2

50	3	9	3	9	6	729

CONUNDRUM

N	I	C	E	Q	U	E	S	T

LETTER GAME 1

D	N	P	U	E	I	K	T	L

LETTER GAME 2

F	C	L	D	I	O	E	V	R

LETTER GAME 3

D	P	E	O	H	S	E	G	O

LETTER GAME 4

H	R	B	A	T	I	A	T	E

NUMBER GAME 1

100	10	10	9	9	1	629

NUMBER GAME 2

25	50	75	100	9	6	840

CONUNDRUM

S	E	M	I	S	T	I	L	L

LETTER GAME 1

L	T	N	G	E	U	O	D	L

LETTER GAME 2

C	R	H	R	W	E	A	O	M

LETTER GAME 3

P	S	I	O	T	G	A	P	H

LETTER GAME 4

N	I	G	Y	E	S	A	V	S

NUMBER GAME 1

25	1	4	1	3	8	622

NUMBER GAME 2

50	100	75	3	4	4	659

CONUNDRUM

I	N	T	R	O	A	I	D	A

LETTER GAME 1

B	H	E	I	D	O	T	U	R

LETTER GAME 2

A	O	P	L	I	Y	E	L	G

LETTER GAME 3

P	R	N	D	E	A	S	O	C

LETTER GAME 4

T	G	Y	I	E	D	S	W	A

NUMBER GAME 1

75	6	2	4	4	8	555

NUMBER GAME 2

2	8	7	7	5	1	343

CONUNDRUM

E	N	O	U	G	H	D	E	T

LETTER GAME 1

G	X	A	H	E	T	P	N	O

LETTER GAME 2

E	F	G	I	N	O	R	V	T

LETTER GAME 3

E	N	Q	T	U	O	L	P	E

LETTER GAME 4

A	D	E	I	L	M	N	S	T

NUMBER GAME 1

100	1	7	9	6	5	248

NUMBER GAME 2

10	2	10	5	4	6	740

CONUNDRUM

L	I	T	T	L	E	S	E	A

LETTER GAME 1

P	A	T	U	R	A	E	V	F

LETTER GAME 2

N	E	T	U	S	T	A	F	E

LETTER GAME 3

G	E	S	I	H	T	E	O	N

LETTER GAME 4

N	U	R	I	S	M	I	V	E

NUMBER GAME 1

50	8	5	4	9	3	784

NUMBER GAME 2

50	25	7	2	8	4	693

CONUNDRUM

R	E	A	L	W	H	I	T	E

LETTER GAME 1

H	W	X	E	I	A	D	S	M

LETTER GAME 2

L	M	W	O	E	O	E	N	T

LETTER GAME 3

L	F	M	I	A	U	R	N	D

LETTER GAME 4

L	R	E	E	A	G	S	C	L

NUMBER GAME 1

6	5	8	7	8	1	308

NUMBER GAME 2

25	2	4	3	3	5	837

CONUNDRUM

N	I	C	E	G	R	O	U	P

LETTER GAME 1

U	C	E	D	P	I	G	N	N

LETTER GAME 2

T	O	R	I	E	I	F	V	L

LETTER GAME 3

A	S	C	O	O	G	R	E	L

LETTER GAME 4

R	M	D	E	I	T	S	A	U

NUMBER GAME 1

50	6	3	7	7	4	264

NUMBER GAME 2

9	7	4	2	1	6	750

CONUNDRUM

D	A	R	N	S	C	E	N	T

LETTER GAME 1

T	A	U	R	H	L	R	B	E

LETTER GAME 2

S	R	T	M	F	O	A	O	K

LETTER GAME 3

D	E	S	R	U	M	O	W	G

LETTER GAME 4

U	A	E	N	C	L	P	O	S

NUMBER GAME 1

25	2	6	3	5	1	882

NUMBER GAME 2

75	50	100	8	3	1	264

CONUNDRUM

R	O	L	L	O	W	H	I	P

LETTER GAME 1

T	R	F	O	E	I	L	Y	R

LETTER GAME 2

R	H	Y	S	E	A	O	C	B

LETTER GAME 3

O	H	E	X	I	D	A	P	E

LETTER GAME 4

G	R	P	Y	O	U	E	N	G

NUMBER GAME 1

6	2	9	5	2	1	580

NUMBER GAME 2

25	5	2	3	2	8	777

CONUNDRUM

S	A	T	A	N	L	I	T	E

LETTER GAME 1

| M | L | T | I | E | O | J | R | S |

LETTER GAME 2

| B | N | A | C | O | T | G | E | S |

LETTER GAME 3

| F | T | S | T | I | E | U | A | M |

LETTER GAME 4

| A | V | E | N | R | I | U | G | A |

NUMBER GAME 1

| 50 | 9 | 6 | 4 | 10 | 6 | 914 |

NUMBER GAME 2

| 100 | 50 | 25 | 3 | 8 | 7 | 819 |

CONUNDRUM

| O | G | R | E | Q | U | E | S | T |

LETTER GAME 1

P	F	A	E	R	D	I	M	E

LETTER GAME 2

M	T	S	H	O	O	R	A	D

LETTER GAME 3

S	C	S	T	O	E	I	R	X

LETTER GAME 4

G	I	C	A	E	T	K	O	D

NUMBER GAME 1

75	9	10	9	10	5	444

NUMBER GAME 2

25	1	6	7	8	8	533

CONUNDRUM

S	P	E	E	D	B	A	R	D

LETTER GAME 1

T	Z	E	N	I	G	N	A	E

LETTER GAME 2

R	P	W	O	E	T	S	O	E

LETTER GAME 3

Y	D	F	A	I	L	R	A	T

LETTER GAME 4

L	Y	P	R	U	E	E	I	Q

NUMBER GAME 1

25	100	7	4	2	3	620

NUMBER GAME 2

75	8	8	6	7	7	931

CONUNDRUM

A	S	K	F	O	R	G	I	N

LETTER GAME 1

R	L	D	O	E	A	V	M	N

LETTER GAME 2

P	R	N	I	E	R	S	I	F

LETTER GAME 3

G	D	B	S	E	T	O	C	E

LETTER GAME 4

G	E	T	N	G	O	R	A	B

NUMBER GAME 1

50	3	2	10	4	8	**642**

NUMBER GAME 2

4	7	8	9	5	2	**253**

CONUNDRUM

T	R	I	C	O	R	N	E	C

LETTER GAME 1

T	D	J	E	I	U	R	T	E

LETTER GAME 2

E	O	T	R	I	A	N	D	P

LETTER GAME 3

M	S	P	F	I	A	E	L	H

LETTER GAME 4

O	F	S	R	E	C	G	U	T

NUMBER GAME 1

100	75	6	2	5	1	464

NUMBER GAME 2

8	10	4	3	1	7	875

CONUNDRUM

I	L	O	V	E	U	N	O	T

LETTER GAME 1

H	U	G	L	A	N	S	E	I

LETTER GAME 2

O	S	L	D	E	N	W	L	A

LETTER GAME 3

A	V	E	N	D	U	G	R	E

LETTER GAME 4

G	O	Y	R	E	H	U	D	N

NUMBER GAME 1

25	75	100	6	9	6	**386**

NUMBER GAME 2

75	6	3	8	8	3	**697**

CONUNDRUM

C	R	U	E	L	B	A	I	T

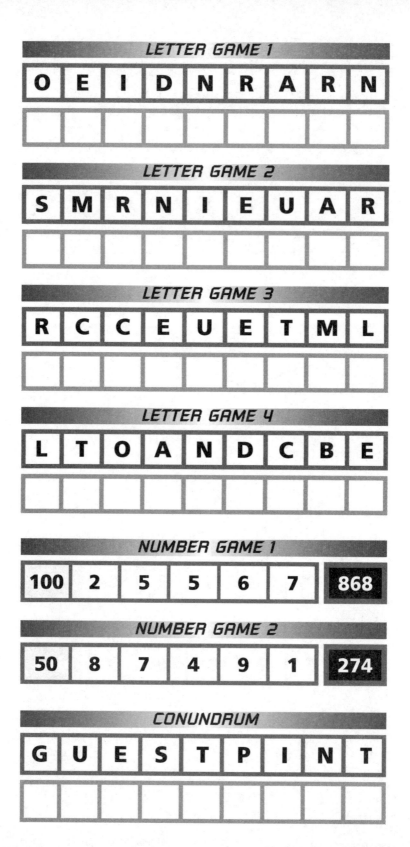

ROUND 129

LETTER GAME 1

O	E	I	D	N	R	A	R	N

LETTER GAME 2

S	M	R	N	I	E	U	A	R

LETTER GAME 3

R	C	C	E	U	E	T	M	L

LETTER GAME 4

L	T	O	A	N	D	C	B	E

NUMBER GAME 1

100	2	5	5	6	7	868

NUMBER GAME 2

50	8	7	4	9	1	274

CONUNDRUM

G	U	E	S	T	P	I	N	T

LETTER GAME 1

T	N	D	E	A	E	L	C	O

LETTER GAME 2

G	U	R	E	S	I	L	O	G

LETTER GAME 3

E	I	A	N	R	K	Z	S	N

LETTER GAME 4

X	U	J	O	I	B	K	E	D

NUMBER GAME 1

25	4	10	5	7	3	523

NUMBER GAME 2

25	2	9	10	9	7	821

CONUNDRUM

S	E	C	U	R	E	P	O	T

LETTER GAME 1

| T | A | G | L | A | V | E | O | C |

LETTER GAME 2

| T | D | N | I | U | I | M | L | O |

LETTER GAME 3

| P | I | N | D | U | S | O | R | E |

LETTER GAME 4

| S | P | V | E | U | A | T | Z | S |

NUMBER GAME 1

| 50 | 4 | 4 | 2 | 3 | 6 | **377** |

NUMBER GAME 2

| 75 | 8 | 3 | 6 | 6 | 7 | **948** |

CONUNDRUM

| C | O | C | O | A | R | I | N | D |

LETTER GAME 1

V	A	T	P	E	C	A	L	O

LETTER GAME 2

E	I	J	N	O	S	S	T	T

LETTER GAME 3

D	S	E	O	G	X	N	E	P

LETTER GAME 4

A	C	E	I	I	M	R	S	T

NUMBER GAME 1

25	50	75	100	3	3	**741**

NUMBER GAME 2

5	2	7	9	7	9	**144**

CONUNDRUM

F	I	G	F	R	I	E	N	D

LETTER GAME 1

Y	D	G	I	E	I	R	N	O

LETTER GAME 2

A	D	D	E	G	I	N	O	S

LETTER GAME 3

U	E	A	R	D	W	V	L	O

LETTER GAME 4

D	D	U	U	N	R	S	E	E

NUMBER GAME 1

25	3	10	4	5	7	937

NUMBER GAME 2

100	6	9	9	2	2	826

CONUNDRUM

D	U	N	D	E	E	P	O	X

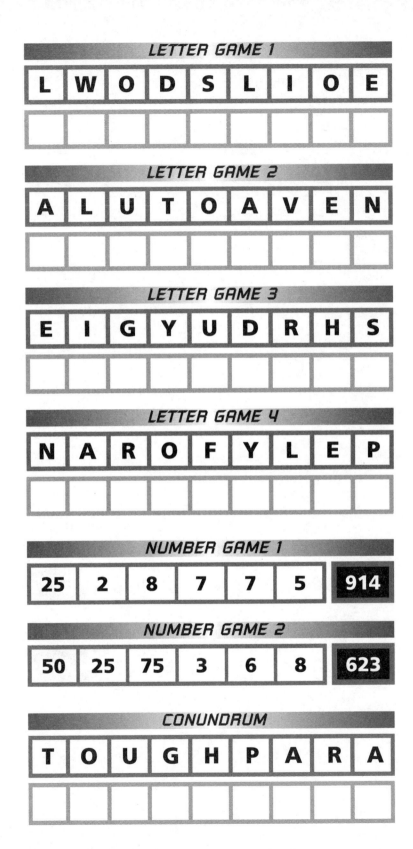

LETTER GAME 1

L	W	O	D	S	L	I	O	E

LETTER GAME 2

A	L	U	T	O	A	V	E	N

LETTER GAME 3

E	I	G	Y	U	D	R	H	S

LETTER GAME 4

N	A	R	O	F	Y	L	E	P

NUMBER GAME 1

25	2	8	7	7	5	914

NUMBER GAME 2

50	25	75	3	6	8	623

CONUNDRUM

T	O	U	G	H	P	A	R	A

LETTER GAME 1

L	E	P	S	E	Z	R	I	Y

LETTER GAME 2

N	O	S	I	H	O	A	R	U

LETTER GAME 3

P	E	L	I	M	T	U	R	C

LETTER GAME 4

D	C	U	E	W	S	O	I	D

NUMBER GAME 1

75	100	2	4	9	7	578

NUMBER GAME 2

50	8	1	7	6	1	239

CONUNDRUM

D	E	P	T	S	T	O	R	E

LETTER GAME 1

O	G	H	A	I	T	L	R	S

LETTER GAME 2

G	R	T	A	D	I	S	E	S

LETTER GAME 3

D	R	A	I	W	I	G	N	P

LETTER GAME 4

C	E	L	E	D	A	T	A	S

NUMBER GAME 1

100	10	5	6	9	2	**471**

NUMBER GAME 2

75	25	100	50	2	2	**704**

CONUNDRUM

S	A	U	C	E	T	O	F	F

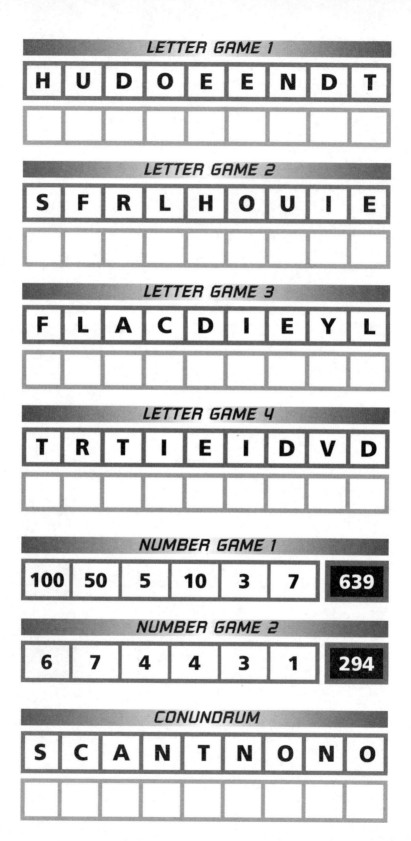

LETTER GAME 1

| H | U | D | O | E | E | N | D | T |

LETTER GAME 2

| S | F | R | L | H | O | U | I | E |

LETTER GAME 3

| F | L | A | C | D | I | E | Y | L |

LETTER GAME 4

| T | R | T | I | E | I | D | V | D |

NUMBER GAME 1

| 100 | 50 | 5 | 10 | 3 | 7 | 639 |

NUMBER GAME 2

| 6 | 7 | 4 | 4 | 3 | 1 | 294 |

CONUNDRUM

| S | C | A | N | T | N | O | N | O |

LETTER GAME 1

A	Y	D	E	I	O	V	P	L

LETTER GAME 2

O	E	I	T	F	S	X	A	D

LETTER GAME 3

Y	H	M	T	P	U	I	D	E

LETTER GAME 4

G	D	C	I	A	E	O	T	B

NUMBER GAME 1

25	10	2	4	7	2	**555**

NUMBER GAME 2

10	3	2	8	9	1	**584**

CONUNDRUM

I	M	N	O	G	H	O	S	T

LETTER GAME 1

L	G	A	I	P	S	A	R	B

LETTER GAME 2

A	S	K	R	O	L	Y	C	I

LETTER GAME 3

L	R	Z	O	A	E	R	M	T

LETTER GAME 4

L	R	Z	L	U	E	I	G	Y

NUMBER GAME 1

75	8	10	9	8	9	244

NUMBER GAME 2

50	75	2	3	1	9	186

CONUNDRUM

E	D	D	Y	H	A	R	T	E

LETTER GAME 1

B	E	I	O	R	S	T	U	V

LETTER GAME 2

B	S	U	X	R	E	L	H	A

LETTER GAME 3

O	C	A	T	G	E	H	P	D

LETTER GAME 4

A	A	C	D	E	I	L	L	N

NUMBER GAME 1

25	4	1	10	10	1	875

NUMBER GAME 2

50	7	10	8	8	5	933

CONUNDRUM

G	O	L	D	E	N	A	C	E

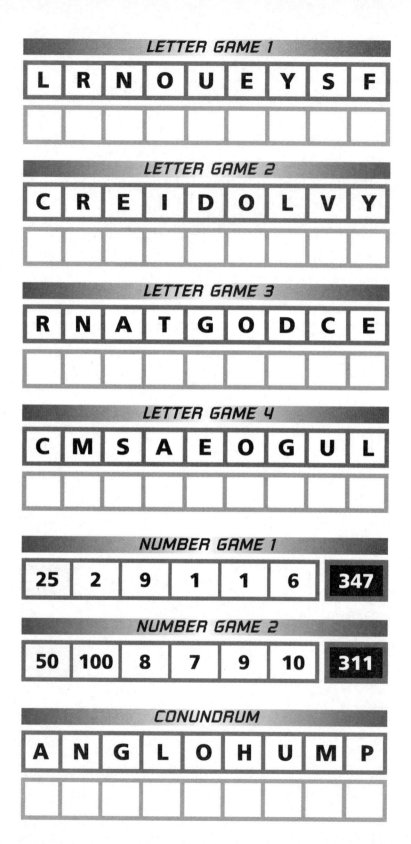

LETTER GAME 1

O	S	T	E	Y	R	A	B	U

LETTER GAME 2

N	L	R	E	U	S	G	W	A

LETTER GAME 3

S	B	I	A	S	T	O	U	S

LETTER GAME 4

B	O	P	D	A	N	G	I	R

NUMBER GAME 1

25	10	7	4	4	2	**812**

NUMBER GAME 2

75	25	50	100	4	9	**606**

CONUNDRUM

T	H	I	S	G	N	O	M	E

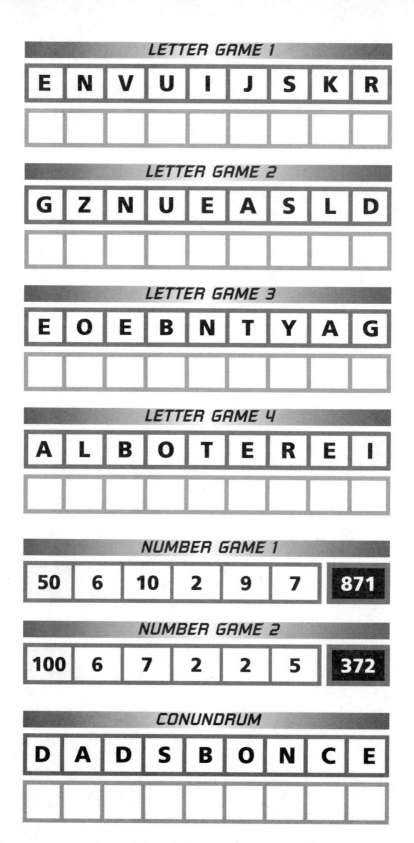

LETTER GAME 1

| E | N | V | U | I | J | S | K | R |

LETTER GAME 2

| G | Z | N | U | E | A | S | L | D |

LETTER GAME 3

| E | O | E | B | N | T | Y | A | G |

LETTER GAME 4

| A | L | B | O | T | E | R | E | I |

NUMBER GAME 1

| 50 | 6 | 10 | 2 | 9 | 7 | 871 |

NUMBER GAME 2

| 100 | 6 | 7 | 2 | 2 | 5 | 372 |

CONUNDRUM

| D | A | D | S | B | O | N | C | E |

LETTER GAME 1

N	G	H	E	I	E	D	T	N

LETTER GAME 2

T	I	M	L	O	P	E	D	S

LETTER GAME 3

T	S	V	N	O	I	U	D	A

LETTER GAME 4

L	K	T	A	E	P	R	A	C

NUMBER GAME 1

4	5	2	3	1	6	840

NUMBER GAME 2

8	3	4	1	2	3	864

CONUNDRUM

T	I	N	Y	T	A	M	E	R

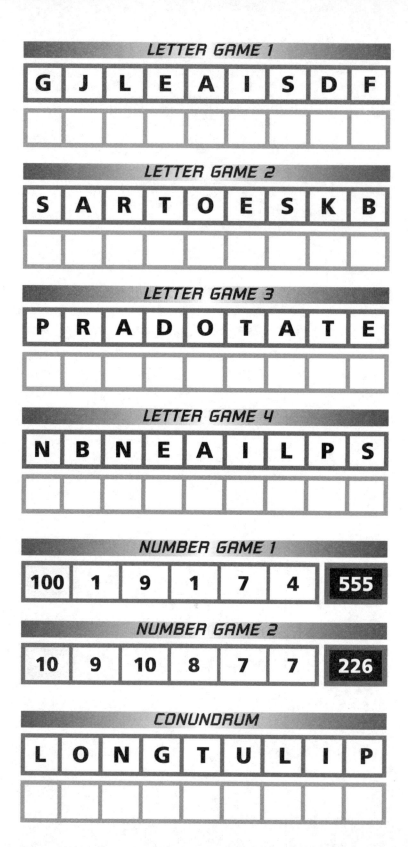

LETTER GAME 1

G	J	L	E	A	I	S	D	F

LETTER GAME 2

S	A	R	T	O	E	S	K	B

LETTER GAME 3

P	R	A	D	O	T	A	T	E

LETTER GAME 4

N	B	N	E	A	I	L	P	S

NUMBER GAME 1

100	1	9	1	7	4	555

NUMBER GAME 2

10	9	10	8	7	7	226

CONUNDRUM

L	O	N	G	T	U	L	I	P

LETTER GAME 1

T	L	R	I	E	G	M	A	R

LETTER GAME 2

C	S	I	N	A	R	P	E	N

LETTER GAME 3

H	I	N	S	A	G	L	O	T

LETTER GAME 4

M	A	R	T	Y	O	R	N	E

NUMBER GAME 1

25	7	5	4	1	10	628

NUMBER GAME 2

50	6	8	2	1	3	867

CONUNDRUM

T	Y	P	I	C	A	L	E	S

LETTER GAME 1

G	I	F	A	T	O	U	E	R

LETTER GAME 2

Y	A	C	D	G	T	E	R	O

LETTER GAME 3

G	H	S	I	U	O	L	F	K

LETTER GAME 4

A	C	E	E	I	F	N	R	T

NUMBER GAME 1

75	25	8	3	9	7	945

NUMBER GAME 2

100	75	50	4	10	5	885

CONUNDRUM

T	R	I	A	D	R	I	T	E

LETTER GAME 1

N	D	E	A	M	L	I	W	R

LETTER GAME 2

E	A	S	S	M	I	T	R	F

LETTER GAME 3

N	O	I	N	I	T	F	G	Y

LETTER GAME 4

I	E	R	F	B	T	O	S	E

NUMBER GAME 1

25	50	7	9	2	3	944

NUMBER GAME 2

50	6	8	8	1	7	867

CONUNDRUM

F	O	R	D	C	O	M	E	T

LETTER GAME 1

A	V	T	I	R	E	D	L	U

LETTER GAME 2

F	G	R	O	I	E	S	H	L

LETTER GAME 3

S	N	E	A	G	L	M	I	G

LETTER GAME 4

Y	V	U	S	D	I	E	N	T

NUMBER GAME 1

75	5	9	7	4	3	573

NUMBER GAME 2

25	50	100	6	6	9	693

CONUNDRUM

D	I	R	T	Y	R	O	O	M

LETTER GAME 1

U	P	N	T	I	A	K	D	O

LETTER GAME 2

L	I	M	A	H	I	G	S	R

LETTER GAME 3

Z	I	U	E	N	X	A	S	D

LETTER GAME 4

K	S	U	P	G	A	O	D	E

NUMBER GAME 1

50	4	10	5	10	3	987

NUMBER GAME 2

75	2	2	3	8	5	704

CONUNDRUM

T	E	L	Y	A	N	G	E	L

LETTER GAME 1

B	I	M	O	N	A	L	M	A

LETTER GAME 2

T	S	O	E	A	C	J	N	I

LETTER GAME 3

L	E	G	A	S	N	Y	I	C

LETTER GAME 4

K	A	T	J	E	A	T	D	N

NUMBER GAME 1

100	10	1	8	3	8	**716**

NUMBER GAME 2

25	2	3	1	10	9	**462**

CONUNDRUM

P	R	E	P	A	G	A	I	N

LETTER GAME 1

P	L	G	O	D	I	A	U	E

LETTER GAME 2

E	H	E	I	L	D	A	N	W

LETTER GAME 3

A	N	Y	I	V	T	E	L	O

LETTER GAME 4

R	O	N	E	T	J	U	I	P

NUMBER GAME 1

75	10	4	8	1	5	779

NUMBER GAME 2

7	2	8	5	6	2	904

CONUNDRUM

K	N	E	W	A	G	E	N	I

LETTER GAME 1

J	N	S	U	A	C	E	N	T

LETTER GAME 2

N	G	T	E	A	O	B	I	J

LETTER GAME 3

G	R	I	E	A	N	W	N	E

LETTER GAME 4

R	D	G	E	A	E	T	V	T

NUMBER GAME 1

100	2	9	7	10	10	404

NUMBER GAME 2

50	5	1	3	4	1	686

CONUNDRUM

D	U	D	R	E	P	O	R	T

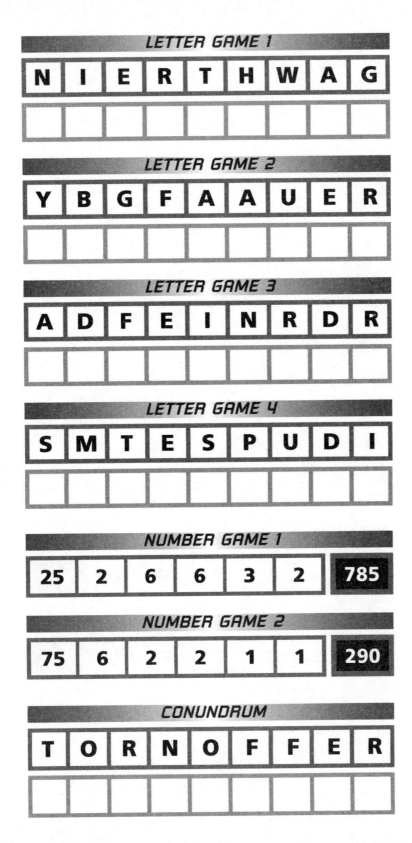

LETTER GAME 1

N	I	E	R	T	H	W	A	G

LETTER GAME 2

Y	B	G	F	A	A	U	E	R

LETTER GAME 3

A	D	F	E	I	N	R	D	R

LETTER GAME 4

S	M	T	E	S	P	U	D	I

NUMBER GAME 1

25	2	6	6	3	2	785

NUMBER GAME 2

75	6	2	2	1	1	290

CONUNDRUM

T	O	R	N	O	F	F	E	R

LETTER GAME 1

B	T	A	A	C	L	E	H	E

LETTER GAME 2

O	S	C	H	A	Z	E	P	Y

LETTER GAME 3

E	L	T	D	T	E	E	R	A

LETTER GAME 4

G	M	R	A	E	N	C	O	H

NUMBER GAME 1

50	7	8	9	10	10	356

NUMBER GAME 2

8	5	2	1	9	9	748

CONUNDRUM

G	I	V	E	R	O	U	N	D

LETTER GAME 1

S	U	O	L	V	I	C	E	S

LETTER GAME 2

D	O	S	R	I	W	O	N	D

LETTER GAME 3

G	O	R	V	I	T	A	N	D

LETTER GAME 4

F	A	L	R	Y	U	P	E	I

NUMBER GAME 1

75	5	7	3	1	9	642

NUMBER GAME 2

100	4	4	2	1	3	960

CONUNDRUM

M	A	N	I	C	A	B	L	E

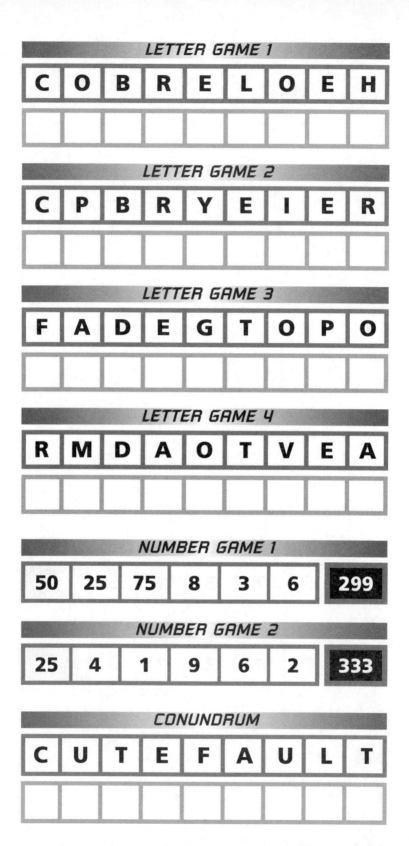

LETTER GAME 1

C	O	B	R	E	L	O	E	H

LETTER GAME 2

C	P	B	R	Y	E	I	E	R

LETTER GAME 3

F	A	D	E	G	T	O	P	O

LETTER GAME 4

R	M	D	A	O	T	V	E	A

NUMBER GAME 1

50	25	75	8	3	6	299

NUMBER GAME 2

25	4	1	9	6	2	333

CONUNDRUM

C	U	T	E	F	A	U	L	T

LETTER GAME 1

G	R	O	W	I	L	M	A	N

LETTER GAME 2

A	P	D	L	U	A	R	G	E

LETTER GAME 3

A	C	H	I	D	N	E	T	S

LETTER GAME 4

R	S	B	I	O	T	D	E	O

NUMBER GAME 1

10	6	7	5	5	3	963

NUMBER GAME 2

100	8	2	3	7	4	966

CONUNDRUM

T	E	A	T	U	L	I	P	S

LETTER GAME 1

A	D	A	C	W	K	R	B	E

LETTER GAME 2

L	L	W	O	E	S	I	R	T

LETTER GAME 3

D	C	R	A	S	P	I	E	P

LETTER GAME 4

F	T	W	E	O	E	S	L	N

NUMBER GAME 1

75	1	2	3	4	5	704

NUMBER GAME 2

25	8	4	3	3	6	527

CONUNDRUM

C	A	N	D	I	D	O	T	I

LETTER GAME 1

S	U	E	Q	Y	B	R	A	L

LETTER GAME 2

D	Y	L	H	I	T	S	O	A

LETTER GAME 3

E	D	H	L	E	A	T	F	I

LETTER GAME 4

O	F	S	G	I	X	D	E	H

NUMBER GAME 1

25	7	1	6	9	2	**478**

NUMBER GAME 2

25	6	3	9	2	4	**938**

CONUNDRUM

C	L	E	A	N	C	O	D	E

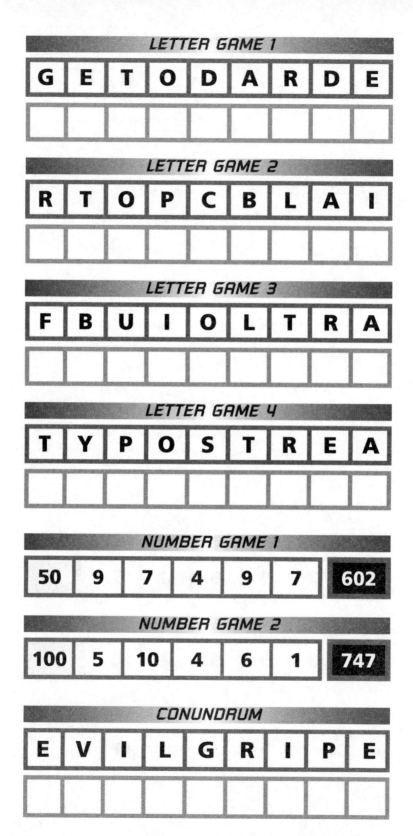

LETTER GAME 1

| G | E | T | O | D | A | R | D | E |

LETTER GAME 2

| R | T | O | P | C | B | L | A | I |

LETTER GAME 3

| F | B | U | I | O | L | T | R | A |

LETTER GAME 4

| T | Y | P | O | S | T | R | E | A |

NUMBER GAME 1

| 50 | 9 | 7 | 4 | 9 | 7 | **602** |

NUMBER GAME 2

| 100 | 5 | 10 | 4 | 6 | 1 | **747** |

CONUNDRUM

| E | V | I | L | G | R | I | P | E |

LETTER GAME 1

A	Y	E	F	D	P	R	M	I

LETTER GAME 2

D	A	I	L	E	I	F	N	Z

LETTER GAME 3

A	B	D	I	L	O	V	T	E

LETTER GAME 4

G	R	Y	O	R	U	A	P	T

NUMBER GAME 1

25	8	8	6	4	5	383

NUMBER GAME 2

7	7	5	5	3	3	444

CONUNDRUM

I	N	T	O	D	I	N	E	R

LETTER GAME 1

| M | G | W | L | I | O | D | E | A |

LETTER GAME 2

| P | A | O | R | T | X | H | S | E |

LETTER GAME 3

| T | E | S | O | D | G | T | A | S |

LETTER GAME 4

| E | S | Y | T | A | L | C | N | R |

NUMBER GAME 1

| 10 | 9 | 4 | 5 | 2 | 7 | 760 |

NUMBER GAME 2

| 75 | 25 | 50 | 6 | 7 | 9 | 665 |

CONUNDRUM

| T | R | A | D | L | A | D | Y | S |

LETTER GAME 1

E	D	R	I	T	G	F	U	R

LETTER GAME 2

T	A	R	E	P	O	C	H	N

LETTER GAME 3

N	E	V	I	O	L	B	O	I

LETTER GAME 4

T	S	L	E	A	I	B	O	P

NUMBER GAME 1

75	6	5	8	4	9	951

NUMBER GAME 2

100	3	8	4	7	2	574

CONUNDRUM

B	L	A	M	E	G	O	L	D

LETTER GAME 1

| F | Y | S | Z | E | U | I | P | T |

LETTER GAME 2

| R | S | O | M | A | E | T | B | D |

LETTER GAME 3

| C | S | N | A | E | O | P | L | A |

LETTER GAME 4

| K | L | D | Y | T | E | A | E | C |

NUMBER GAME 1

| 25 | 3 | 7 | 2 | 4 | 5 | 980 |

NUMBER GAME 2

| 25 | 5 | 10 | 10 | 1 | 5 | 864 |

CONUNDRUM

| L | I | V | I | D | I | C | E | S |

LETTER GAME 1

A	M	I	U	M	E	D	S	L

LETTER GAME 2

A	S	C	T	O	R	V	R	E

LETTER GAME 3

G	A	I	R	M	Y	E	S	T

LETTER GAME 4

Y	L	I	N	P	R	T	E	A

NUMBER GAME 1

5	6	3	3	4	4	271

NUMBER GAME 2

75	2	7	1	10	6	347

CONUNDRUM

S	T	U	M	P	F	I	R	E

LETTER GAME 1

O	D	R	Y	U	R	S	V	E

LETTER GAME 2

J	O	T	W	A	N	S	E	B

LETTER GAME 3

A	I	T	H	K	R	C	S	O

LETTER GAME 4

D	B	E	A	T	S	L	U	W

NUMBER GAME 1

50	25	75	6	5	7	417

NUMBER GAME 2

50	5	4	3	1	3	801

CONUNDRUM

B	O	R	E	S	H	A	C	K

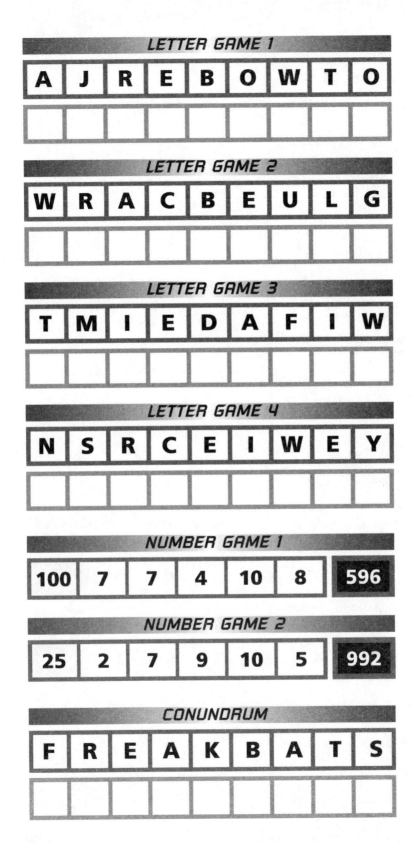

LETTER GAME 1

A	J	R	E	B	O	W	T	O

LETTER GAME 2

W	R	A	C	B	E	U	L	G

LETTER GAME 3

T	M	I	E	D	A	F	I	W

LETTER GAME 4

N	S	R	C	E	I	W	E	Y

NUMBER GAME 1

100	7	7	4	10	8	596

NUMBER GAME 2

25	2	7	9	10	5	992

CONUNDRUM

F	R	E	A	K	B	A	T	S

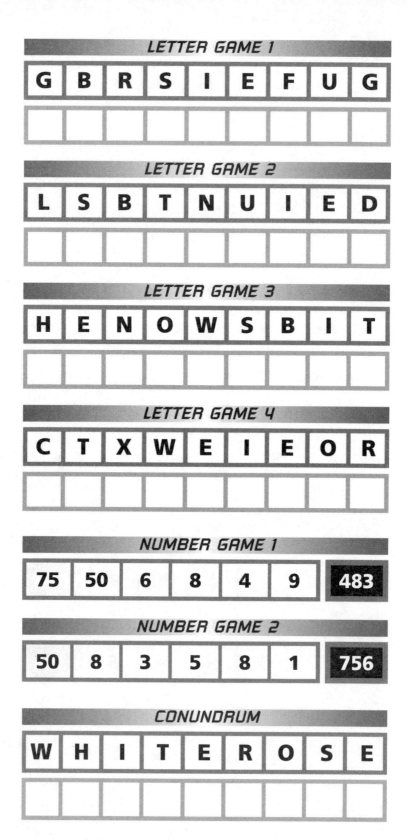

LETTER GAME 1

G	B	R	S	I	E	F	U	G

LETTER GAME 2

L	S	B	T	N	U	I	E	D

LETTER GAME 3

H	E	N	O	W	S	B	I	T

LETTER GAME 4

C	T	X	W	E	I	E	O	R

NUMBER GAME 1

75	50	6	8	4	9	483

NUMBER GAME 2

50	8	3	5	8	1	756

CONUNDRUM

W	H	I	T	E	R	O	S	E

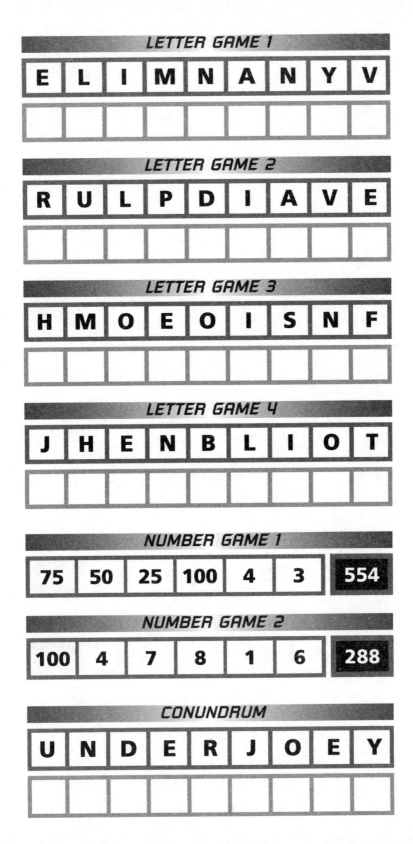

LETTER GAME 1

E	L	I	M	N	A	N	Y	V

LETTER GAME 2

R	U	L	P	D	I	A	V	E

LETTER GAME 3

H	M	O	E	O	I	S	N	F

LETTER GAME 4

J	H	E	N	B	L	I	O	T

NUMBER GAME 1

75	50	25	100	4	3	554

NUMBER GAME 2

100	4	7	8	1	6	288

CONUNDRUM

U	N	D	E	R	J	O	E	Y

LETTER GAME 1

N	S	M	E	U	C	O	E	P

LETTER GAME 2

E	F	G	H	I	L	W	T	Y

LETTER GAME 3

N	R	L	U	E	O	Y	S	D

LETTER GAME 4

O	K	R	Y	B	A	N	D	E

NUMBER GAME 1

75	100	8	4	2	6	719

NUMBER GAME 2

100	1	1	2	2	3	927

CONUNDRUM

A	C	E	F	I	B	R	E	S

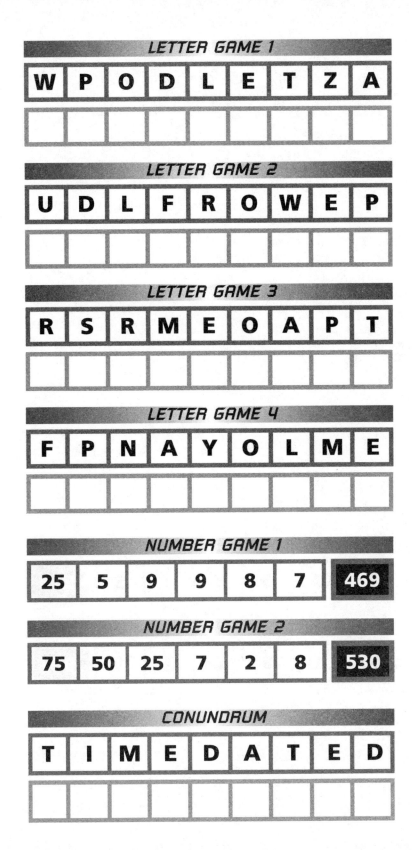

LETTER GAME 1

W	P	O	D	L	E	T	Z	A

LETTER GAME 2

U	D	L	F	R	O	W	E	P

LETTER GAME 3

R	S	R	M	E	O	A	P	T

LETTER GAME 4

F	P	N	A	Y	O	L	M	E

NUMBER GAME 1

25	5	9	9	8	7	469

NUMBER GAME 2

75	50	25	7	2	8	530

CONUNDRUM

T	I	M	E	D	A	T	E	D

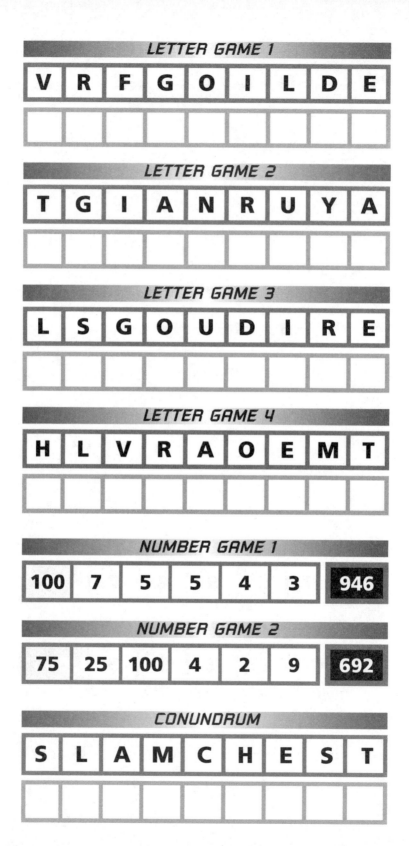

LETTER GAME 1

V	R	F	G	O	I	L	D	E

LETTER GAME 2

T	G	I	A	N	R	U	Y	A

LETTER GAME 3

L	S	G	O	U	D	I	R	E

LETTER GAME 4

H	L	V	R	A	O	E	M	T

NUMBER GAME 1

100	7	5	5	4	3	946

NUMBER GAME 2

75	25	100	4	2	9	692

CONUNDRUM

S	L	A	M	C	H	E	S	T

LETTER GAME 1

N	H	N	I	A	R	M	E	K

LETTER GAME 2

P	Y	S	T	A	L	I	O	C

LETTER GAME 3

N	E	E	O	X	Y	T	A	G

LETTER GAME 4

V	C	E	S	O	T	E	N	A

NUMBER GAME 1

100	50	10	8	4	7	925

NUMBER GAME 2

25	7	3	1	5	9	666

CONUNDRUM

P	O	L	A	R	A	N	E	E

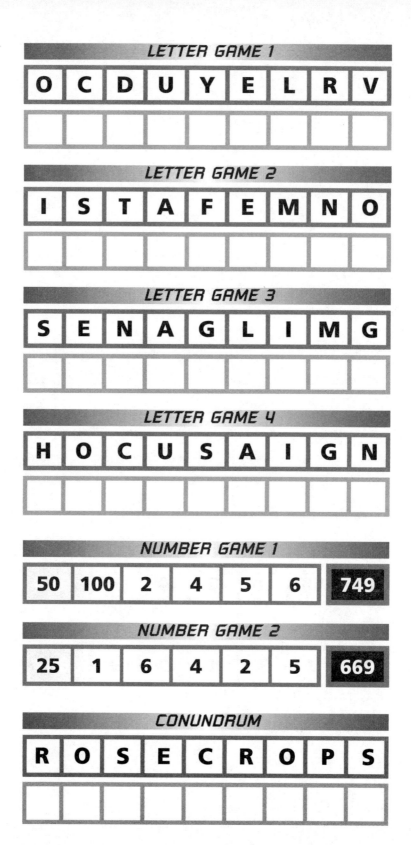

LETTER GAME 1

O	C	D	U	Y	E	L	R	V

LETTER GAME 2

I	S	T	A	F	E	M	N	O

LETTER GAME 3

S	E	N	A	G	L	I	M	G

LETTER GAME 4

H	O	C	U	S	A	I	G	N

NUMBER GAME 1

50	100	2	4	5	6	749

NUMBER GAME 2

25	1	6	4	2	5	669

CONUNDRUM

R	O	S	E	C	R	O	P	S

LETTER GAME 1

| H | U | B | E | A | S | R | D | N |

LETTER GAME 2

| G | Y | O | O | B | R | I | E | N |

LETTER GAME 3

| N | L | E | U | C | A | R | E | L |

LETTER GAME 4

| S | C | U | O | R | A | B | I | L |

NUMBER GAME 1

| 100 | 10 | 8 | 7 | 8 | 10 | **246** |

NUMBER GAME 2

| 25 | 8 | 7 | 2 | 2 | 4 | **888** |

CONUNDRUM

| E | A | R | T | H | C | L | A | D |

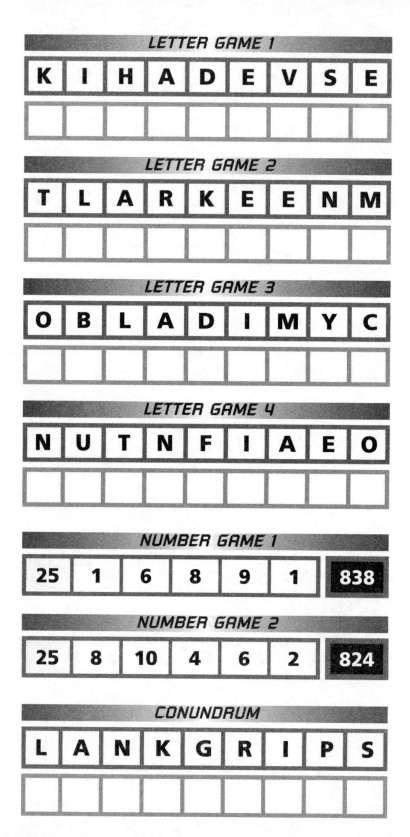

LETTER GAME 1

K	I	H	A	D	E	V	S	E

LETTER GAME 2

T	L	A	R	K	E	E	N	M

LETTER GAME 3

O	B	L	A	D	I	M	Y	C

LETTER GAME 4

N	U	T	N	F	I	A	E	O

NUMBER GAME 1

25	1	6	8	9	1	838

NUMBER GAME 2

25	8	10	4	6	2	824

CONUNDRUM

L	A	N	K	G	R	I	P	S

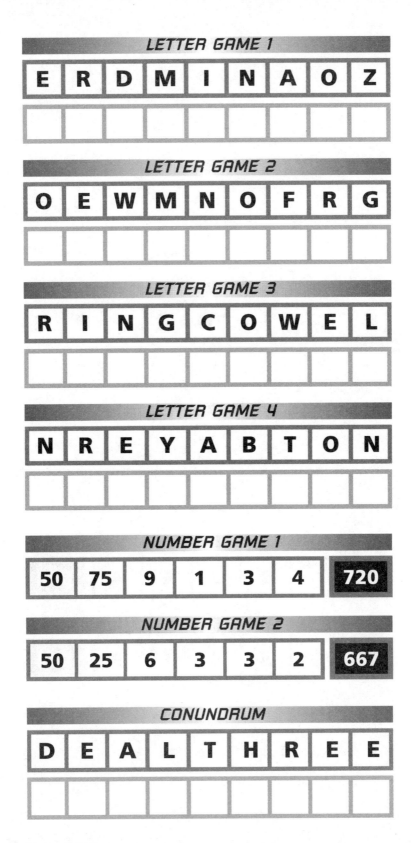

LETTER GAME 1
E R D M I N A O Z

LETTER GAME 2
O E W M N O F R G

LETTER GAME 3
R I N G C O W E L

LETTER GAME 4
N R E Y A B T O N

NUMBER GAME 1
50 75 9 1 3 4 — 720

NUMBER GAME 2
50 25 6 3 3 2 — 667

CONUNDRUM
D E A L T H R E E

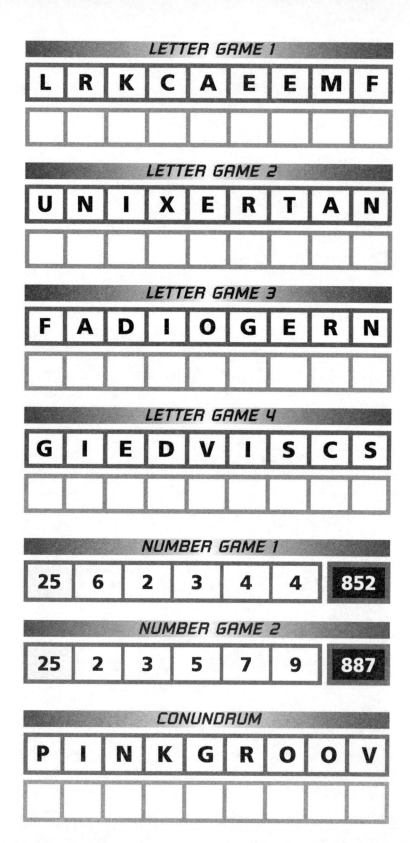

LETTER GAME 1

L	R	K	C	A	E	E	M	F

LETTER GAME 2

U	N	I	X	E	R	T	A	N

LETTER GAME 3

F	A	D	I	O	G	E	R	N

LETTER GAME 4

G	I	E	D	V	I	S	C	S

NUMBER GAME 1

25	6	2	3	4	4	852

NUMBER GAME 2

25	2	3	5	7	9	887

CONUNDRUM

P	I	N	K	G	R	O	O	V

LETTER GAME 1

O	N	I	F	E	S	H	A	D

LETTER GAME 2

S	I	N	C	D	R	E	E	E

LETTER GAME 3

V	I	R	E	S	T	E	C	E

LETTER GAME 4

C	R	I	D	T	E	M	I	H

NUMBER GAME 1

25	5	2	1	7	3	782

NUMBER GAME 2

75	100	2	3	4	9	844

CONUNDRUM

N	I	N	O	R	O	U	G	H

LETTER GAME 1

R	I	M	E	D	I	A	L	A

LETTER GAME 2

D	Y	P	O	L	E	M	E	R

LETTER GAME 3

B	E	D	R	I	E	S	A	F

LETTER GAME 4

A	R	R	I	P	D	E	E	H

NUMBER GAME 1

75	5	3	6	8	4	**760**

NUMBER GAME 2

10	1	6	7	8	5	**841**

CONUNDRUM

T	H	R	E	E	D	A	V	S

LETTER GAME 1

M	O	T	O	R	P	E	D	A

LETTER GAME 2

K	I	N	P	L	O	G	R	A

LETTER GAME 3

S	M	O	R	K	I	G	A	S

LETTER GAME 4

M	E	D	E	S	A	C	R	U

NUMBER GAME 1

100	25	7	4	1	8	629

NUMBER GAME 2

25	50	8	3	7	5	317

CONUNDRUM

P	A	M	E	L	I	T	I	C

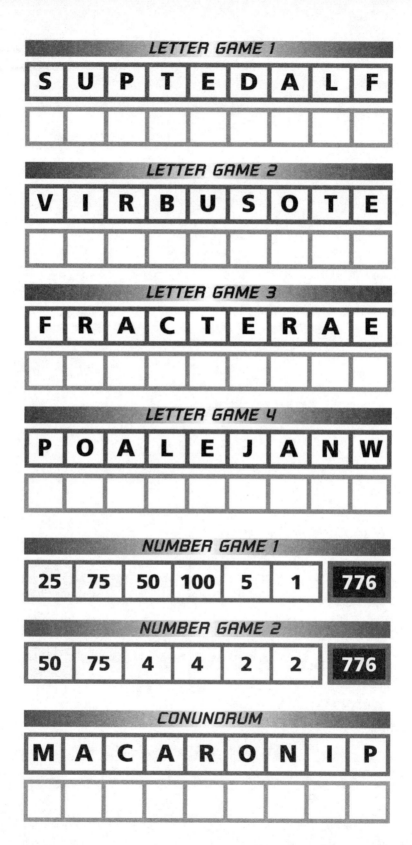

LETTER GAME 1

S	U	P	T	E	D	A	L	F

LETTER GAME 2

V	I	R	B	U	S	O	T	E

LETTER GAME 3

F	R	A	C	T	E	R	A	E

LETTER GAME 4

P	O	A	L	E	J	A	N	W

NUMBER GAME 1

25	75	50	100	5	1	776

NUMBER GAME 2

50	75	4	4	2	2	776

CONUNDRUM

M	A	C	A	R	O	N	I	P

LETTER GAME 1

U	R	I	N	C	A	P	S	G

LETTER GAME 2

G	I	O	L	I	N	E	R	A

LETTER GAME 3

S	U	R	G	L	E	B	A	S

LETTER GAME 4

O	X	E	D	L	S	I	Y	C

NUMBER GAME 1

75	6	10	4	3	2	538

NUMBER GAME 2

50	7	5	7	2	4	820

CONUNDRUM

D	I	N	A	M	I	T	T	E

193

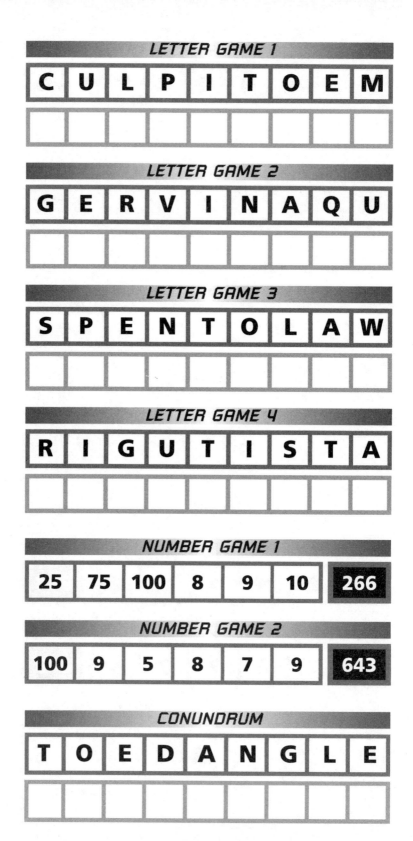

LETTER GAME 1

C	U	L	P	I	T	O	E	M

LETTER GAME 2

G	E	R	V	I	N	A	Q	U

LETTER GAME 3

S	P	E	N	T	O	L	A	W

LETTER GAME 4

R	I	G	U	T	I	S	T	A

NUMBER GAME 1

25	75	100	8	9	10	266

NUMBER GAME 2

100	9	5	8	7	9	643

CONUNDRUM

T	O	E	D	A	N	G	L	E

LETTER GAME 1

X	U	U	B	R	Y	P	E	A

LETTER GAME 2

C	H	E	A	R	U	P	S	C

LETTER GAME 3

B	L	U	F	E	T	A	R	E

LETTER GAME 4

P	E	L	B	K	E	A	E	R

NUMBER GAME 1

8	3	4	2	10	9	**734**

NUMBER GAME 2

50	25	8	7	7	5	**543**

CONUNDRUM

A	N	O	I	N	T	E	S	S

LETTER GAME 1

R	A	M	I	S	T	I	C	Y

LETTER GAME 2

N	I	F	A	N	C	E	R	E

LETTER GAME 3

O	C	B	T	R	A	I	A	E

LETTER GAME 4

C	O	D	I	M	A	G	T	U

NUMBER GAME 1

75	25	1	10	4	4	841

NUMBER GAME 2

2	5	9	8	9	4	570

CONUNDRUM

M	A	G	I	C	T	R	A	P

LETTER GAME 1

S	O	N	D	E	M	A	H	I

LETTER GAME 2

H	O	N	C	O	R	E	S	P

LETTER GAME 3

H	U	N	D	R	E	N	A	D

LETTER GAME 4

D	E	R	N	O	M	A	T	N

NUMBER GAME 1

25	2	3	8	3	6	667

NUMBER GAME 2

25	75	100	10	10	9	416

CONUNDRUM

L	I	L	Y	Q	U	O	O	S

LETTER GAME 1

D	I	N	R	E	E	T	S	K

LETTER GAME 2

C	O	N	E	J	A	T	D	K

LETTER GAME 3

D	E	L	B	U	R	E	N	A

LETTER GAME 4

T	H	O	R	O	S	P	A	C

NUMBER GAME 1

75	100	2	1	3	3	936

NUMBER GAME 2

50	75	25	5	5	1	386

CONUNDRUM

R	A	C	I	E	T	E	X	T

LETTER GAME 1

D	I	L	T	E	R	E	B	S

LETTER GAME 2

D	A	V	E	P	I	J	T	A

LETTER GAME 3

M	M	I	T	U	R	E	A	E

LETTER GAME 4

L	I	S	T	E	A	C	S	B

NUMBER GAME 1

100	7	10	9	10	1	244

NUMBER GAME 2

25	75	50	100	8	7	942

CONUNDRUM

D	E	V	I	L	D	A	T	A

LETTER GAME 1

Y O V E L S A S T

LETTER GAME 2

D I L L E N T A C

LETTER GAME 3

L A P P O R E S I

LETTER GAME 4

C R E P O T I N E

NUMBER GAME 1

9 4 3 7 5 2 | 999

NUMBER GAME 2

25 100 7 7 4 3 | 578

CONUNDRUM

N O T E D M A I D

LETTER GAME 1

R	O	D	L	D	A	N	L	E

LETTER GAME 2

B	L	O	N	E	A	M	E	T

LETTER GAME 3

S	C	U	T	O	I	C	A	W

LETTER GAME 4

L	I	K	C	P	I	R	E	R

NUMBER GAME 1

100	75	25	2	4	2	683

NUMBER GAME 2

50	100	1	10	10	1	630

CONUNDRUM

F	O	R	R	H	E	I	D	I

LETTER GAME 1

D	R	U	I	I	F	E	P	F

LETTER GAME 2

A	R	R	W	E	D	R	A	T

LETTER GAME 3

A	N	I	G	E	R	D	A	T

LETTER GAME 4

R	E	C	S	T	O	O	E	S

NUMBER GAME 1

50	4	6	10	1	7	972

NUMBER GAME 2

25	9	1	4	5	6	848

CONUNDRUM

G	R	A	N	D	P	I	N	E

LETTER GAME 1

O	D	R	I	N	A	T	O	V

LETTER GAME 2

S	T	I	E	R	L	A	I	C

LETTER GAME 3

A	C	D	E	E	R	S	T	E

LETTER GAME 4

F	I	M	P	R	E	C	A	T

NUMBER GAME 1

50	25	75	3	1	2	407

NUMBER GAME 2

50	25	9	2	5	7	828

CONUNDRUM

S	P	E	E	D	C	U	T	S

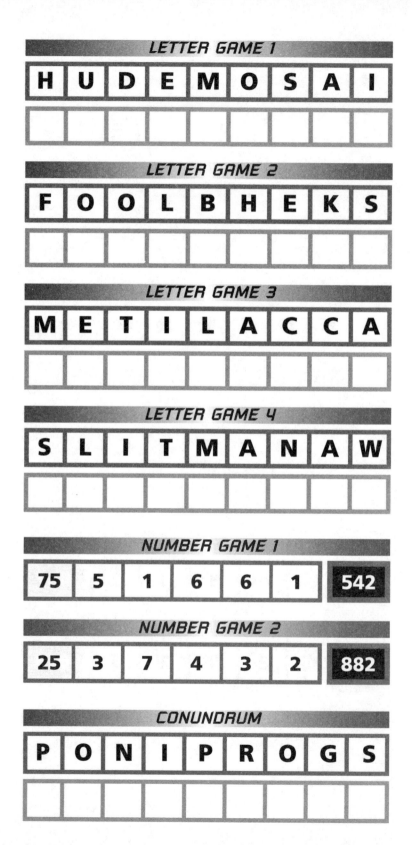

LETTER GAME 1

H	U	D	E	M	O	S	A	I

LETTER GAME 2

F	O	O	L	B	H	E	K	S

LETTER GAME 3

M	E	T	I	L	A	C	C	A

LETTER GAME 4

S	L	I	T	M	A	N	A	W

NUMBER GAME 1

75	5	1	6	6	1	542

NUMBER GAME 2

25	3	7	4	3	2	882

CONUNDRUM

P	O	N	I	P	R	O	G	S

LETTER GAME 1

V	A	G	I	B	A	L	E	N

LETTER GAME 2

C	U	M	D	E	L	A	T	I

LETTER GAME 3

A	B	L	O	U	R	D	E	G

LETTER GAME 4

W	A	R	D	I	Y	E	V	J

NUMBER GAME 1

2	8	4	5	4	1	657

NUMBER GAME 2

75	25	2	9	2	6	830

CONUNDRUM

R	I	T	E	C	I	G	A	R

LETTER GAME 1

P	R	Y	T	E	E	A	R	A

LETTER GAME 2

M	O	N	I	S	T	A	D	V

LETTER GAME 3

A	N	E	E	R	U	D	S	W

LETTER GAME 4

H	O	S	L	E	F	A	O	D

NUMBER GAME 1

50	6	7	5	8	6	729

NUMBER GAME 2

50	25	8	2	7	10	564

CONUNDRUM

T	I	N	Y	M	E	T	A	L

LETTER GAME 1

G	E	L	T	A	I	A	T	P

LETTER GAME 2

D	R	O	K	E	B	N	W	A

LETTER GAME 3

I	H	B	E	N	S	T	A	L

LETTER GAME 4

G	I	N	E	R	S	T	A	X

NUMBER GAME 1

25	75	100	50	3	6	429

NUMBER GAME 2

75	2	2	1	5	8	695

CONUNDRUM

N	E	C	K	B	L	A	D	E

LETTER GAME 1

L	O	B	A	I	T	A	S	F

LETTER GAME 2

C	O	N	T	R	A	I	A	W

LETTER GAME 3

B	A	L	C	T	R	I	E	A

LETTER GAME 4

S	L	I	K	E	D	A	E	H

NUMBER GAME 1

100	25	9	4	4	8	956

NUMBER GAME 2

25	10	6	6	3	1	628

CONUNDRUM

G	I	A	N	T	T	I	E	S

ROUND 200

LETTER GAME 1

R	I	N	L	I	O	N	C	E

LETTER GAME 2

H	A	R	G	L	I	N	E	O

LETTER GAME 3

B	T	I	H	E	W	T	I	A

LETTER GAME 4

T	I	S	E	L	I	N	W	A

NUMBER GAME 1

7	6	3	3	8	2	591

NUMBER GAME 2

25	8	3	10	2	10	731

CONUNDRUM

O	U	R	T	E	M	P	L	E

209

LETTER GAME 1

E	H	A	S	R	E	O	S	T

LETTER GAME 2

F	U	H	C	E	G	L	A	N

LETTER GAME 3

A	R	S	P	I	T	E	A	F

LETTER GAME 4

D	R	R	D	W	E	A	A	T

NUMBER GAME 1

50	8	7	1	1	5	676

NUMBER GAME 2

25	10	2	9	2	4	841

CONUNDRUM

A	S	T	A	R	D	U	E	T

LETTER GAME 1

A	D	E	E	L	I	N	S	T

LETTER GAME 2

C	C	K	E	N	L	E	A	D

LETTER GAME 3

A	D	L	E	O	M	L	S	T

LETTER GAME 4

M	A	I	S	R	H	C	A	E

NUMBER GAME 1

75	100	6	3	4	5	**917**

NUMBER GAME 2

25	100	50	4	3	8	**690**

CONUNDRUM

S	O	N	I	C	G	R	U	B

LETTER GAME 1

B	E	T	H	A	S	N	U	E

LETTER GAME 2

L	L	K	Y	D	E	I	A	T

LETTER GAME 3

A	A	T	H	M	O	R	N	T

LETTER GAME 4

A	N	T	O	W	Y	P	N	E

NUMBER GAME 1

25	50	8	8	7	7	222

NUMBER GAME 2

100	9	10	7	1	2	843

CONUNDRUM

D	O	E	C	A	R	R	O	T

LETTER GAME 1

A	A	L	I	C	S	T	R	I

LETTER GAME 2

P	O	R	T	O	V	E	S	I

LETTER GAME 3

L	A	B	W	D	A	R	T	E

LETTER GAME 4

B	L	E	N	C	A	M	E	S

NUMBER GAME 1

25	50	75	100	5	5	749

NUMBER GAME 2

75	2	4	3	2	4	964

CONUNDRUM

L	A	N	A	D	I	M	B	O

213

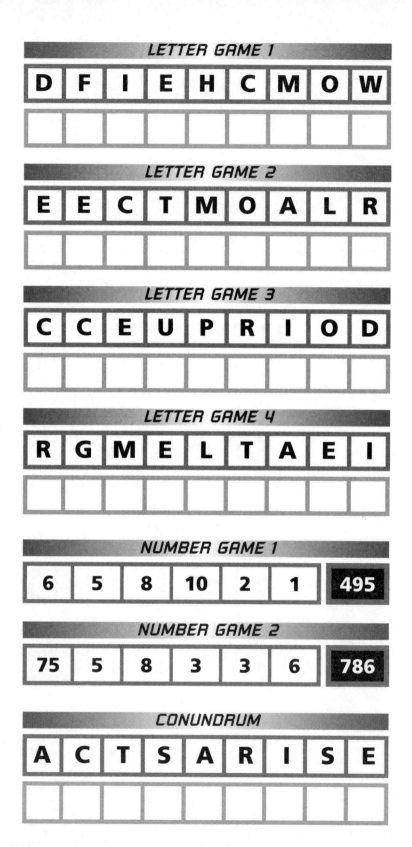

LETTER GAME 1

D	F	I	E	H	C	M	O	W

LETTER GAME 2

E	E	C	T	M	O	A	L	R

LETTER GAME 3

C	C	E	U	P	R	I	O	D

LETTER GAME 4

R	G	M	E	L	T	A	E	I

NUMBER GAME 1

6	5	8	10	2	1	495

NUMBER GAME 2

75	5	8	3	3	6	786

CONUNDRUM

A	C	T	S	A	R	I	S	E

LETTER GAME 1

G	I	N	U	F	A	T	R	E

LETTER GAME 2

E	E	G	I	N	R	P	N	I

LETTER GAME 3

X	D	U	R	E	D	E	D	L

LETTER GAME 4

M	T	R	O	C	H	A	E	E

NUMBER GAME 1

100	8	7	7	9	10	995

NUMBER GAME 2

50	25	8	2	3	7	588

CONUNDRUM

B	A	L	D	I	S	I	G	N

LETTER GAME 1

G	A	E	T	I	O	N	E	Y

LETTER GAME 2

H	I	V	Z	C	E	R	A	T

LETTER GAME 3

N	O	B	I	G	T	E	R	O

LETTER GAME 4

R	O	L	B	Y	M	E	W	A

NUMBER GAME 1

100	50	75	6	6	1	887

NUMBER GAME 2

8	1	7	2	10	10	850

CONUNDRUM

P	E	T	R	E	S	C	U	E

LETTER GAME 1

D	R	A	H	E	E	K	S	T

LETTER GAME 2

L	J	T	I	S	O	N	E	T

LETTER GAME 3

G	R	U	S	I	P	I	N	H

LETTER GAME 4

M	M	O	S	R	E	A	T	H

NUMBER GAME 1

50	9	10	2	3	2	668

NUMBER GAME 2

25	100	4	4	5	7	339

CONUNDRUM

C	A	V	E	S	H	A	R	K

ROUND 209

LETTER GAME 1

S I W R G N O T B

LETTER GAME 2

D I N H E S A V D

LETTER GAME 3

Y H N U T C E P O

LETTER GAME 4

N S L I T O N E A

NUMBER GAME 1

75 9 6 2 4 9 | 950

NUMBER GAME 2

100 5 6 8 3 3 | 472

CONUNDRUM

G U N G I B I L E

LETTER GAME 1

N	E	L	I	M	S	L	I	T

LETTER GAME 2

P	R	E	M	I	L	E	N	C

LETTER GAME 3

O	R	E	V	S	U	N	Y	L

LETTER GAME 4

R	U	N	T	E	R	O	C	A

NUMBER GAME 1

25	7	7	3	9	6	**894**

NUMBER GAME 2

25	8	1	7	1	9	**730**

CONUNDRUM

E	V	I	L	M	A	M	B	O

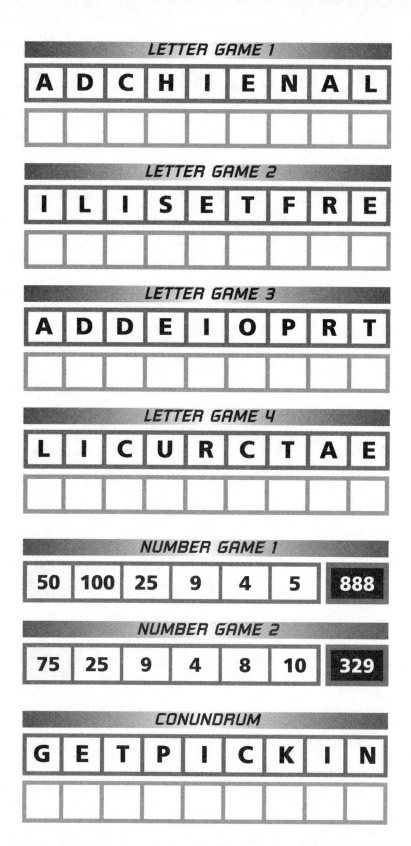

LETTER GAME 1

A	D	C	H	I	E	N	A	L

LETTER GAME 2

I	L	I	S	E	T	F	R	E

LETTER GAME 3

A	D	D	E	I	O	P	R	T

LETTER GAME 4

L	I	C	U	R	C	T	A	E

NUMBER GAME 1

50	100	25	9	4	5	888

NUMBER GAME 2

75	25	9	4	8	10	329

CONUNDRUM

G	E	T	P	I	C	K	I	N

LETTER GAME 1

R	R	L	L	D	E	E	B	A

LETTER GAME 2

R	T	U	S	M	L	P	I	E

LETTER GAME 3

S	H	R	E	N	O	M	O	I

LETTER GAME 4

D	E	E	P	L	I	T	A	G

NUMBER GAME 1

50	7	10	4	2	6	**911**

NUMBER GAME 2

25	10	9	9	10	4	**634**

CONUNDRUM

T	A	L	K	S	E	N	S	H

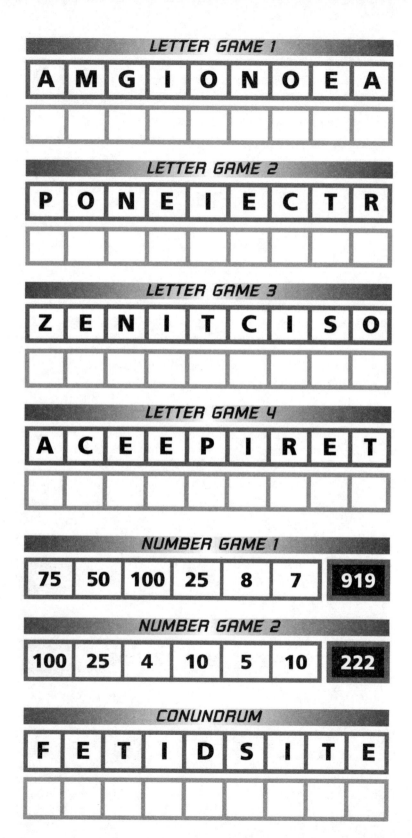

LETTER GAME 1

| A | M | G | I | O | N | O | E | A |

LETTER GAME 2

| P | O | N | E | I | E | C | T | R |

LETTER GAME 3

| Z | E | N | I | T | C | I | S | O |

LETTER GAME 4

| A | C | E | E | P | I | R | E | T |

NUMBER GAME 1

| 75 | 50 | 100 | 25 | 8 | 7 | 919 |

NUMBER GAME 2

| 100 | 25 | 4 | 10 | 5 | 10 | 222 |

CONUNDRUM

| F | E | T | I | D | S | I | T | E |

LETTER GAME 1

E	E	M	I	R	R	P	E	D

LETTER GAME 2

G	O	R	I	E	U	S	B	O

LETTER GAME 3

M	E	R	I	S	A	P	W	O

LETTER GAME 4

I	A	N	N	E	R	I	T	T

NUMBER GAME 1

50	6	7	4	1	3	786

NUMBER GAME 2

8	9	10	1	2	3	694

CONUNDRUM

I	D	I	N	N	A	J	O	G

LETTER GAME 1

E	N	T	H	U	M	I	S	T

LETTER GAME 2

Y	M	R	E	O	L	C	A	J

LETTER GAME 3

V	I	N	D	R	E	B	U	D

LETTER GAME 4

G	L	U	T	I	N	Q	I	F

NUMBER GAME 1

50	6	8	4	9	9	**681**

NUMBER GAME 2

75	2	8	7	1	3	**186**

CONUNDRUM

F	I	N	E	S	T	Y	I	N

LETTER GAME 1

P	E	S	A	T	E	B	A	L

LETTER GAME 2

I	I	A	E	R	L	T	N	Y

LETTER GAME 3

A	C	E	I	N	N	L	O	T

LETTER GAME 4

F	G	G	I	L	A	N	I	N

NUMBER GAME 1

25	100	50	75	2	9	343

NUMBER GAME 2

50	100	3	2	7	7	468

CONUNDRUM

D	E	P	A	R	T	E	E	S

LETTER GAME 1

F	R	E	S	T	U	L	A	M

LETTER GAME 2

B	R	O	I	D	A	P	L	C

LETTER GAME 3

L	O	O	H	K	N	T	E	I

LETTER GAME 4

T	W	O	R	K	S	E	N	I

NUMBER GAME 1

5	7	6	3	4	8	963

NUMBER GAME 2

75	9	9	10	8	8	874

CONUNDRUM

A	P	O	O	R	N	I	T	E

LETTER GAME 1

A	A	S	H	I	M	N	P	R

LETTER GAME 2

G	R	O	N	S	T	E	A	F

LETTER GAME 3

T	I	S	U	E	N	B	C	O

LETTER GAME 4

D	U	L	E	C	I	S	O	T

NUMBER GAME 1

25	8	4	3	3	8	540

NUMBER GAME 2

100	25	2	7	5	5	368

CONUNDRUM

P	A	N	T	O	G	E	A	R

LETTER GAME 1

G	N	K	I	R	M	S	I	A

LETTER GAME 2

A	D	E	E	V	N	R	L	I

LETTER GAME 3

L	O	N	I	C	O	M	E	S

LETTER GAME 4

P	E	T	H	O	L	A	T	I

NUMBER GAME 1

75	50	25	3	4	3	645

NUMBER GAME 2

100	10	7	6	6	2	537

CONUNDRUM

F	I	E	R	C	E	T	A	N

LETTER GAME 1

V	L	I	S	E	C	U	R	E

LETTER GAME 2

T	R	O	N	E	G	A	S	W

LETTER GAME 3

D	E	C	I	E	P	O	C	L

LETTER GAME 4

B	I	T	H	O	R	P	I	E

NUMBER GAME 1

50	10	4	9	5	8	**876**

NUMBER GAME 2

25	75	100	6	9	9	**402**

CONUNDRUM

G	N	O	M	I	C	L	I	P

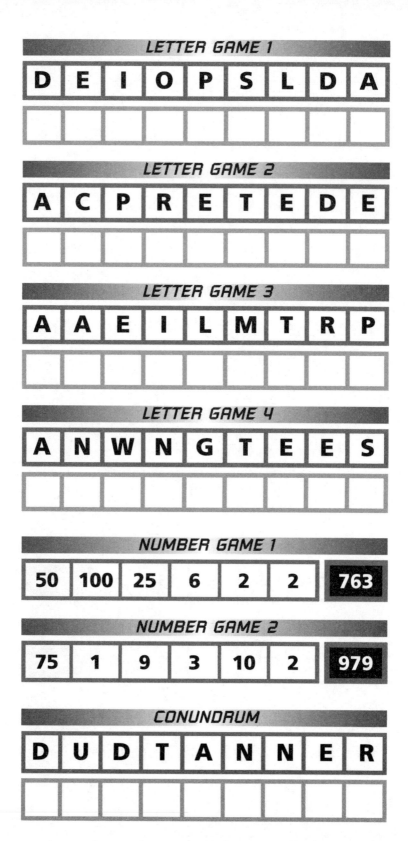

LETTER GAME 1

D	E	I	O	P	S	L	D	A

LETTER GAME 2

A	C	P	R	E	T	E	D	E

LETTER GAME 3

A	A	E	I	L	M	T	R	P

LETTER GAME 4

A	N	W	N	G	T	E	E	S

NUMBER GAME 1

50	100	25	6	2	2	763

NUMBER GAME 2

75	1	9	3	10	2	979

CONUNDRUM

D	U	D	T	A	N	N	E	R

LETTER GAME 1

T	T	E	L	B	E	X	A	A

LETTER GAME 2

C	S	E	L	I	S	O	S	E

LETTER GAME 3

P	L	M	E	C	A	O	T	R

LETTER GAME 4

A	E	G	N	T	T	I	P	N

NUMBER GAME 1

25	75	4	4	7	8	536

NUMBER GAME 2

50	1	7	5	7	5	634

CONUNDRUM

C	O	C	O	A	H	I	L	L

LETTER GAME 1

Y	O	R	N	S	T	E	D	K

LETTER GAME 2

H	O	F	I	S	L	W	B	E

LETTER GAME 3

E	F	Q	N	I	S	H	U	E

LETTER GAME 4

F	F	U	N	O	T	A	B	I

NUMBER GAME 1

100	8	2	7	5	4	666

NUMBER GAME 2

10	6	9	7	2	1	850

CONUNDRUM

M	A	I	D	E	N	T	O	N

LETTER GAME 1

D	D	E	M	O	N	T	S	I

LETTER GAME 2

D	E	U	C	M	P	O	T	I

LETTER GAME 3

C	L	Y	B	O	M	I	S	A

LETTER GAME 4

A	C	T	N	E	L	T	E	M

NUMBER GAME 1

25	50	75	100	8	5	**344**

NUMBER GAME 2

25	9	8	7	10	4	**922**

CONUNDRUM

R	I	S	K	Q	U	I	E	T

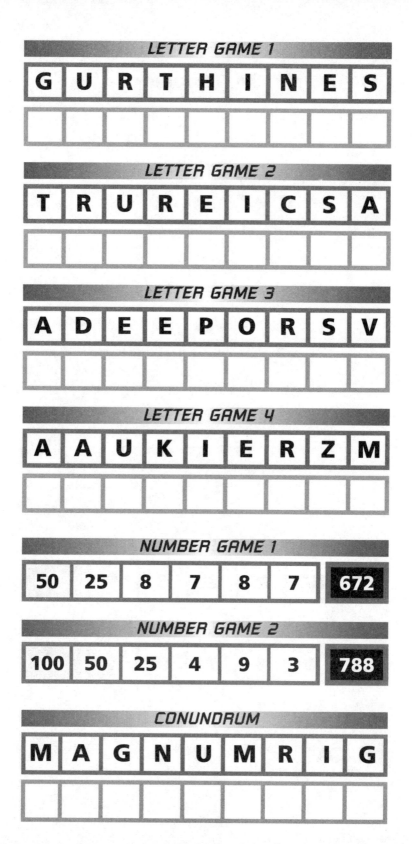

LETTER GAME 1

G	U	R	T	H	I	N	E	S

LETTER GAME 2

T	R	U	R	E	I	C	S	A

LETTER GAME 3

A	D	E	E	P	O	R	S	V

LETTER GAME 4

A	A	U	K	I	E	R	Z	M

NUMBER GAME 1

50	25	8	7	8	7	672

NUMBER GAME 2

100	50	25	4	9	3	788

CONUNDRUM

M	A	G	N	U	M	R	I	G

LETTER GAME 1

| D | E | E | P | R | A | S | E | F |

LETTER GAME 2

| X | E | R | I | F | U | T | S | A |

LETTER GAME 3

| P | H | S | T | O | S | N | A | E |

LETTER GAME 4

| S | D | U | N | C | T | I | O | F |

NUMBER GAME 1

| 75 | 100 | 2 | 2 | 3 | 4 | **519** |

NUMBER GAME 2

| 3 | 1 | 9 | 7 | 6 | 5 | **346** |

CONUNDRUM

| R | A | C | E | C | H | A | R | T |

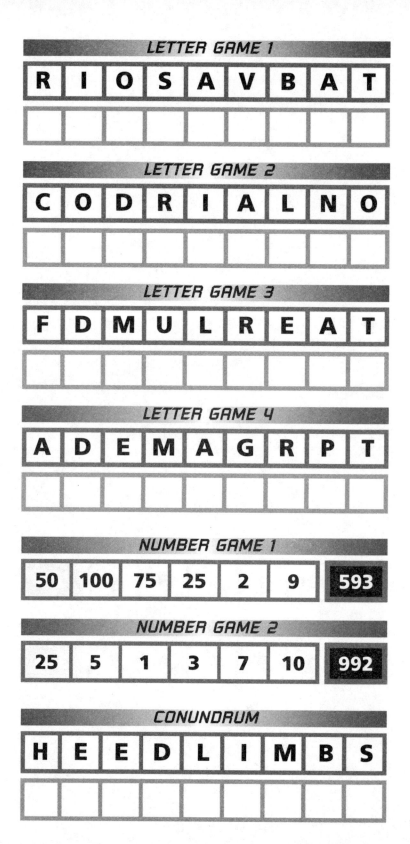

LETTER GAME 1

R	I	O	S	A	V	B	A	T

LETTER GAME 2

C	O	D	R	I	A	L	N	O

LETTER GAME 3

F	D	M	U	L	R	E	A	T

LETTER GAME 4

A	D	E	M	A	G	R	P	T

NUMBER GAME 1

50	100	75	25	2	9	593

NUMBER GAME 2

25	5	1	3	7	10	992

CONUNDRUM

H	E	E	D	L	I	M	B	S

LETTER GAME 1

G	P	O	N	G	L	E	T	A

LETTER GAME 2

E	M	I	N	B	S	U	S	D

LETTER GAME 3

R	E	T	I	E	V	S	T	E

LETTER GAME 4

S	T	R	B	O	O	K	E	T

NUMBER GAME 1

50	3	5	3	5	2	731

NUMBER GAME 2

100	7	9	8	9	7	178

CONUNDRUM

C	U	T	S	U	N	C	L	E

LETTER GAME 1

A	C	H	E	R	I	P	E	T

LETTER GAME 2

F	D	E	U	N	T	C	O	A

LETTER GAME 3

G	E	S	T	O	P	R	E	H

LETTER GAME 4

C	R	O	E	P	I	T	Y	H

NUMBER GAME 1

50	75	3	9	4	4	777

NUMBER GAME 2

100	75	6	2	5	9	339

CONUNDRUM

S	O	G	I	M	A	R	K	S

LETTER GAME 1

F	E	F	O	T	B	A	L	P

LETTER GAME 2

E	C	H	S	L	U	F	A	B

LETTER GAME 3

D	E	I	P	N	A	S	T	P

LETTER GAME 4

E	N	N	I	F	A	C	R	E

NUMBER GAME 1

25	50	75	100	9	10	834

NUMBER GAME 2

50	5	6	8	6	8	477

CONUNDRUM

T	E	N	N	I	S	F	A	G

LETTER GAME 1

G	N	R	U	N	E	T	O	C

LETTER GAME 2

T	H	I	R	E	P	I	W	R

LETTER GAME 3

H	P	J	O	U	R	D	S	I

LETTER GAME 4

P	D	S	E	U	T	S	I	T

NUMBER GAME 1

8	1	5	10	10	7	925

NUMBER GAME 2

25	2	5	5	3	6	766

CONUNDRUM

B	Y	E	V	O	R	D	E	Y

LETTER GAME 1

R	O	D	P	U	W	N	O	T

LETTER GAME 2

S	E	T	L	I	X	E	P	T

LETTER GAME 3

W	C	H	E	E	R	A	B	A

LETTER GAME 4

F	E	L	I	D	F	S	N	A

NUMBER GAME 1

50	100	4	1	10	9	376

NUMBER GAME 2

75	100	25	6	9	9	520

CONUNDRUM

F	I	N	A	L	L	Y	U	P

ROUND 233

LETTER GAME 1

C	I	P	L	A	M	A	S	E

LETTER GAME 2

D	E	M	G	A	R	P	A	I

LETTER GAME 3

B	O	O	M	I	H	E	N	T

LETTER GAME 4

A	A	E	L	L	B	T	M	I

NUMBER GAME 1

25	100	50	9	9	6	**876**

NUMBER GAME 2

50	75	2	10	10	1	**674**

CONUNDRUM

T	U	F	F	B	I	N	G	E

LETTER GAME 1

E	E	F	T	L	O	R	V	I

LETTER GAME 2

D	G	E	E	E	I	P	R	W

LETTER GAME 3

A	P	I	N	P	L	A	F	T

LETTER GAME 4

A	N	E	M	T	T	I	I	R

NUMBER GAME 1

100	1	2	3	4	5	678

NUMBER GAME 2

75	4	4	9	7	1	494

CONUNDRUM

N	O	V	O	P	R	O	F	E

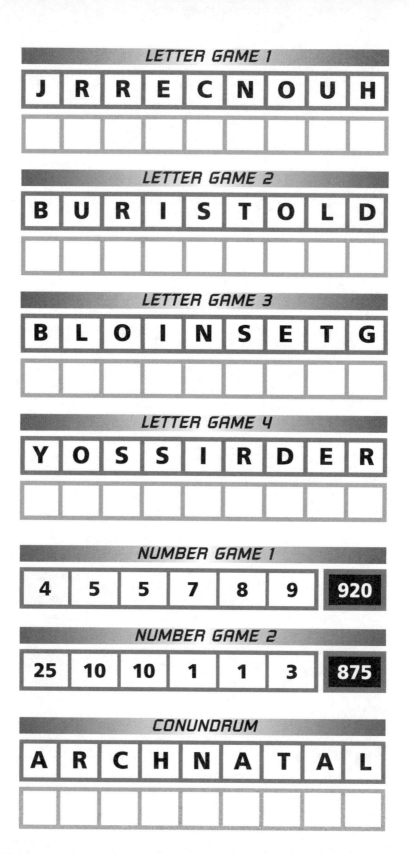

LETTER GAME 1

J	R	R	E	C	N	O	U	H

LETTER GAME 2

B	U	R	I	S	T	O	L	D

LETTER GAME 3

B	L	O	I	N	S	E	T	G

LETTER GAME 4

Y	O	S	S	I	R	D	E	R

NUMBER GAME 1

4	5	5	7	8	9	**920**

NUMBER GAME 2

25	10	10	1	1	3	**875**

CONUNDRUM

A	R	C	H	N	A	T	A	L

LETTER GAME 1

R	I	V	E	T	Y	S	I	D

LETTER GAME 2

M	E	N	I	T	R	O	Y	W

LETTER GAME 3

F	R	U	B	T	E	L	A	E

LETTER GAME 4

A	A	I	R	T	Y	V	N	N

NUMBER GAME 1

50	100	75	25	9	8	555

NUMBER GAME 2

25	100	7	5	6	6	844

CONUNDRUM

N	I	G	E	L	N	E	S	S

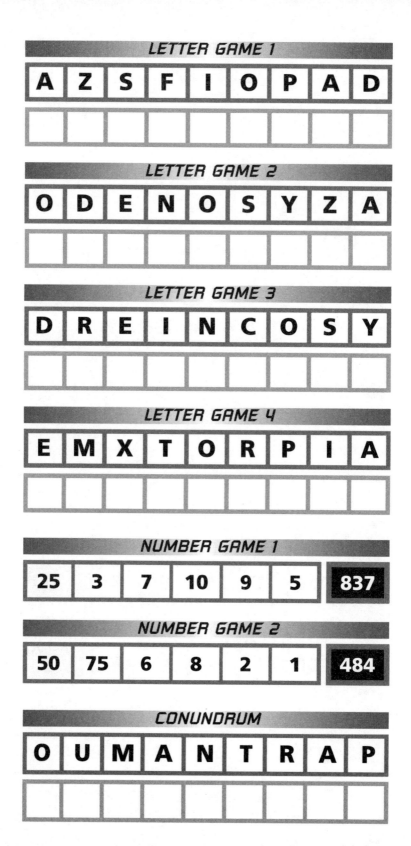

LETTER GAME 1

A	Z	S	F	I	O	P	A	D

LETTER GAME 2

O	D	E	N	O	S	Y	Z	A

LETTER GAME 3

D	R	E	I	N	C	O	S	Y

LETTER GAME 4

E	M	X	T	O	R	P	I	A

NUMBER GAME 1

25	3	7	10	9	5	837

NUMBER GAME 2

50	75	6	8	2	1	484

CONUNDRUM

O	U	M	A	N	T	R	A	P

LETTER GAME 1

G	U	R	E	L	T	O	N	J

LETTER GAME 2

I	B	R	S	N	A	K	E	T

LETTER GAME 3

C	O	T	B	B	A	M	I	S

LETTER GAME 4

N	E	U	T	E	R	H	O	T

NUMBER GAME 1

9	10	5	3	2	4	621

NUMBER GAME 2

50	100	75	2	4	7	945

CONUNDRUM

I	C	O	U	N	T	B	A	D

LETTER GAME 1

A	C	D	E	L	I	M	O	T

LETTER GAME 2

S	E	R	I	M	U	F	P	T

LETTER GAME 3

A	B	D	E	G	O	P	R	Y

LETTER GAME 4

B	U	D	I	E	S	S	I	D

NUMBER GAME 1

100	4	7	8	5	9	276

NUMBER GAME 2

25	10	1	7	2	4	529

CONUNDRUM

G	O	L	D	E	N	Y	I	P

ROUND 240

LETTER GAME 1

S	E	B	T	L	O	N	C	A

LETTER GAME 2

S	E	R	H	I	V	A	D	W

LETTER GAME 3

A	C	I	N	B	M	A	L	E

LETTER GAME 4

G	I	R	N	I	O	L	E	L

NUMBER GAME 1

50	100	6	7	8	6	970

NUMBER GAME 2

75	25	9	6	8	7	829

CONUNDRUM

N	U	T	D	E	A	D	U	N

249

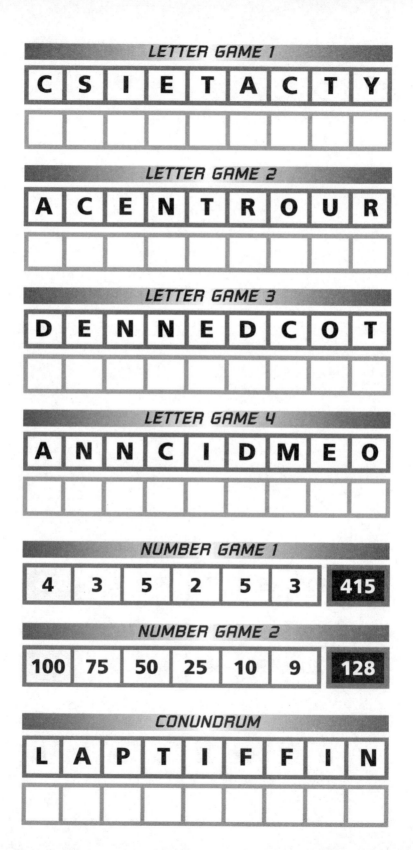

LETTER GAME 1

C S I E T A C T Y

LETTER GAME 2

A C E N T R O U R

LETTER GAME 3

D E N N E D C O T

LETTER GAME 4

A N N C I D M E O

NUMBER GAME 1

4 3 5 2 5 3 | 415

NUMBER GAME 2

100 75 50 25 10 9 | 128

CONUNDRUM

L A P T I F F I N

LETTER GAME 1

S	E	I	P	Q	T	U	R	N

LETTER GAME 2

C	L	N	U	T	O	R	A	N

LETTER GAME 3

A	G	E	L	U	F	S	E	I

LETTER GAME 4

G	I	E	B	E	R	A	V	N

NUMBER GAME 1

100	75	5	5	10	10	230

NUMBER GAME 2

25	75	100	2	8	9	636

CONUNDRUM

B	L	E	W	N	I	G	E	L

LETTER GAME 1

S T I C E S D A E

LETTER GAME 2

H O G B E L B I S

LETTER GAME 3

S S I E A T M Z I

LETTER GAME 4

V R G E N O C E F

NUMBER GAME 1

50 100 25 75 8 8 → 414

NUMBER GAME 2

3 9 10 9 6 1 → 500

CONUNDRUM

I N A B A R R I L

LETTER GAME 1

A	E	I	N	N	S	P	L	U

LETTER GAME 2

P	H	N	D	E	E	R	S	A

LETTER GAME 3

A	R	T	E	S	T	Q	U	Y

LETTER GAME 4

E	E	C	N	T	O	R	T	E

NUMBER GAME 1

25	50	7	3	4	4	928

NUMBER GAME 2

75	4	9	5	2	2	879

CONUNDRUM

O	X	E	N	R	I	G	H	T

LETTER GAME 1

B	R	U	P	T	E	H	G	Y

LETTER GAME 2

H	O	O	E	S	N	W	S	I

LETTER GAME 3

N	D	G	I	R	Y	O	I	J

LETTER GAME 4

W	K	O	O	C	R	A	E	D

NUMBER GAME 1

50	7	9	4	5	7	886

NUMBER GAME 2

50	100	8	9	6	6	222

CONUNDRUM

F	A	R	W	A	L	L	E	T

LETTER GAME 1

F	O	B	E	T	A	I	L	D

LETTER GAME 2

C	E	D	L	R	O	T	A	E

LETTER GAME 3

R	U	S	B	I	D	R	E	G

LETTER GAME 4

D	I	T	R	E	L	A	O	I

NUMBER GAME 1

25	4	8	6	5	5	643

NUMBER GAME 2

75	50	7	9	4	1	882

CONUNDRUM

L	I	Q	U	I	F	A	D	E

LETTER GAME 1

B	K	I	E	R	A	S	L	T

LETTER GAME 2

D	E	C	O	U	D	L	E	B

LETTER GAME 3

E	I	S	N	T	E	O	T	H

LETTER GAME 4

C	D	E	I	I	K	T	W	M

NUMBER GAME 1

100	6	4	2	1	5	340

NUMBER GAME 2

50	7	4	9	10	10	844

CONUNDRUM

P	I	G	S	H	R	I	N	E

LETTER GAME 1

Q	K	T	I	H	O	O	L	C

LETTER GAME 2

D	E	R	E	R	I	P	M	L

LETTER GAME 3

A	A	E	M	G	P	L	Y	T

LETTER GAME 4

T	I	M	E	D	A	R	S	E

NUMBER GAME 1

100	50	75	25	7	7	999

NUMBER GAME 2

6	2	5	8	1	4	435

CONUNDRUM

S	I	D	E	G	R	A	D	E

LETTER GAME 1

L	T	E	D	I	M	O	P	A

LETTER GAME 2

D	A	M	E	P	E	I	N	C

LETTER GAME 3

A	S	R	E	P	E	E	D	T

LETTER GAME 4

T	Q	U	E	O	C	Y	R	A

NUMBER GAME 1

100	7	8	9	9	7	533

NUMBER GAME 2

50	25	3	5	2	7	894

CONUNDRUM

E	E	E	S	T	H	I	C	K

LETTER GAME 1

T	E	R	U	Q	I	N	A	S

LETTER GAME 2

A	C	F	B	O	P	S	O	X

LETTER GAME 3

A	A	T	Y	W	U	P	N	C

LETTER GAME 4

A	C	T	R	I	A	L	S	F

NUMBER GAME 1

75	100	50	3	2	1	582

NUMBER GAME 2

25	3	7	10	9	9	645

CONUNDRUM

R	E	D	P	A	R	E	N	T

LETTER GAME 1

A	E	R	I	D	P	E	R	H

LETTER GAME 2

R	O	U	D	I	S	E	R	F

LETTER GAME 3

R	I	D	B	E	N	D	D	E

LETTER GAME 4

B	K	U	H	S	E	I	P	T

NUMBER GAME 1

50	100	75	4	8	4	338

NUMBER GAME 2

50	100	6	9	5	6	777

CONUNDRUM

L	O	U	N	G	E	M	O	O

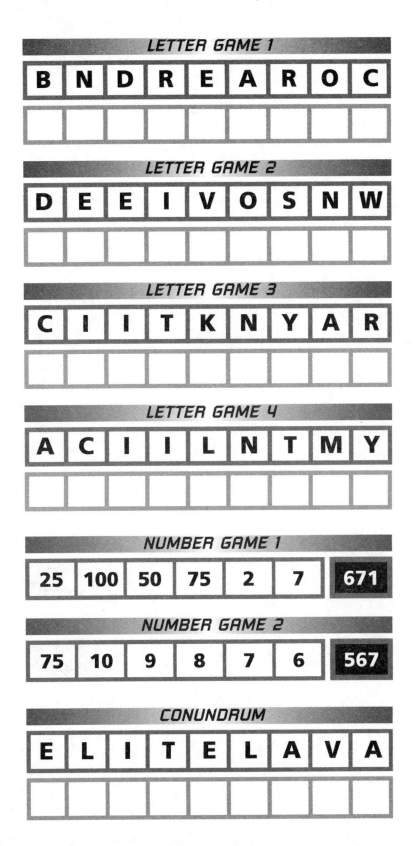

LETTER GAME 1

B	N	D	R	E	A	R	O	C

LETTER GAME 2

D	E	E	I	V	O	S	N	W

LETTER GAME 3

C	I	I	T	K	N	Y	A	R

LETTER GAME 4

A	C	I	I	L	N	T	M	Y

NUMBER GAME 1

25	100	50	75	2	7	671

NUMBER GAME 2

75	10	9	8	7	6	567

CONUNDRUM

E	L	I	T	E	L	A	V	A

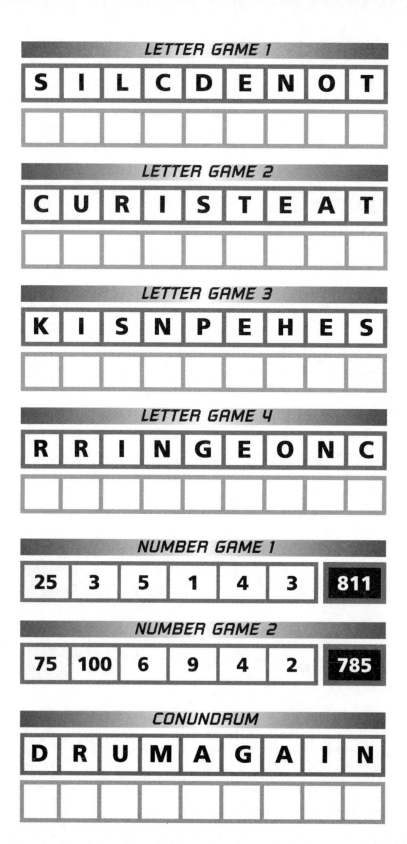

LETTER GAME 1

| S | I | L | C | D | E | N | O | T |

LETTER GAME 2

| C | U | R | I | S | T | E | A | T |

LETTER GAME 3

| K | I | S | N | P | E | H | E | S |

LETTER GAME 4

| R | R | I | N | G | E | O | N | C |

NUMBER GAME 1

| 25 | 3 | 5 | 1 | 4 | 3 | 811 |

NUMBER GAME 2

| 75 | 100 | 6 | 9 | 4 | 2 | 785 |

CONUNDRUM

| D | R | U | M | A | G | A | I | N |

LETTER GAME 1

S	T	I	N	S	E	L	A	S

LETTER GAME 2

G	E	F	T	O	A	S	F	Y

LETTER GAME 3

L	R	E	P	H	M	E	A	E

LETTER GAME 4

E	D	N	E	R	G	A	D	L

NUMBER GAME 1

50	3	9	10	8	1	920

NUMBER GAME 2

25	75	5	10	5	1	824

CONUNDRUM

I	L	U	V	B	E	E	T	S

LETTER GAME 1

A	H	S	N	E	T	A	P	X

LETTER GAME 2

P	L	U	N	T	E	O	R	C

LETTER GAME 3

D	A	L	O	S	T	E	I	M

LETTER GAME 4

F	E	T	E	B	R	E	A	E

NUMBER GAME 1

8	10	7	9	6	5	778

NUMBER GAME 2

25	5	6	1	6	1	846

CONUNDRUM

D	U	B	L	L	Z	E	R	O

LETTER GAME 1

M	E	R	N	I	T	A	E	A

LETTER GAME 2

A	C	N	N	U	S	E	I	G

LETTER GAME 3

D	N	C	F	I	E	E	T	S

LETTER GAME 4

E	B	I	T	L	U	E	S	T

NUMBER GAME 1

50	75	2	9	1	8	**503**

NUMBER GAME 2

75	100	25	50	10	10	**431**

CONUNDRUM

F	U	N	N	I	G	U	R	L

LETTER GAME 1

P	I	N	B	U	L	T	E	R

LETTER GAME 2

G	E	E	S	T	O	R	C	I

LETTER GAME 3

H	E	R	T	E	E	M	O	S

LETTER GAME 4

C	T	P	E	H	A	D	S	I

NUMBER GAME 1

100	6	5	8	7	3	942

NUMBER GAME 2

50	75	100	1	7	4	558

CONUNDRUM

T	A	C	A	T	I	N	G	L

LETTER GAME 1

C	D	I	N	I	M	S	I	A

LETTER GAME 2

T	I	N	R	E	G	A	S	C

LETTER GAME 3

C	H	I	N	T	E	U	L	A

LETTER GAME 4

S	R	I	G	O	N	A	R	W

NUMBER GAME 1

25	2	3	4	3	1	840

NUMBER GAME 2

75	100	6	4	8	5	655

CONUNDRUM

D	U	B	L	E	H	I	P	S

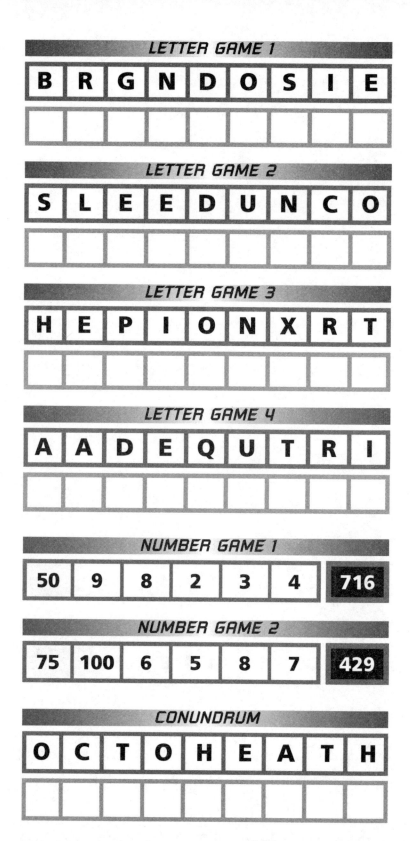

LETTER GAME 1

| B | R | G | N | D | O | S | I | E |

LETTER GAME 2

| S | L | E | E | D | U | N | C | O |

LETTER GAME 3

| H | E | P | I | O | N | X | R | T |

LETTER GAME 4

| A | A | D | E | Q | U | T | R | I |

NUMBER GAME 1

| 50 | 9 | 8 | 2 | 3 | 4 | **716** |

NUMBER GAME 2

| 75 | 100 | 6 | 5 | 8 | 7 | **429** |

CONUNDRUM

| O | C | T | O | H | E | A | T | H |

LETTER GAME 1

C	E	R	I	B	I	N	S	A

LETTER GAME 2

D	R	U	N	I	M	E	T	O

LETTER GAME 3

V	T	L	E	N	A	C	O	W

LETTER GAME 4

D	N	E	M	O	A	B	E	G

NUMBER GAME 1

25	50	75	2	6	9	862

NUMBER GAME 2

100	6	4	7	7	5	984

CONUNDRUM

D	E	A	T	H	G	R	I	N

LETTER GAME 1

C	H	U	R	L	I	E	V	A

LETTER GAME 2

H	T	E	M	P	I	A	S	E

LETTER GAME 3

E	R	U	S	T	I	M	O	T

LETTER GAME 4

G	A	N	B	T	I	E	R	J

NUMBER GAME 1

50	10	10	5	5	4	**723**

NUMBER GAME 2

75	6	10	6	9	9	**321**

CONUNDRUM

R	E	T	I	N	T	W	I	G

LETTER GAME 1

E	H	N	O	T	O	U	S	B

LETTER GAME 2

G	R	E	E	V	O	C	A	S

LETTER GAME 3

T	E	I	M	N	O	T	N	C

LETTER GAME 4

P	H	E	P	T	I	S	O	S

NUMBER GAME 1

25	50	75	100	8	8	**739**

NUMBER GAME 2

50	75	4	5	1	7	**666**

CONUNDRUM

E	U	R	E	S	I	L	L	Y

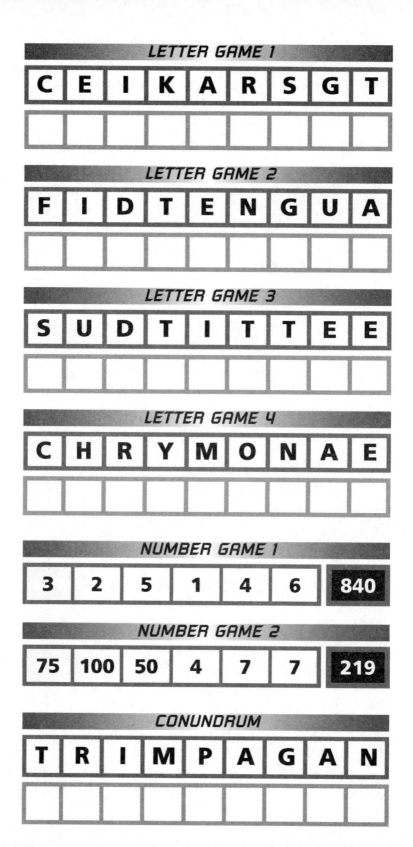

LETTER GAME 1

C E I K A R S G T

LETTER GAME 2

F I D T E N G U A

LETTER GAME 3

S U D T I T T E E

LETTER GAME 4

C H R Y M O N A E

NUMBER GAME 1

| 3 | 2 | 5 | 1 | 4 | 6 | 840 |

NUMBER GAME 2

| 75 | 100 | 50 | 4 | 7 | 7 | 219 |

CONUNDRUM

T R I M P A G A N

LETTER GAME 1

H	I	S	D	A	V	E	R	B

LETTER GAME 2

W	H	S	C	O	D	E	I	K

LETTER GAME 3

B	H	C	E	E	O	T	I	A

LETTER GAME 4

B	E	D	L	E	C	A	O	D

NUMBER GAME 1

100	25	9	5	1	1	**307**

NUMBER GAME 2

75	8	8	9	5	7	**326**

CONUNDRUM

G	E	T	S	I	N	D	E	T

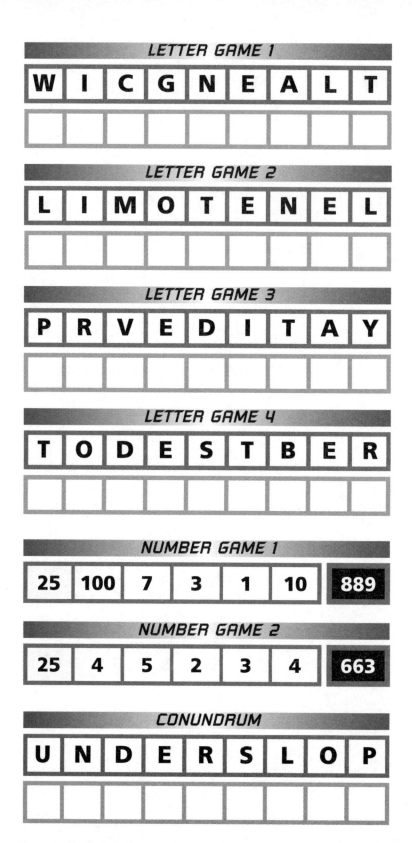

LETTER GAME 1

W	I	C	G	N	E	A	L	T

LETTER GAME 2

L	I	M	O	T	E	N	E	L

LETTER GAME 3

P	R	V	E	D	I	T	A	Y

LETTER GAME 4

T	O	D	E	S	T	B	E	R

NUMBER GAME 1

25	100	7	3	1	10	889

NUMBER GAME 2

25	4	5	2	3	4	663

CONUNDRUM

U	N	D	E	R	S	L	O	P

LETTER GAME 1

P	A	T	R	O	E	V	A	E

LETTER GAME 2

K	E	W	L	I	N	G	A	P

LETTER GAME 3

B	R	I	E	L	A	C	K	N

LETTER GAME 4

W	H	O	B	O	L	E	L	I

NUMBER GAME 1

50	75	25	7	8	6	**485**

NUMBER GAME 2

100	50	10	10	9	9	**779**

CONUNDRUM

D	A	R	K	B	E	H	A	N

LETTER GAME 1

A	D	G	E	I	I	L	P	T

LETTER GAME 2

C	O	N	E	R	K	E	R	F

LETTER GAME 3

T	I	R	O	V	E	T	H	A

LETTER GAME 4

P	U	R	S	O	S	U	S	T

NUMBER GAME 1

50	7	8	3	1	3	947

NUMBER GAME 2

25	100	2	8	3	6	524

CONUNDRUM

O	S	I	M	M	E	R	E	D

LETTER GAME 1

E	A	D	I	E	D	E	N	T

LETTER GAME 2

Y	N	O	R	E	C	D	A	G

LETTER GAME 3

F	L	O	P	T	H	I	S	U

LETTER GAME 4

B	E	B	Q	A	U	L	S	R

NUMBER GAME 1

10	7	5	3	9	8	957

NUMBER GAME 2

25	1	7	4	1	5	608

CONUNDRUM

T	A	U	N	T	L	A	R	A

LETTER GAME 1

H	P	E	T	I	S	E	E	W

LETTER GAME 2

F	I	G	T	R	A	W	E	L

LETTER GAME 3

O	R	E	N	I	M	O	V	T

LETTER GAME 4

S	T	L	O	R	T	H	E	I

NUMBER GAME 1

75	50	6	6	8	9	858

NUMBER GAME 2

75	50	6	9	4	3	860

CONUNDRUM

P	I	P	S	N	U	G	L	Y

LETTER GAME 1

Y	A	B	A	T	E	R	L	P

LETTER GAME 2

C	L	U	M	R	E	T	P	I

LETTER GAME 3

A	E	G	M	O	N	T	I	R

LETTER GAME 4

T	E	N	S	I	T	S	R	A

NUMBER GAME 1

100	5	7	7	1	2	948

NUMBER GAME 2

25	7	9	10	8	8	562

CONUNDRUM

I	P	O	F	E	R	R	E	T

LETTER GAME 1

S	S	L	C	O	R	E	A	I

LETTER GAME 2

A	B	E	E	L	K	O	T	U

LETTER GAME 3

C	T	E	N	R	O	R	E	H

LETTER GAME 4

T	I	I	E	E	F	L	M	H

NUMBER GAME 1

50	100	25	3	8	5	764

NUMBER GAME 2

75	5	10	6	7	6	637

CONUNDRUM

R	E	P	A	V	E	I	N	G

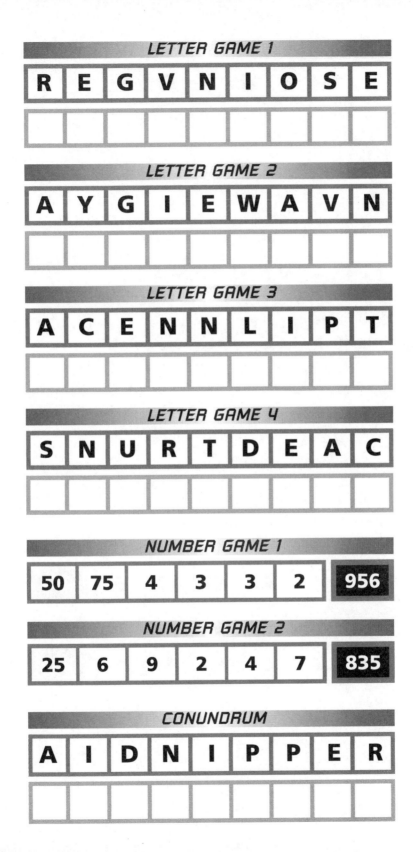

LETTER GAME 1

R E G V N I O S E

LETTER GAME 2

A Y G I E W A V N

LETTER GAME 3

A C E N N L I P T

LETTER GAME 4

S N U R T D E A C

NUMBER GAME 1

50 75 4 3 3 2 | 956

NUMBER GAME 2

25 6 9 2 4 7 | 835

CONUNDRUM

A I D N I P P E R

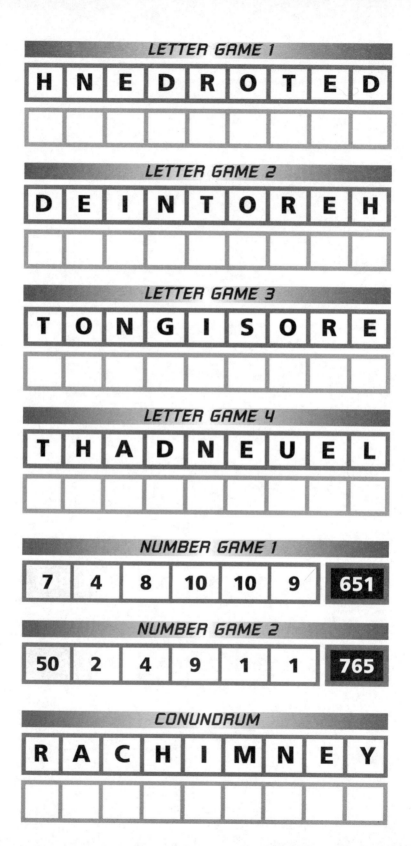

LETTER GAME 1

H	N	E	D	R	O	T	E	D

LETTER GAME 2

D	E	I	N	T	O	R	E	H

LETTER GAME 3

T	O	N	G	I	S	O	R	E

LETTER GAME 4

T	H	A	D	N	E	U	E	L

NUMBER GAME 1

7	4	8	10	10	9	651

NUMBER GAME 2

50	2	4	9	1	1	765

CONUNDRUM

R	A	C	H	I	M	N	E	Y

LETTER GAME 1

| B | V | E | R | S | O | I | T | Y |

LETTER GAME 2

| A | L | L | I | S | E | B | O | G |

LETTER GAME 3

| O | O | I | L | A | M | N | T | P |

LETTER GAME 4

| S | T | E | R | A | V | E | R | H |

NUMBER GAME 1

| 100 | 75 | 3 | 3 | 4 | 4 | **849** |

NUMBER GAME 2

| 75 | 5 | 2 | 2 | 1 | 4 | **274** |

CONUNDRUM

| M | I | N | O | R | G | L | I | P |

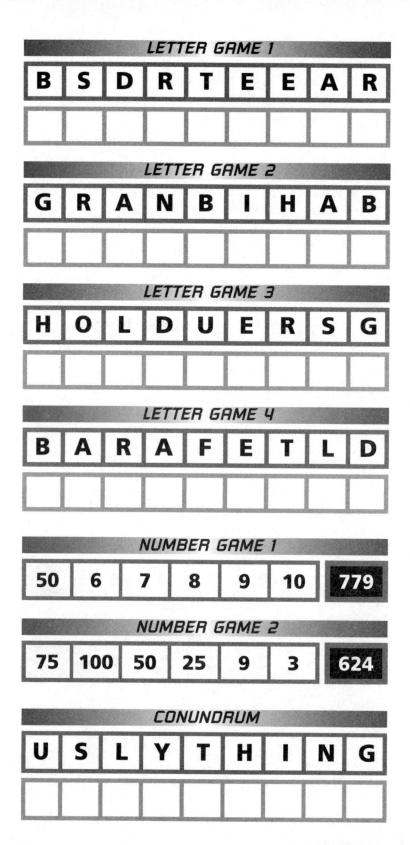

LETTER GAME 1

B	S	D	R	T	E	E	A	R

LETTER GAME 2

G	R	A	N	B	I	H	A	B

LETTER GAME 3

H	O	L	D	U	E	R	S	G

LETTER GAME 4

B	A	R	A	F	E	T	L	D

NUMBER GAME 1

50	6	7	8	9	10	**779**

NUMBER GAME 2

75	100	50	25	9	3	**624**

CONUNDRUM

U	S	L	Y	T	H	I	N	G

LETTER GAME 1

G	R	E	G	G	N	I	N	I

LETTER GAME 2

R	O	V	E	G	N	A	I	R

LETTER GAME 3

V	E	R	P	I	T	O	A	E

LETTER GAME 4

M	I	R	S	T	E	A	D	P

NUMBER GAME 1

25	3	6	8	7	3	**987**

NUMBER GAME 2

50	75	6	10	2	2	**536**

CONUNDRUM

S	P	E	E	D	R	O	C	S

285

LETTER GAME 1

T	Y	E	R	P	I	A	S	U

LETTER GAME 2

E	S	B	D	I	V	A	L	E

LETTER GAME 3

C	R	E	M	K	A	T	I	D

LETTER GAME 4

C	L	O	M	E	G	I	N	W

NUMBER GAME 1

25	50	100	75	9	5	644

NUMBER GAME 2

75	8	9	3	9	4	816

CONUNDRUM

L	O	U	S	I	E	R	I	G

LETTER GAME 1

I	D	I	H	N	A	U	J	M

LETTER GAME 2

Z	H	I	K	P	O	R	I	T

LETTER GAME 3

P	E	R	N	O	D	T	A	G

LETTER GAME 4

B	S	T	E	R	A	D	E	I

NUMBER GAME 1

2	7	8	8	5	5	900

NUMBER GAME 2

100	25	50	4	3	6	782

CONUNDRUM

H	O	W	D	O	O	M	A	N

LETTER GAME 1

D	I	L	E	S	O	C	K	R

LETTER GAME 2

T	H	O	L	I	A	N	B	E

LETTER GAME 3

B	U	R	O	N	A	I	L	T

LETTER GAME 4

S	E	V	I	T	U	B	L	E

NUMBER GAME 1

25	4	1	3	3	2	**429**

NUMBER GAME 2

100	6	9	4	5	7	**338**

CONUNDRUM

B	I	G	M	E	R	L	I	N

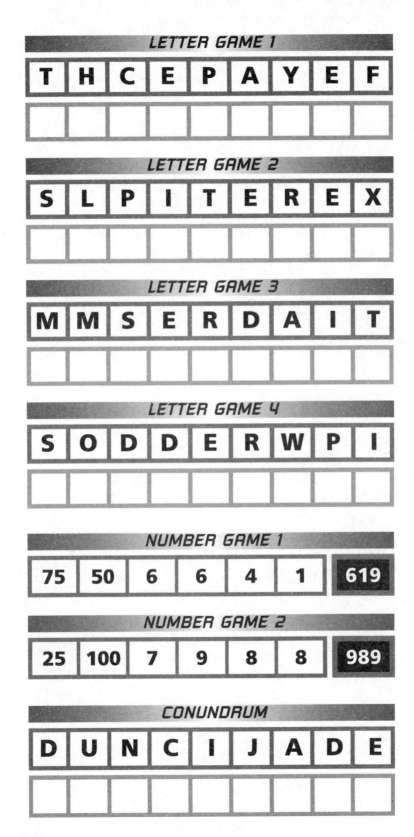

LETTER GAME 1

T	H	C	E	P	A	Y	E	F

LETTER GAME 2

S	L	P	I	T	E	R	E	X

LETTER GAME 3

M	M	S	E	R	D	A	I	T

LETTER GAME 4

S	O	D	D	E	R	W	P	I

NUMBER GAME 1

75	50	6	6	4	1	619

NUMBER GAME 2

25	100	7	9	8	8	989

CONUNDRUM

D	U	N	C	I	J	A	D	E

LETTER GAME 1

T	A	I	N	G	E	O	T	N

LETTER GAME 2

C	I	L	H	A	M	Y	T	E

LETTER GAME 3

H	E	N	K	A	R	D	S	I

LETTER GAME 4

K	I	R	E	H	U	N	S	I

NUMBER GAME 1

75	50	100	4	7	10	812

NUMBER GAME 2

25	2	4	5	4	3	751

CONUNDRUM

C	O	V	E	T	S	I	L	K

LETTER GAME 1

E	E	I	R	S	C	O	G	R

LETTER GAME 2

A	T	A	K	F	P	L	U	S

LETTER GAME 3

T	H	E	W	S	A	C	I	K

LETTER GAME 4

C	U	T	R	I	F	A	E	B

NUMBER GAME 1

50	25	9	8	8	6	447

NUMBER GAME 2

75	50	25	100	5	2	815

CONUNDRUM

L	O	U	S	I	H	A	I	R

LETTER GAME 1

P	R	T	I	I	S	M	A	U

LETTER GAME 2

E	E	A	I	K	B	L	L	Y

LETTER GAME 3

P	L	E	T	A	N	A	L	A

LETTER GAME 4

M	E	L	X	I	C	A	D	E

NUMBER GAME 1

25	10	2	5	10	4	745

NUMBER GAME 2

100	25	8	7	3	9	680

CONUNDRUM

G	R	E	E	N	L	I	N	T

LETTER GAME 1

A	C	E	N	I	P	T	T	M

LETTER GAME 2

C	I	I	A	N	P	O	T	V

LETTER GAME 3

C	H	E	R	G	B	I	A	P

LETTER GAME 4

D	U	N	I	O	R	N	E	L

NUMBER GAME 1

75	5	7	2	2	8	944

NUMBER GAME 2

75	6	10	2	5	5	721

CONUNDRUM

A	C	U	T	E	P	U	N	T

LETTER GAME 1

S	P	O	R	E	E	N	S	A

LETTER GAME 2

T	R	S	E	D	O	X	E	I

LETTER GAME 3

M	O	T	F	E	R	A	R	B

LETTER GAME 4

N	O	V	A	T	I	E	X	C

NUMBER GAME 1

3	4	2	5	7	8	693

NUMBER GAME 2

8	3	6	2	10	8	940

CONUNDRUM

W	A	N	S	I	N	G	E	R

LETTER GAME 1

L	L	A	T	I	E	R	B	A

LETTER GAME 2

A	E	N	I	M	E	A	R	T

LETTER GAME 3

E	E	E	D	I	P	S	T	S

LETTER GAME 4

M	R	R	A	I	D	E	R	E

NUMBER GAME 1

50	100	25	9	9	4	286

NUMBER GAME 2

50	4	6	9	1	1	598

CONUNDRUM

N	E	E	D	A	T	U	R	K

LETTER GAME 1

A	A	C	D	E	E	P	S	T

LETTER GAME 2

M	I	S	U	N	E	L	A	R

LETTER GAME 3

A	C	I	S	S	O	R	T	E

LETTER GAME 4

C	R	U	N	E	S	S	I	E

NUMBER GAME 1

50	25	6	7	4	4	**465**

NUMBER GAME 2

4	10	1	3	5	8	**999**

CONUNDRUM

T	I	D	Y	I	N	G	I	N

LETTER GAME 1

L	L	M	U	T	E	I	G	O

LETTER GAME 2

V	S	I	E	R	B	A	L	E

LETTER GAME 3

S	H	E	R	D	W	I	P	E

LETTER GAME 4

P	R	A	S	N	I	T	E	R

NUMBER GAME 1

75	100	50	25	3	5	627

NUMBER GAME 2

100	75	9	8	8	9	844

CONUNDRUM

C	L	A	P	T	R	A	C	I

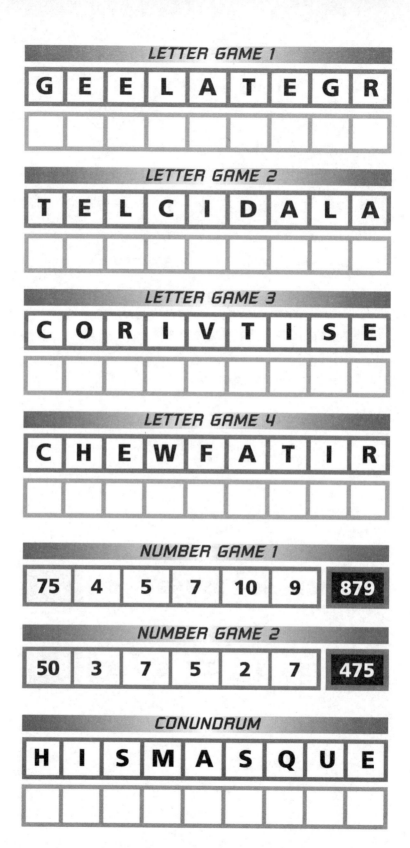

LETTER GAME 1

G	E	E	L	A	T	E	G	R

LETTER GAME 2

T	E	L	C	I	D	A	L	A

LETTER GAME 3

C	O	R	I	V	T	I	S	E

LETTER GAME 4

C	H	E	W	F	A	T	I	R

NUMBER GAME 1

75	4	5	7	10	9	879

NUMBER GAME 2

50	3	7	5	2	7	475

CONUNDRUM

H	I	S	M	A	S	Q	U	E

LETTER GAME 1

D	E	T	S	A	L	N	B	I

LETTER GAME 2

D	E	R	R	I	G	O	N	T

LETTER GAME 3

A	G	L	I	N	I	P	N	U

LETTER GAME 4

B	D	E	E	R	I	S	C	K

NUMBER GAME 1

25	100	10	9	10	9	**745**

NUMBER GAME 2

100	3	5	5	2	1	**846**

CONUNDRUM

B	I	G	B	I	N	G	E	R

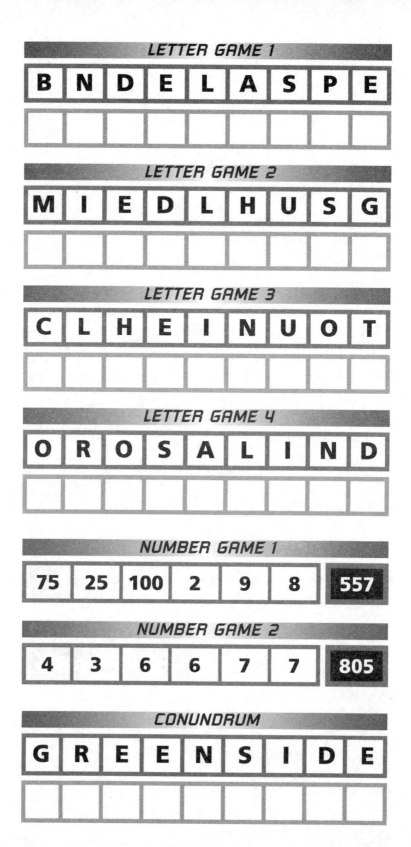

LETTER GAME 1

B	N	D	E	L	A	S	P	E

LETTER GAME 2

M	I	E	D	L	H	U	S	G

LETTER GAME 3

C	L	H	E	I	N	U	O	T

LETTER GAME 4

O	R	O	S	A	L	I	N	D

NUMBER GAME 1

75	25	100	2	9	8	**557**

NUMBER GAME 2

4	3	6	6	7	7	**805**

CONUNDRUM

G	R	E	E	N	S	I	D	E

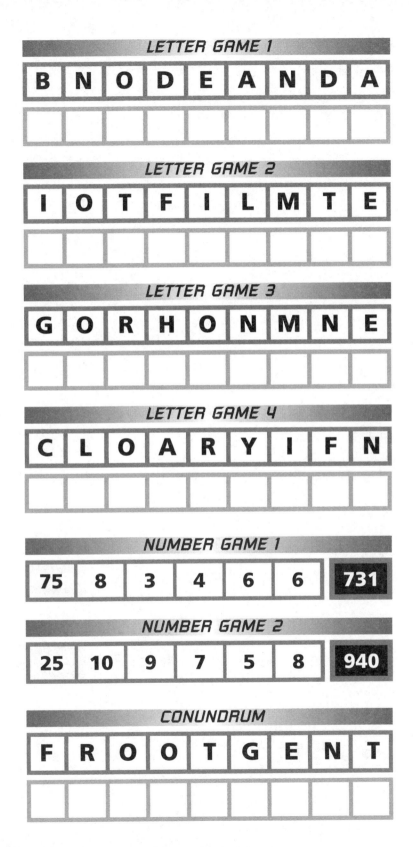

LETTER GAME 1

B	N	O	D	E	A	N	D	A

LETTER GAME 2

I	O	T	F	I	L	M	T	E

LETTER GAME 3

G	O	R	H	O	N	M	N	E

LETTER GAME 4

C	L	O	A	R	Y	I	F	N

NUMBER GAME 1

75	8	3	4	6	6	731

NUMBER GAME 2

25	10	9	7	5	8	940

CONUNDRUM

F	R	O	O	T	G	E	N	T

LETTER GAME 1

C	K	I	M	T	E	R	L	A

LETTER GAME 2

G	E	R	O	N	S	T	I	P

LETTER GAME 3

A	D	I	C	E	N	T	D	O

LETTER GAME 4

B	F	E	E	R	A	L	R	E

NUMBER GAME 1

50	100	6	5	4	1	888

NUMBER GAME 2

100	25	75	4	9	8	689

CONUNDRUM

G	U	M	P	T	O	N	I	C

ROUND 294

LETTER GAME 1

V	I	E	D	L	A	S	T	O

LETTER GAME 2

A	P	I	B	O	G	H	R	A

LETTER GAME 3

L	A	T	E	R	I	C	U	C

LETTER GAME 4

T	I	N	B	E	E	D	O	S

NUMBER GAME 1

7	8	8	2	1	3	527

NUMBER GAME 2

50	100	9	4	4	8	639

CONUNDRUM

L	A	R	R	Y	G	U	L	E

303

LETTER GAME 1

C	C	L	A	E	K	N	E	I

LETTER GAME 2

H	H	O	O	O	M	P	B	E

LETTER GAME 3

N	N	G	I	L	O	P	A	T

LETTER GAME 4

V	I	E	T	A	L	T	E	N

NUMBER GAME 1

25	50	75	100	5	7	**291**

NUMBER GAME 2

25	6	7	3	4	9	**772**

CONUNDRUM

W	A	L	E	S	W	O	L	D

LETTER GAME 1

D	I	S	F	E	R	I	A	L

LETTER GAME 2

C	H	E	T	I	N	D	S	O

LETTER GAME 3

P	L	I	I	S	T	A	N	E

LETTER GAME 4

C	H	I	L	E	T	U	N	O

NUMBER GAME 1

50	8	5	9	10	8	644

NUMBER GAME 2

100	6	1	2	5	7	811

CONUNDRUM

H	A	T	T	Y	P	E	E	L

LETTER GAME 1

A	D	W	P	I	P	N	E	I

LETTER GAME 2

H	O	D	E	M	A	T	F	O

LETTER GAME 3

D	V	C	E	L	I	A	R	S

LETTER GAME 4

L	O	R	G	I	N	A	E	S

NUMBER GAME 1

75	25	6	5	5	6	588

NUMBER GAME 2

25	2	9	1	3	1	703

CONUNDRUM

D	I	N	C	I	L	U	N	G

LETTER GAME 1

A	R	O	P	T	E	P	Y	R

LETTER GAME 2

T	H	I	N	W	E	R	E	A

LETTER GAME 3

M	U	T	F	C	A	T	O	I

LETTER GAME 4

M	O	R	O	T	A	P	E	S

NUMBER GAME 1

25	75	50	2	4	6	**595**

NUMBER GAME 2

50	2	5	7	8	7	**942**

CONUNDRUM

M	I	S	S	F	L	I	T	E

LETTER GAME 1

B	B	L	L	W	I	R	E	O

LETTER GAME 2

W	R	A	D	E	T	S	O	F

LETTER GAME 3

G	C	E	L	Y	E	D	A	I

LETTER GAME 4

T	T	E	E	N	W	S	H	O

NUMBER GAME 1

75	4	1	2	3	4	779

NUMBER GAME 2

100	25	75	50	10	10	455

CONUNDRUM

G	R	E	E	N	S	E	A	S

LETTER GAME 1

A	O	R	T	I	S	C	H	I

LETTER GAME 2

T	T	R	R	D	U	E	O	B

LETTER GAME 3

M	E	B	E	T	A	N	A	T

LETTER GAME 4

T	T	E	R	I	S	A	T	B

NUMBER GAME 1

25	100	8	9	9	1	**513**

NUMBER GAME 2

7	10	6	6	5	3	**787**

CONUNDRUM

S	O	D	F	E	N	C	E	S

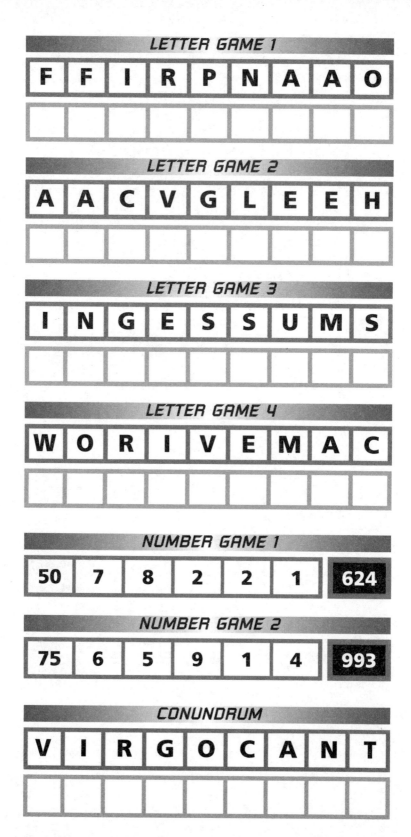

LETTER GAME 1

F	F	I	R	P	N	A	A	O

LETTER GAME 2

A	A	C	V	G	L	E	E	H

LETTER GAME 3

I	N	G	E	S	S	U	M	S

LETTER GAME 4

W	O	R	I	V	E	M	A	C

NUMBER GAME 1

50	7	8	2	2	1	624

NUMBER GAME 2

75	6	5	9	1	4	993

CONUNDRUM

V	I	R	G	O	C	A	N	T

LETTER GAME 1

G	L	T	T	Y	U	R	E	I

LETTER GAME 2

B	H	O	L	W	E	N	A	E

LETTER GAME 3

B	U	T	Q	A	A	I	N	C

LETTER GAME 4

M	I	S	T	E	N	I	F	G

NUMBER GAME 1

25	10	9	10	9	8	**548**

NUMBER GAME 2

100	75	5	8	10	6	**768**

CONUNDRUM

A	D	I	E	M	U	S	O	H

LETTER GAME 1

K	I	R	E	E	D	M	A	R

LETTER GAME 2

T	T	L	L	O	R	I	A	P

LETTER GAME 3

B	R	W	Y	E	E	S	O	T

LETTER GAME 4

T	T	T	E	L	O	E	A	C

NUMBER GAME 1

50	100	25	3	7	8	491

NUMBER GAME 2

6	3	1	1	7	5	535

CONUNDRUM

T	I	N	Y	T	E	N	O	N

LETTER GAME 1

X	N	D	H	I	E	R	E	D

LETTER GAME 2

K	N	I	L	B	R	E	E	D

LETTER GAME 3

A	D	I	V	O	P	R	E	S

LETTER GAME 4

V	E	G	A	N	T	I	E	S

NUMBER GAME 1

50	75	100	25	2	2	369

NUMBER GAME 2

75	4	4	3	7	9	580

CONUNDRUM

I	C	O	N	S	P	I	R	E

LETTER GAME 1

E	E	D	D	N	I	T	R	O

LETTER GAME 2

E	E	N	D	E	K	R	W	E

LETTER GAME 3

X	I	U	M	N	U	R	A	P

LETTER GAME 4

D	I	L	G	I	C	E	A	V

NUMBER GAME 1

25	100	2	3	3	5	424

NUMBER GAME 2

100	1	3	1	3	6	865

CONUNDRUM

B	A	L	D	M	E	R	C	S

LETTER GAME 1

D	R	W	P	O	S	S	A	I

LETTER GAME 2

C	O	L	F	I	K	E	S	T

LETTER GAME 3

B	L	O	F	A	W	N	S	E

LETTER GAME 4

C	H	K	W	O	O	R	A	A

NUMBER GAME 1

2	8	7	5	6	3	921

NUMBER GAME 2

25	7	10	1	5	9	449

CONUNDRUM

C	H	I	N	O	G	A	R	B

LETTER GAME 1

P	I	P	S	T	O	E	S	R

LETTER GAME 2

C	E	P	E	R	A	T	E	D

LETTER GAME 3

S	T	N	E	A	L	E	R	S

LETTER GAME 4

R	O	N	D	O	A	T	E	S

NUMBER GAME 1

50	25	100	8	3	3	768

NUMBER GAME 2

75	100	25	50	8	8	899

CONUNDRUM

V	E	R	Y	S	T	A	I	D

LETTER GAME 1

R	R	B	Y	B	U	E	L	E

LETTER GAME 2

H	E	L	P	T	E	A	T	G

LETTER GAME 3

J	I	T	E	H	A	S	T	E

LETTER GAME 4

D	U	C	L	O	D	C	E	A

NUMBER GAME 1

50	100	5	6	2	7	967

NUMBER GAME 2

8	7	2	4	7	3	904

CONUNDRUM

R	D	I	C	K	S	T	U	M

LETTER GAME 1

E	L	X	M	O	P	A	S	L

LETTER GAME 2

H	C	I	D	A	A	T	E	B

LETTER GAME 3

S	E	P	O	R	E	X	S	I

LETTER GAME 4

C	B	U	M	I	N	P	L	A

NUMBER GAME 1

25	8	3	5	3	1	686

NUMBER GAME 2

75	4	4	7	10	9	653

CONUNDRUM

M	I	S	T	E	R	T	E	X

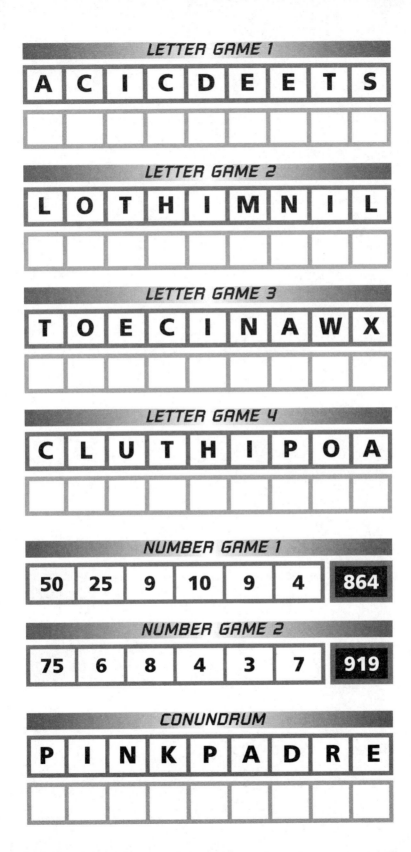

LETTER GAME 1

A	C	I	C	D	E	E	T	S

LETTER GAME 2

L	O	T	H	I	M	N	I	L

LETTER GAME 3

T	O	E	C	I	N	A	W	X

LETTER GAME 4

C	L	U	T	H	I	P	O	A

NUMBER GAME 1

50	25	9	10	9	4	**864**

NUMBER GAME 2

75	6	8	4	3	7	**919**

CONUNDRUM

P	I	N	K	P	A	D	R	E

LETTER GAME 1

S	E	U	H	M	I	O	D	A

LETTER GAME 2

D	U	N	N	I	G	O	S	E

LETTER GAME 3

R	R	E	E	C	A	D	T	I

LETTER GAME 4

L	E	R	O	C	K	E	M	C

NUMBER GAME 1

50	75	100	4	8	5	653

NUMBER GAME 2

8	7	5	6	4	4	996

CONUNDRUM

V	I	R	G	O	L	E	N	T

LETTER GAME 1

M	E	B	G	A	T	L	I	N

LETTER GAME 2

B	U	R	G	I	N	H	O	E

LETTER GAME 3

A	B	O	N	L	I	D	Y	E

LETTER GAME 4

G	D	D	R	E	U	P	A	I

NUMBER GAME 1

25	1	6	8	2	7	555

NUMBER GAME 2

100	75	25	3	4	8	960

CONUNDRUM

L	A	M	B	E	R	I	E	S

LETTER GAME 1

P	H	O	L	E	M	A	I	S

LETTER GAME 2

M	E	S	I	N	B	S	A	T

LETTER GAME 3

L	O	E	D	A	T	E	S	H

LETTER GAME 4

C	L	W	E	N	M	U	O	E

NUMBER GAME 1

50	100	6	8	10	10	**278**

NUMBER GAME 2

75	4	3	5	7	2	**867**

CONUNDRUM

T	O	G	A	C	A	P	E	S

LETTER GAME 1

C	H	E	N	D	E	R	W	I

LETTER GAME 2

G	H	E	R	E	T	E	D	T

LETTER GAME 3

S	N	C	L	O	E	S	D	I

LETTER GAME 4

W	A	R	R	S	O	P	E	S

NUMBER GAME 1

25	100	50	75	10	4	780

NUMBER GAME 2

50	9	4	5	1	9	527

CONUNDRUM

K	E	E	N	D	O	O	R	S

323

LETTER GAME 1

B	U	R	P	I	C	A	L	E

LETTER GAME 2

O	C	O	T	L	A	B	W	E

LETTER GAME 3

M	A	N	R	O	Y	L	U	P

LETTER GAME 4

A	A	S	T	M	R	P	Y	E

NUMBER GAME 1

3	8	7	7	5	2	678

NUMBER GAME 2

75	25	2	6	3	9	848

CONUNDRUM

S	I	N	S	R	A	T	E	D

LETTER GAME 1

C	O	O	P	L	I	T	S	A

LETTER GAME 2

T	I	Y	F	E	C	K	W	A

LETTER GAME 3

A	S	H	O	L	P	I	S	D

LETTER GAME 4

Q	I	B	D	O	U	T	S	M

NUMBER GAME 1

75	50	8	6	7	5	885

NUMBER GAME 2

100	2	1	2	1	10	624

CONUNDRUM

L	U	N	A	R	H	Y	T	E

LETTER GAME 1

H	U	E	R	D	G	E	N	I

LETTER GAME 2

M	I	S	T	P	O	N	E	D

LETTER GAME 3

M	I	X	H	U	N	G	O	E

LETTER GAME 4

R	E	D	T	B	E	A	T	S

NUMBER GAME 1

25	100	50	75	9	3	**772**

NUMBER GAME 2

50	25	8	2	5	10	**667**

CONUNDRUM

S	T	O	R	E	P	U	M	P

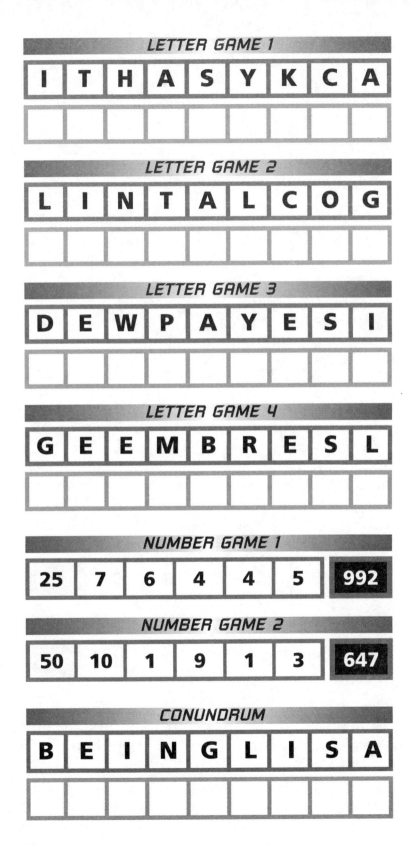

LETTER GAME 1

I	T	H	A	S	Y	K	C	A

LETTER GAME 2

L	I	N	T	A	L	C	O	G

LETTER GAME 3

D	E	W	P	A	Y	E	S	I

LETTER GAME 4

G	E	E	M	B	R	E	S	L

NUMBER GAME 1

25	7	6	4	4	5	992

NUMBER GAME 2

50	10	1	9	1	3	647

CONUNDRUM

B	E	I	N	G	L	I	S	A

LETTER GAME 1

R	I	V	S	T	E	R	A	E

LETTER GAME 2

D	Y	S	T	E	A	U	N	I

LETTER GAME 3

A	N	V	R	E	Y	W	S	I

LETTER GAME 4

A	R	U	X	T	E	D	E	T

NUMBER GAME 1

75	100	25	6	8	9	**548**

NUMBER GAME 2

3	5	8	4	2	10	**835**

CONUNDRUM

Q	U	A	I	L	C	O	V	E

LETTER GAME 1

A	L	C	O	B	I	T	A	N

LETTER GAME 2

S	T	U	U	N	R	I	L	E

LETTER GAME 3

H	P	E	R	I	A	S	Y	T

LETTER GAME 4

F	L	U	T	I	P	E	S	C

NUMBER GAME 1

50	4	5	6	1	8	**939**

NUMBER GAME 2

75	25	8	6	2	4	**705**

CONUNDRUM

G	A	F	F	S	F	L	A	T

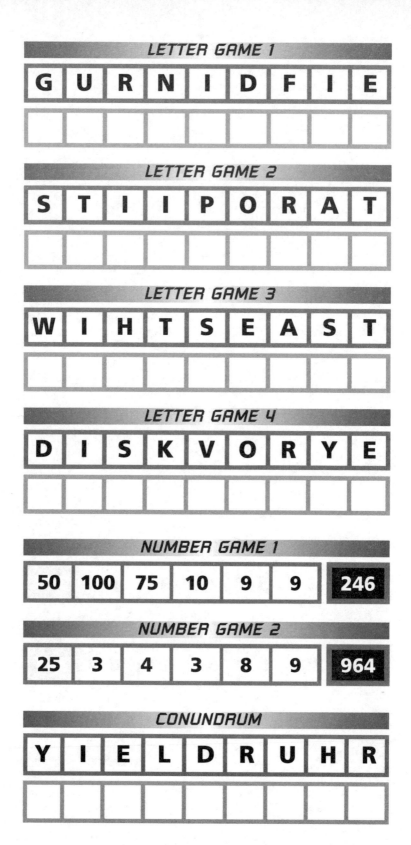

LETTER GAME 1

G	U	R	N	I	D	F	I	E

LETTER GAME 2

S	T	I	I	P	O	R	A	T

LETTER GAME 3

W	I	H	T	S	E	A	S	T

LETTER GAME 4

D	I	S	K	V	O	R	Y	E

NUMBER GAME 1

50	100	75	10	9	9	246

NUMBER GAME 2

25	3	4	3	8	9	964

CONUNDRUM

Y	I	E	L	D	R	U	H	R

LETTER GAME 1

C	L	O	E	D	A	C	A	S

LETTER GAME 2

T	R	E	E	V	I	E	R	D

LETTER GAME 3

E	E	Z	L	I	P	N	A	D

LETTER GAME 4

P	R	E	M	O	D	E	C	A

NUMBER GAME 1

5	3	8	7	2	6	**624**

NUMBER GAME 2

75	50	10	4	9	3	**888**

CONUNDRUM

A	G	N	E	S	Q	U	I	K

LETTER GAME 1

S	I	N	G	E	L	E	D	T

LETTER GAME 2

S	I	R	E	B	A	R	S	H

LETTER GAME 3

S	U	S	I	S	P	U	R	T

LETTER GAME 4

D	A	M	I	A	N	G	E	T

NUMBER GAME 1

25	100	4	9	1	4	735

NUMBER GAME 2

100	75	50	25	5	5	610

CONUNDRUM

T	R	U	E	C	R	I	T	S

LETTER GAME 1

S	T	I	E	E	R	N	D	J

LETTER GAME 2

S	E	M	T	U	I	O	Q	D

LETTER GAME 3

B	L	U	N	V	E	T	E	F

LETTER GAME 4

C	R	O	H	I	M	A	N	A

NUMBER GAME 1

25	8	2	6	7	8	740

NUMBER GAME 2

75	100	8	9	1	10	583

CONUNDRUM

Z	E	R	O	G	E	N	I	C

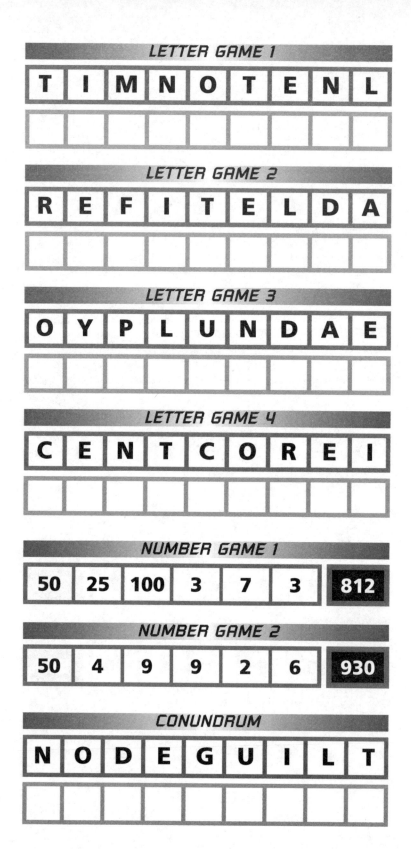

LETTER GAME 1

T	I	M	N	O	T	E	N	L

LETTER GAME 2

R	E	F	I	T	E	L	D	A

LETTER GAME 3

O	Y	P	L	U	N	D	A	E

LETTER GAME 4

C	E	N	T	C	O	R	E	I

NUMBER GAME 1

50	25	100	3	7	3	812

NUMBER GAME 2

50	4	9	9	2	6	930

CONUNDRUM

N	O	D	E	G	U	I	L	T

LETTER GAME 1

K	N	S	S	E	O	M	P	A

LETTER GAME 2

S	I	R	E	K	A	T	S	F

LETTER GAME 3

C	H	E	T	R	I	T	A	O

LETTER GAME 4

S	S	T	T	O	O	I	E	N

NUMBER GAME 1

75	50	6	10	9	7	**927**

NUMBER GAME 2

25	3	1	2	6	1	**804**

CONUNDRUM

F	A	G	P	R	I	N	C	E

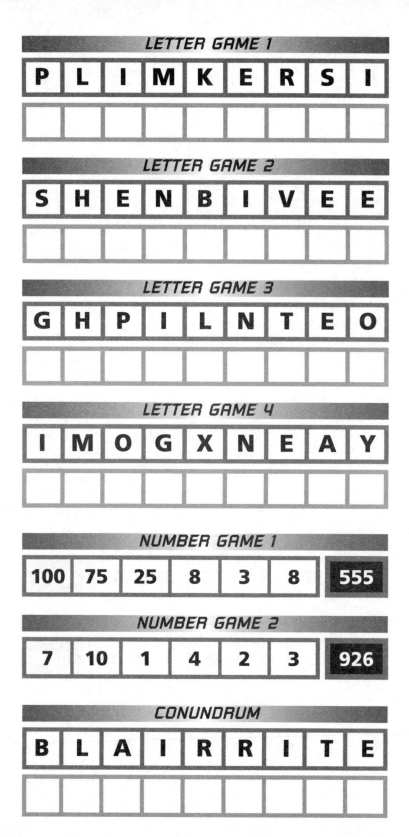

LETTER GAME 1

| P | L | I | M | K | E | R | S | I |

LETTER GAME 2

| S | H | E | N | B | I | V | E | E |

LETTER GAME 3

| G | H | P | I | L | N | T | E | O |

LETTER GAME 4

| I | M | O | G | X | N | E | A | Y |

NUMBER GAME 1

| 100 | 75 | 25 | 8 | 3 | 8 | **555** |

NUMBER GAME 2

| 7 | 10 | 1 | 4 | 2 | 3 | **926** |

CONUNDRUM

| B | L | A | I | R | R | I | T | E |

LETTER GAME 1

A	L	M	O	F	G	I	N	U

LETTER GAME 2

V	O	L	I	E	B	A	S	L

LETTER GAME 3

M	O	T	R	B	I	N	E	S

LETTER GAME 4

A	C	R	T	I	P	E	Y	O

NUMBER GAME 1

25	7	10	9	4	4	598

NUMBER GAME 2

50	75	25	2	8	6	437

CONUNDRUM

D	I	S	C	U	L	O	U	R

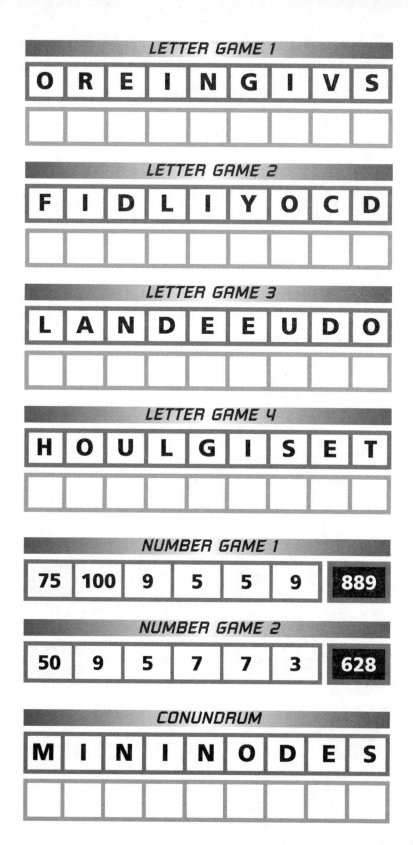

LETTER GAME 1

| O | R | E | I | N | G | I | V | S |

LETTER GAME 2

| F | I | D | L | I | Y | O | C | D |

LETTER GAME 3

| L | A | N | D | E | E | U | D | O |

LETTER GAME 4

| H | O | U | L | G | I | S | E | T |

NUMBER GAME 1

| 75 | 100 | 9 | 5 | 5 | 9 | 889 |

NUMBER GAME 2

| 50 | 9 | 5 | 7 | 7 | 3 | 628 |

CONUNDRUM

| M | I | N | I | N | O | D | E | S |

LETTER GAME 1

C	N	D	R	Q	U	E	E	O

LETTER GAME 2

P	C	C	E	T	I	A	V	E

LETTER GAME 3

H	T	O	C	H	O	T	E	A

LETTER GAME 4

B	I	N	G	A	H	D	A	S

NUMBER GAME 1

25	1	6	3	3	6	540

NUMBER GAME 2

100	3	4	9	10	10	788

CONUNDRUM

T	I	G	E	R	B	A	R	N

LETTER GAME 1

M	M	N	N	O	I	C	E	R

LETTER GAME 2

S	A	U	R	B	I	E	R	S

LETTER GAME 3

S	P	O	G	N	K	I	R	E

LETTER GAME 4

D	R	E	E	K	T	O	W	N

NUMBER GAME 1

50	75	100	1	5	5	886

NUMBER GAME 2

75	2	7	8	7	3	484

CONUNDRUM

B	L	U	E	M	A	N	C	A

LETTER GAME 1

I	N	A	S	T	U	D	I	O

LETTER GAME 2

S	H	E	T	T	I	P	R	A

LETTER GAME 3

T	O	F	O	R	I	A	L	N

LETTER GAME 4

F	L	U	D	E	N	R	U	I

NUMBER GAME 1

50	100	9	10	8	7	396

NUMBER GAME 2

25	8	4	3	9	2	666

CONUNDRUM

N	O	G	R	I	P	T	O	M

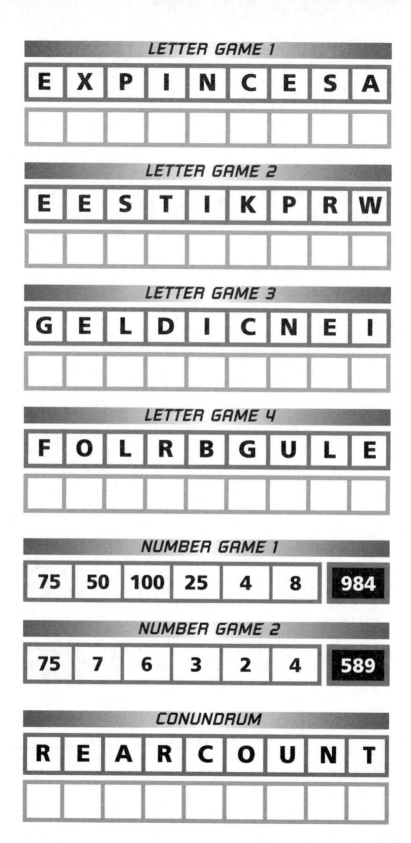

LETTER GAME 1

E	X	P	I	N	C	E	S	A

LETTER GAME 2

E	E	S	T	I	K	P	R	W

LETTER GAME 3

G	E	L	D	I	C	N	E	I

LETTER GAME 4

F	O	L	R	B	G	U	L	E

NUMBER GAME 1

75	50	100	25	4	8	984

NUMBER GAME 2

75	7	6	3	2	4	589

CONUNDRUM

R	E	A	R	C	O	U	N	T

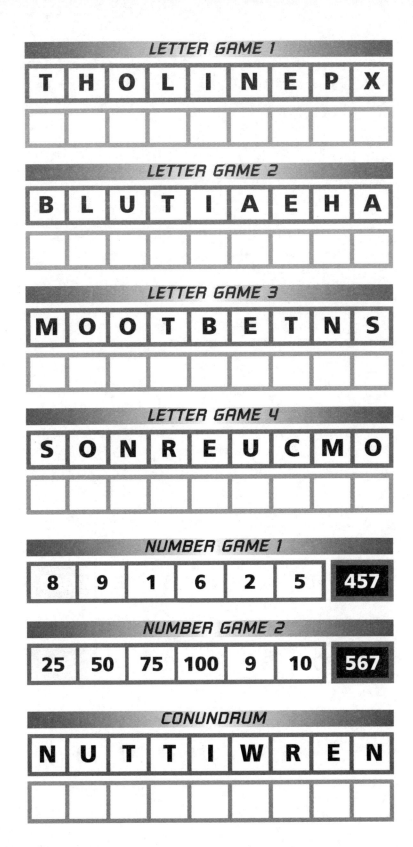

LETTER GAME 1

T	H	O	L	I	N	E	P	X

LETTER GAME 2

B	L	U	T	I	A	E	H	A

LETTER GAME 3

M	O	O	T	B	E	T	N	S

LETTER GAME 4

S	O	N	R	E	U	C	M	O

NUMBER GAME 1

8	9	1	6	2	5	457

NUMBER GAME 2

25	50	75	100	9	10	567

CONUNDRUM

N	U	T	T	I	W	R	E	N

LETTER GAME 1

F	R	E	E	D	I	L	U	N

LETTER GAME 2

B	B	V	R	R	H	U	A	E

LETTER GAME 3

P	L	U	Q	U	A	R	E	D

LETTER GAME 4

K	N	B	R	E	D	E	U	L

NUMBER GAME 1

75	6	5	9	3	2	940

NUMBER GAME 2

50	100	2	4	3	7	845

CONUNDRUM

T	E	N	T	D	R	O	M	E

LETTER GAME 1

G	H	O	O	R	L	N	N	U

LETTER GAME 2

D	L	R	Y	A	W	O	N	E

LETTER GAME 3

P	I	F	P	L	N	T	A	E

LETTER GAME 4

D	O	B	E	N	I	A	G	S

NUMBER GAME 1

25	5	9	7	5	3	722

NUMBER GAME 2

100	10	9	10	8	8	521

CONUNDRUM

G	A	L	L	O	P	W	I	N

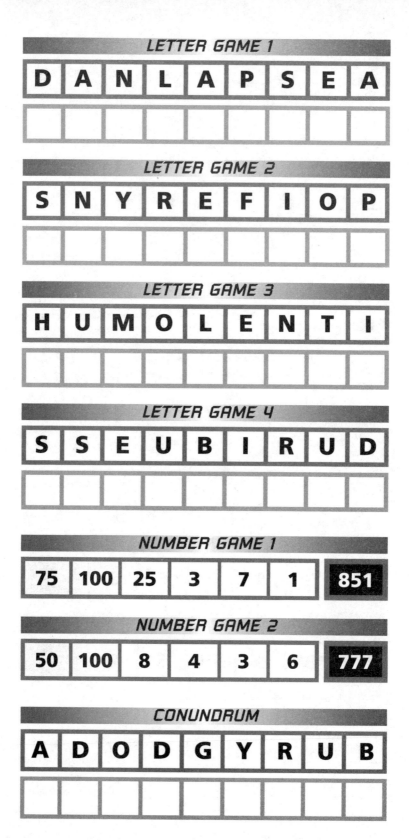

LETTER GAME 1

D	A	N	L	A	P	S	E	A

LETTER GAME 2

S	N	Y	R	E	F	I	O	P

LETTER GAME 3

H	U	M	O	L	E	N	T	I

LETTER GAME 4

S	S	E	U	B	I	R	U	D

NUMBER GAME 1

75	100	25	3	7	1	851

NUMBER GAME 2

50	100	8	4	3	6	777

CONUNDRUM

A	D	O	D	G	Y	R	U	B

LETTER GAME 1

M	E	W	R	O	N	C	E	A

LETTER GAME 2

C	C	D	E	A	M	I	A	S

LETTER GAME 3

C	O	R	O	P	Y	G	E	S

LETTER GAME 4

C	I	L	T	U	M	S	A	S

NUMBER GAME 1

3	5	4	6	6	9	**576**

NUMBER GAME 2

50	100	75	7	6	9	**234**

CONUNDRUM

N	I	G	H	T	R	O	B	E

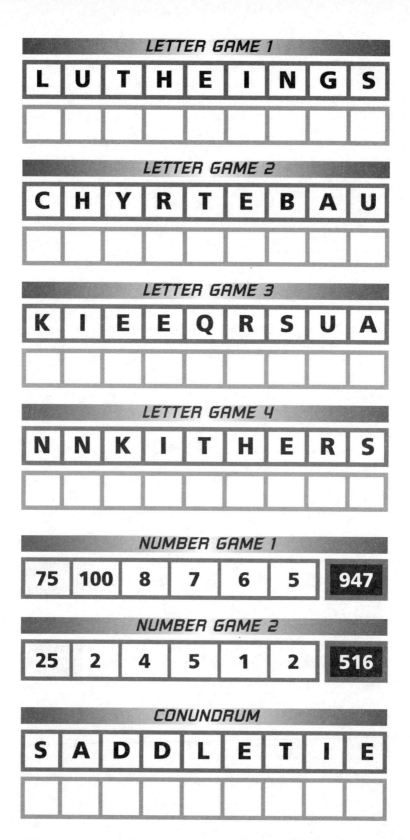

LETTER GAME 1

L	U	T	H	E	I	N	G	S

LETTER GAME 2

C	H	Y	R	T	E	B	A	U

LETTER GAME 3

K	I	E	E	Q	R	S	U	A

LETTER GAME 4

N	N	K	I	T	H	E	R	S

NUMBER GAME 1

75	100	8	7	6	5	947

NUMBER GAME 2

25	2	4	5	1	2	516

CONUNDRUM

S	A	D	D	L	E	T	I	E

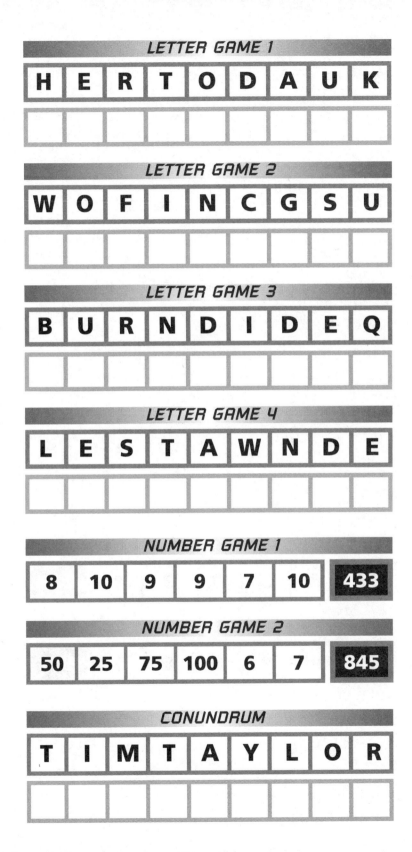

LETTER GAME 1

H	E	R	T	O	D	A	U	K

LETTER GAME 2

W	O	F	I	N	C	G	S	U

LETTER GAME 3

B	U	R	N	D	I	D	E	Q

LETTER GAME 4

L	E	S	T	A	W	N	D	E

NUMBER GAME 1

8	10	9	9	7	10	433

NUMBER GAME 2

50	25	75	100	6	7	845

CONUNDRUM

T	I	M	T	A	Y	L	O	R

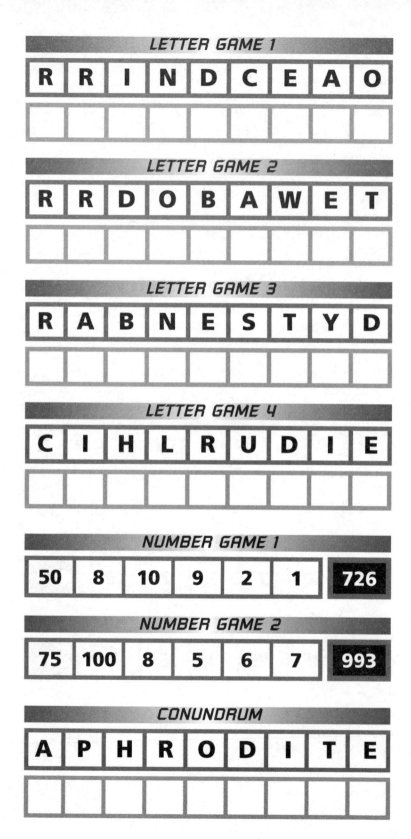

LETTER GAME 1

R	R	I	N	D	C	E	A	O

LETTER GAME 2

R	R	D	O	B	A	W	E	T

LETTER GAME 3

R	A	B	N	E	S	T	Y	D

LETTER GAME 4

C	I	H	L	R	U	D	I	E

NUMBER GAME 1

50	8	10	9	2	1	726

NUMBER GAME 2

75	100	8	5	6	7	993

CONUNDRUM

A	P	H	R	O	D	I	T	E

LETTER GAME 1

C	K	I	S	U	Q	E	I	O

LETTER GAME 2

G	E	N	O	L	I	D	A	S

LETTER GAME 3

P	R	E	T	O	V	I	A	E

LETTER GAME 4

E	U	G	T	H	I	N	F	G

NUMBER GAME 1

25	2	7	5	8	8	955

NUMBER GAME 2

100	6	1	3	6	7	429

CONUNDRUM

M	A	I	N	F	R	E	S	H

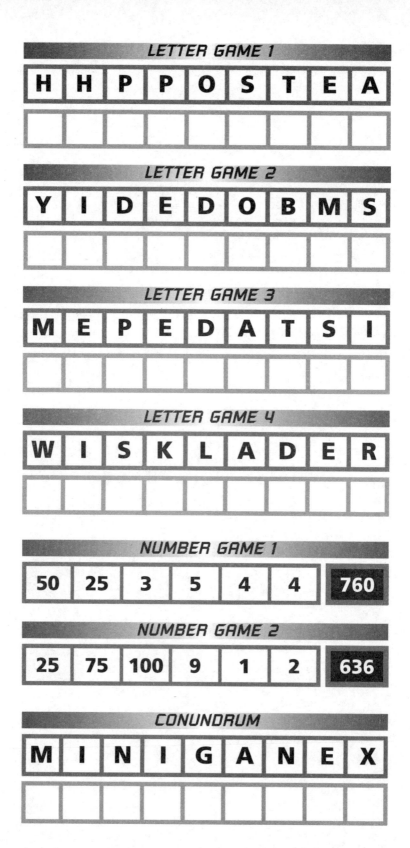

LETTER GAME 1

H	H	P	P	O	S	T	E	A

LETTER GAME 2

Y	I	D	E	D	O	B	M	S

LETTER GAME 3

M	E	P	E	D	A	T	S	I

LETTER GAME 4

W	I	S	K	L	A	D	E	R

NUMBER GAME 1

50	25	3	5	4	4	760

NUMBER GAME 2

25	75	100	9	1	2	636

CONUNDRUM

M	I	N	I	G	A	N	E	X

LETTER GAME 1

S	L	O	R	N	A	M	T	E

LETTER GAME 2

D	E	C	O	M	N	C	A	O

LETTER GAME 3

H	O	R	S	T	E	A	H	D

LETTER GAME 4

B	L	E	P	H	Y	O	R	E

NUMBER GAME 1

4	5	10	10	2	8	756

NUMBER GAME 2

25	1	6	5	7	3	822

CONUNDRUM

J	E	E	R	C	U	P	I	D

LETTER GAME 1

L	U	N	G	I	R	E	W	S

LETTER GAME 2

R	E	R	I	U	S	E	Q	E

LETTER GAME 3

N	N	C	H	G	E	D	A	U

LETTER GAME 4

P	O	R	R	O	T	E	C	A

NUMBER GAME 1

100	25	9	8	1	6	**737**

NUMBER GAME 2

50	75	100	8	5	10	**943**

CONUNDRUM

S	I	L	L	I	B	A	R	D

LETTER GAME 1

F	F	L	I	N	G	A	W	E

LETTER GAME 2

B	O	L	O	T	F	L	A	E

LETTER GAME 3

E	E	H	L	L	U	A	C	K

LETTER GAME 4

G	R	I	T	U	L	V	A	Y

NUMBER GAME 1

50	100	25	75	6	5	692

NUMBER GAME 2

100	6	9	9	8	10	427

CONUNDRUM

A	L	G	A	E	H	O	N	X

LETTER GAME 1

P	N	E	S	I	D	E	S	D

LETTER GAME 2

E	L	I	N	G	I	D	U	E

LETTER GAME 3

B	L	U	S	T	I	G	E	A

LETTER GAME 4

B	O	E	D	A	R	S	B	T

NUMBER GAME 1

75	2	1	10	10	2	844

NUMBER GAME 2

1	7	8	4	4	3	350

CONUNDRUM

N	U	T	T	I	S	I	D	E

LETTER GAME 1

F	T	T	S	E	E	A	D	S

LETTER GAME 2

A	H	R	E	K	D	I	E	S

LETTER GAME 3

B	V	O	E	R	I	L	D	Y

LETTER GAME 4

D	D	I	O	R	A	S	E	W

NUMBER GAME 1

50	75	100	8	8	7	**681**

NUMBER GAME 2

25	50	100	7	4	8	**977**

CONUNDRUM

P	I	P	E	C	A	N	A	L

LETTER GAME 1

I	X	G	O	N	M	N	Y	I

LETTER GAME 2

D	I	L	E	A	R	T	H	L

LETTER GAME 3

C	I	T	E	D	K	P	E	X

LETTER GAME 4

R	E	T	I	N	C	U	O	S

NUMBER GAME 1

50	6	7	8	3	6	826

NUMBER GAME 2

75	8	4	3	1	5	692

CONUNDRUM

D	I	N	N	E	R	B	U	G

LETTER GAME 1

X	O	F	T	I	C	Q	U	I

LETTER GAME 2

C	N	N	D	R	O	E	A	I

LETTER GAME 3

C	O	R	I	F	E	S	U	N

LETTER GAME 4

T	H	I	R	E	G	N	W	A

NUMBER GAME 1

100	75	1	2	1	2	544

NUMBER GAME 2

2	7	6	8	5	9	999

CONUNDRUM

M	O	O	D	Y	T	I	C	H

LETTER GAME 1

A A I L R C A M E

LETTER GAME 2

C E R I O S G E R

LETTER GAME 3

H I S L O R T A M

LETTER GAME 4

H I E P T T E A A

NUMBER GAME 1

| 50 | 100 | 75 | 1 | 5 | 7 | **812** |

NUMBER GAME 2

| 75 | 10 | 9 | 8 | 2 | 2 | **433** |

CONUNDRUM

N I G H T R U S T

LETTER GAME 1

S	O	C	U	H	R	E	V	A

LETTER GAME 2

A	U	C	D	I	T	R	I	E

LETTER GAME 3

D	R	I	G	A	M	E	Y	P

LETTER GAME 4

C	T	T	P	S	Y	E	A	I

NUMBER GAME 1

25	4	3	1	6	6	953

NUMBER GAME 2

100	50	5	10	1	2	369

CONUNDRUM

E	D	D	T	I	F	F	I	N

LETTER GAME 1

| R | R | E | E | D | I | O | S | T |

LETTER GAME 2

| L | O | S | H | E | I | N | R | E |

LETTER GAME 3

| S | I | N | T | E | S | D | I | O |

LETTER GAME 4

| P | I | O | N | A | S | M | C | E |

NUMBER GAME 1

| 25 | 7 | 5 | 9 | 4 | 7 | 687 |

NUMBER GAME 2

| 75 | 6 | 4 | 3 | 5 | 3 | 987 |

CONUNDRUM

| F | O | U | L | N | O | I | S | E |

LETTER GAME 1

I	I	R	C	K	S	T	E	L

LETTER GAME 2

L	T	Y	R	V	E	C	O	A

LETTER GAME 3

O	R	K	E	N	G	A	A	O

LETTER GAME 4

G	E	T	S	I	R	F	O	N

NUMBER GAME 1

25	50	100	2	9	10	818

NUMBER GAME 2

50	75	2	4	6	3	833

CONUNDRUM

N	A	R	C	O	S	I	S	T

LETTER GAME 1

H	O	R	K	I	P	P	E	W

LETTER GAME 2

C	U	R	N	T	I	P	O	N

LETTER GAME 3

L	U	E	D	I	S	A	B	E

LETTER GAME 4

C	A	N	T	M	O	D	U	E

NUMBER GAME 1

100	50	75	3	8	9	742

NUMBER GAME 2

25	6	4	3	10	5	948

CONUNDRUM

S	O	U	P	L	A	T	T	E

LETTER GAME 1

R	A	M	I	L	G	I	N	K

LETTER GAME 2

U	L	M	I	N	P	A	T	S

LETTER GAME 3

R	R	T	U	O	M	A	G	Y

LETTER GAME 4

P	U	M	S	T	I	L	E	A

NUMBER GAME 1

50	25	75	100	5	8	**637**

NUMBER GAME 2

5	3	2	6	4	3	**297**

CONUNDRUM

L	I	F	E	G	L	I	N	T

LETTER GAME 1

P	I	E	N	O	C	A	Z	D

LETTER GAME 2

G	G	P	O	H	R	A	U	E

LETTER GAME 3

I	H	N	T	O	A	N	D	O

LETTER GAME 4

T	T	A	A	G	I	M	S	N

NUMBER GAME 1

50	10	1	4	5	6	781

NUMBER GAME 2

25	2	1	2	1	7	534

CONUNDRUM

T	A	N	G	Y	P	E	A	R

LETTER GAME 1

G	T	T	I	U	N	O	R	A

LETTER GAME 2

C	T	T	U	R	I	N	E	A

LETTER GAME 3

S	T	O	C	L	U	S	A	I

LETTER GAME 4

S	R	E	U	R	C	T	E	A

NUMBER GAME 1

75	8	7	5	3	1	943

NUMBER GAME 2

75	100	8	5	4	1	939

CONUNDRUM

M	E	R	E	G	I	A	N	T

LETTER GAME 1

N	N	B	H	K	O	I	S	E

LETTER GAME 2

F	G	C	R	P	L	A	A	E

LETTER GAME 3

T	T	E	E	I	N	R	Y	A

LETTER GAME 4

E	I	I	M	T	Y	R	U	P

NUMBER GAME 1

25	7	7	5	5	9	860

NUMBER GAME 2

50	75	25	7	4	8	341

CONUNDRUM

H	E	M	A	N	L	A	N	D

LETTER GAME 1

D	I	Y	C	Q	U	R	E	A

LETTER GAME 2

T	D	E	S	I	I	V	T	E

LETTER GAME 3

L	E	R	C	U	T	F	A	R

LETTER GAME 4

P	P	O	R	A	G	T	E	S

NUMBER GAME 1

50	8	9	3	4	4	**768**

NUMBER GAME 2

100	25	2	5	8	7	**571**

CONUNDRUM

T	H	R	E	E	L	I	D	S

LETTER GAME 1

D	L	O	S	I	T	R	E	W

LETTER GAME 2

P	A	R	D	I	N	A	G	C

LETTER GAME 3

R	I	V	A	N	R	O	G	E

LETTER GAME 4

B	O	L	M	U	T	R	E	S

NUMBER GAME 1

25	75	50	8	10	1	851

NUMBER GAME 2

75	6	6	2	2	5	989

CONUNDRUM

N	A	S	T	Y	L	E	E	R

LETTER GAME 1

F	U	L	R	O	M	O	N	I

LETTER GAME 2

G	R	O	B	E	T	A	A	L

LETTER GAME 3

A	L	L	I	R	C	U	Y	P

LETTER GAME 4

B	I	N	N	A	M	O	L	E

NUMBER GAME 1

5	9	7	1	3	9	734

NUMBER GAME 2

25	3	5	6	8	10	933

CONUNDRUM

S	I	G	H	B	R	I	B	E

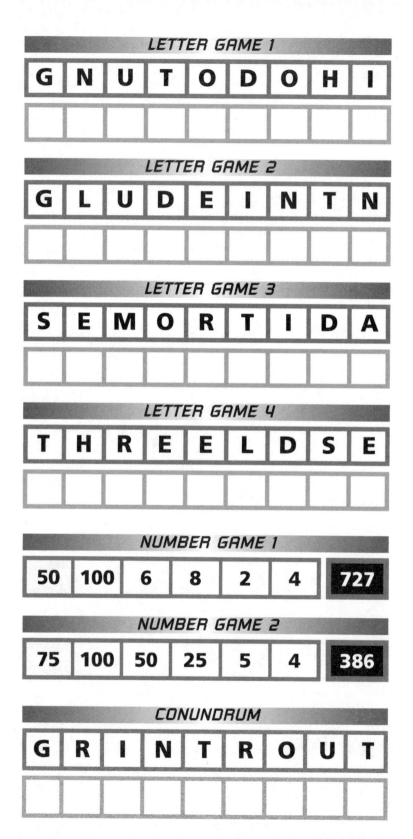

LETTER GAME 1

G	N	U	T	O	D	O	H	I

LETTER GAME 2

G	L	U	D	E	I	N	T	N

LETTER GAME 3

S	E	M	O	R	T	I	D	A

LETTER GAME 4

T	H	R	E	E	L	D	S	E

NUMBER GAME 1

50	100	6	8	2	4	**727**

NUMBER GAME 2

75	100	50	25	5	4	**386**

CONUNDRUM

G	R	I	N	T	R	O	U	T

LETTER GAME 1

| D | Y | I | F | I | R | G | I | T |

LETTER GAME 2

| C | R | I | A | L | S | I | T | A |

LETTER GAME 3

| D | E | R | I | C | E | S | V | C |

LETTER GAME 4

| G | R | Y | I | P | L | A | O | L |

NUMBER GAME 1

| 50 | 5 | 1 | 3 | 1 | 6 | **942** |

NUMBER GAME 2

| 75 | 100 | 25 | 9 | 6 | 3 | **987** |

CONUNDRUM

| P | P | I | T | I | L | E | S | S |

LETTER GAME 1

T	T	R	E	M	O	U	S	O

LETTER GAME 2

R	E	V	O	R	I	N	C	A

LETTER GAME 3

G	R	U	N	I	S	E	N	O

LETTER GAME 4

R	U	M	N	D	A	O	G	E

NUMBER GAME 1

5	10	6	1	7	5	**408**

NUMBER GAME 2

25	5	7	6	8	3	**888**

CONUNDRUM

D	I	E	T	W	A	R	T	S

LETTER GAME 1

G	U	R	I	M	E	N	E	D

LETTER GAME 2

A	B	U	M	I	L	R	N	G

LETTER GAME 3

N	N	R	O	P	I	L	A	E

LETTER GAME 4

K	E	L	D	I	C	F	O	R

NUMBER GAME 1

50	7	4	7	5	6	525

NUMBER GAME 2

25	75	4	7	10	3	928

CONUNDRUM

V	A	U	L	T	E	T	I	C

LETTER GAME 1

M	E	E	S	T	R	A	D	I

LETTER GAME 2

B	L	E	N	I	F	A	T	D

LETTER GAME 3

W	O	N	P	R	D	U	E	O

LETTER GAME 4

R	E	E	S	S	L	I	T	N

NUMBER GAME 1

100	25	6	2	2	9	839

NUMBER GAME 2

50	25	100	5	8	7	976

CONUNDRUM

G	I	N	G	E	R	V	A	N

LETTER GAME 1

S	N	W	R	E	E	S	A	A

LETTER GAME 2

U	L	L	M	P	G	I	N	A

LETTER GAME 3

S	O	M	M	E	T	L	R	A

LETTER GAME 4

B	U	R	E	C	S	T	I	M

NUMBER GAME 1

100	9	10	8	9	8	**621**

NUMBER GAME 2

75	25	3	9	10	7	**442**

CONUNDRUM

G	R	A	N	D	P	O	E	T

LETTER GAME 1

E	O	L	H	A	S	T	L	S

LETTER GAME 2

I	N	C	A	R	S	H	T	A

LETTER GAME 3

T	T	N	M	U	S	E	N	A

LETTER GAME 4

Q	U	J	I	N	I	R	E	S

NUMBER GAME 1

50	100	75	6	8	7	935

NUMBER GAME 2

25	6	3	4	7	9	849

CONUNDRUM

A	L	Y	X	S	U	I	T	E

LETTER GAME 1

C	N	M	O	R	T	I	A	A

LETTER GAME 2

S	T	E	M	P	U	L	P	O

LETTER GAME 3

A	G	E	S	A	T	I	T	C

LETTER GAME 4

L	U	T	A	C	A	I	S	E

NUMBER GAME 1

100	50	8	9	2	2	**776**

NUMBER GAME 2

25	1	7	4	8	1	**669**

CONUNDRUM

B	R	E	D	M	I	M	E	S

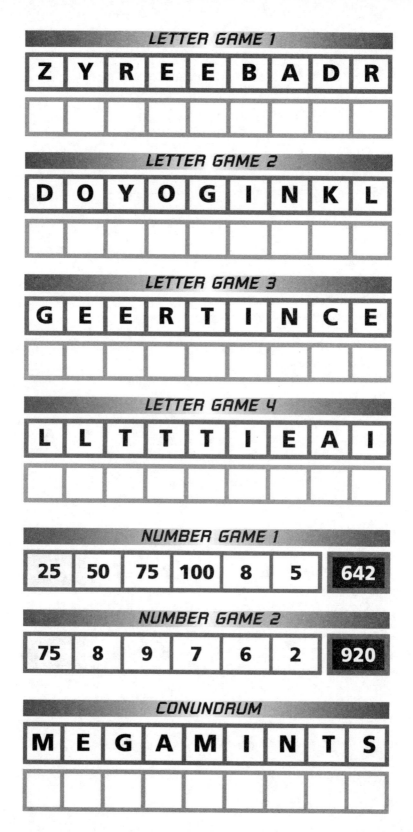

LETTER GAME 1

| Z | Y | R | E | E | B | A | D | R |

LETTER GAME 2

| D | O | Y | O | G | I | N | K | L |

LETTER GAME 3

| G | E | E | R | T | I | N | C | E |

LETTER GAME 4

| L | L | T | T | T | I | E | A | I |

NUMBER GAME 1

| 25 | 50 | 75 | 100 | 8 | 5 | **642** |

NUMBER GAME 2

| 75 | 8 | 9 | 7 | 6 | 2 | **920** |

CONUNDRUM

| M | E | G | A | M | I | N | T | S |

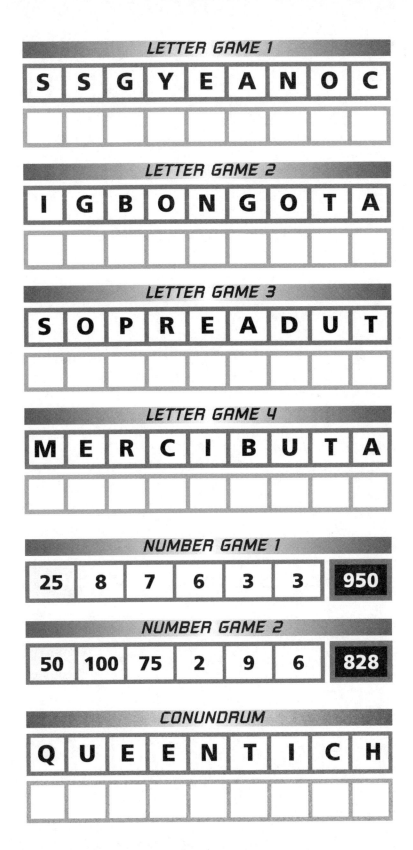

ROUND 372

LETTER GAME 1

S	S	G	Y	E	A	N	O	C

LETTER GAME 2

I	G	B	O	N	G	O	T	A

LETTER GAME 3

S	O	P	R	E	A	D	U	T

LETTER GAME 4

M	E	R	C	I	B	U	T	A

NUMBER GAME 1

25	8	7	6	3	3	**950**

NUMBER GAME 2

50	100	75	2	9	6	**828**

CONUNDRUM

Q	U	E	E	N	T	I	C	H

381

ROUND 373

LETTER GAME 1

| S | K | H | E | F | I | T | A | M |

LETTER GAME 2

| F | O | D | L | I | S | O | H | G |

LETTER GAME 3

| L | E | T | G | I | N | A | P | R |

LETTER GAME 4

| D | R | R | Y | V | E | S | A | A |

NUMBER GAME 1

| 25 | 50 | 5 | 10 | 4 | 7 | 671 |

NUMBER GAME 2

| 100 | 75 | 50 | 25 | 10 | 10 | 741 |

CONUNDRUM

| R | N | C | R | U | E | L | T | Y |

LETTER GAME 1

R	E	M	U	T	I	E	N	Z

LETTER GAME 2

A	H	C	I	L	A	R	E	V

LETTER GAME 3

A	L	M	U	N	I	T	E	C

LETTER GAME 4

P	E	R	V	E	S	I	T	Y

NUMBER GAME 1

3	6	7	2	3	7	**589**

NUMBER GAME 2

75	2	1	3	3	8	**799**

CONUNDRUM

V	I	R	G	I	N	F	O	G

LETTER GAME 1

| F | R | A | B | E | M | U | S | I |

LETTER GAME 2

| E | R | R | A | I | D | E | R | N |

LETTER GAME 3

| E | S | C | T | I | T | O | A | S |

LETTER GAME 4

| G | N | N | T | R | O | P | A | I |

NUMBER GAME 1

| 100 | 6 | 8 | 10 | 5 | 2 | 333 |

NUMBER GAME 2

| 50 | 100 | 1 | 7 | 9 | 4 | 862 |

CONUNDRUM

| B | U | T | N | E | L | L | I | E |

LETTER GAME 1

P	L	I	N	T	E	R	A	Y

LETTER GAME 2

V	E	R	E	B	A	D	E	H

LETTER GAME 3

C	A	R	I	F	I	S	E	C

LETTER GAME 4

R	U	D	S	H	I	N	F	E

NUMBER GAME 1

75	100	5	6	6	7	**915**

NUMBER GAME 2

50	1	9	2	1	3	**611**

CONUNDRUM

M	I	S	T	E	R	S	A	M

LETTER GAME 1

S	I	L	D	N	I	K	E	R

LETTER GAME 2

L	A	I	N	D	O	M	A	B

LETTER GAME 3

C	U	S	E	N	D	T	R	E

LETTER GAME 4

M	O	W	N	A	L	S	I	E

NUMBER GAME 1

25	100	50	4	10	7	542

NUMBER GAME 2

25	9	8	1	3	4	887

CONUNDRUM

D	O	T	S	P	R	I	D	E

LETTER GAME 1

F	R	E	L	I	C	U	S	T

LETTER GAME 2

S	S	S	D	E	B	I	U	L

LETTER GAME 3

E	L	U	L	S	O	E	C	L

LETTER GAME 4

D	A	M	B	I	L	E	N	O

NUMBER GAME 1

50	6	5	7	4	8	**936**

NUMBER GAME 2

25	100	5	7	10	9	**324**

CONUNDRUM

G	I	A	N	T	C	O	M	B

LETTER GAME 1

D	R	E	U	P	T	A	R	I

LETTER GAME 2

P	O	G	U	P	I	N	R	D

LETTER GAME 3

A	P	P	E	E	T	R	O	N

LETTER GAME 4

O	B	S	L	E	I	A	N	C

NUMBER GAME 1

2	6	7	8	1	3	**777**

NUMBER GAME 2

50	100	25	8	5	3	**846**

CONUNDRUM

Y	O	U	C	I	V	I	L	S

LETTER GAME 1

S	T	U	M	P	I	Q	E	Y

LETTER GAME 2

T	H	O	N	G	A	D	E	R

LETTER GAME 3

F	I	R	G	T	E	A	I	R

LETTER GAME 4

R	H	E	N	T	R	O	B	A

NUMBER GAME 1

50	75	1	4	2	9	656

NUMBER GAME 2

25	2	5	7	7	10	834

CONUNDRUM

G	I	V	E	N	D	I	R	T

LETTER GAME 1

C	E	R	O	V	S	T	E	A

LETTER GAME 2

F	O	T	U	F	A	C	E	S

LETTER GAME 3

L	O	T	E	I	N	L	P	A

LETTER GAME 4

N	N	Y	G	I	N	A	O	B

NUMBER GAME 1

6	10	8	7	7	9	248

NUMBER GAME 2

100	75	5	2	2	3	444

CONUNDRUM

N	E	U	T	R	O	F	A	T

LETTER GAME 1

H	O	S	T	I	N	D	A	O

LETTER GAME 2

N	M	E	N	A	S	T	I	C

LETTER GAME 3

A	N	C	U	D	I	O	S	T

LETTER GAME 4

L	D	E	O	N	W	K	E	G

NUMBER GAME 1

75	10	10	9	9	8	**360**

NUMBER GAME 2

25	4	3	7	2	2	**679**

CONUNDRUM

T	E	D	S	T	R	A	C	E

Answers

Round 1
BLOCKAGES 9, BACKLOGS 8, LOCKAGE 7
DANDELION 9, ADENOID 7, LOADED 6
PLURALISE 9, PERUSAL 7, ALLURE 6
SAFEGUARD 9, SUGARED 7, GRADES 6
$(7 \times 25) - 3 = 172$; $6 - (8 - 7) = 5$; $172 \times 5 = 860$
$2 \times 9 \times 50 = 900$; $2 \times 8 = 16$; $900 + 16 = 916$
ADMIRABLE

Round 2
BACTERIA 8, ABREACT 7, CATERS 6
UNLOADED 8, DUODENA 7, NODULE 6
HAILSTONE 9, HOTLINES 8, ELATION 7
WAGONETTE 9, TENTAGE 7, GOATEE 6
$6 \times 100 = 600$; $75 + 4 + 3 = 82$; $600 + (2 \times 82) = 764$
$100 - (9 - 1) = 92$; $92 \times 5 = 460$; $460 + 10 - 1 = 469$
FORTIFIED

Round 3
NAARTJIE 8, KERATIN 7, RETAIN 6
OBELISK 7, BLOKES 6, SHEIK 5
UPSTAGED 8, GATEAUS 7, ADAPTS 6
DESCRIES 8, RESIDES 7, SLICES 6
$75 + 50 + (5 - 3) = 127$; $127 \times 7 = 889$; $889 + 25 = 914$
$9 \times 9 = 81$; $81 + (6 - 4) = 83$; $(83 \times 10) + 3 = 833$
MASSAGING

Round 4
WINDPIPE 8, PAWNED, 6, WIPED 5
HAMBURGER 9, UMBRAGE 7, RHUMBA 6
SALESGIRL 9, GLASSIER 8, AIRLESS 7
CACOETHES 9, TEACHES 7, SCOTCH 6
$75 + 6 = 81$; $8 - (50/25) = 6$; $6 \times 81 = 486$
$2 \times 4 \times 25 = 200$; $200 + 5 = 205$; $205 \times 3 = 615$
VIOLINIST

Round 5
STATIONED 9, SEDATION 8, INSTEAD 7
VACCINATE 9, CAVATINE 8, VACCINE 7
RACEHORSE 9, RESEARCH 8, CAREERS 7
YARDAGE 7, DEARLY 6, GRAVE 5
$50 - 8 = 42$; $42 \times 7 = 294$; $294 - 3 = 291$
$75 + 7 + 5 = 87$; $87 \times 6 = 522$
RETRACTED

Round 6
HANKERED 8, THANKED 7, ADHERE 6
SIGNATURE 9, URINATES 8, GRANITE 7
VULCANIZE 9, VINCULA 7, VENIAL 6
JACKPOTS 8, TOECAPS 7, POCKET 6
$(8 \times 4) + 3 = 35$; $35 \times 25 = 875$; $875 + 2 = 877$
$8 \times (50 - 6) = 352$; $352 - 5 = 347$
ENTAILING

Round 7
CRABMEAT 8, MACABRE 7, DREAMT 6
WALLOPED 8, TADPOLE 7, PALLET 6
CASUISTRY 9, SACRISTY 8, RACISTS 7
OUTNUMBER 9, BURNOUT 7, TUMOUR 6
$9 + 8 - 6 = 11$; $(75 + 11) \times 9 = 774$; $774 + 3 = 777$
$(5 + 3) \times 10 = 80$; $80 - (2/2) = 79$; $79 \times 6 = 474$
GENTLEMAN

Round 8
WAKENING 8, WEANING 7, OWNING 6
BAGATELLE 9, EATABLE 7, EAGLET 6
YUMMIEST 8, TUMMIES 7, MOIETY 6
BLACKOUT 8, OUTBACK 7, COBALT 6
$(9 \times 3) - 1 = 26$; $26 \times 25 = 650$; $650 + 4 + 1 = 655$
$7 \times (100/2) = 350$; $350 - (10 + 2) = 338$
UNFOUNDED

Round 9
UNPOPULAR 9, POPULAR 7, POPLAR 6
WOBBLIER 8, BLOWIER 7, RABBLE 6
CITYSCAPE 9, ASEPTIC 7, ACCEPT 6
CADAVERIC 9, AVARICE 7, CRAVED 6
$100 + 50 + (8/8) = 151$; $151 \times 5 = 755$; $755 + 4 = 759$
$75 + 25 - 7 = 93$; $93 \times 10 = 930$; $930 - 6 = 924$
SHADOWING

Round 10
STEADILY 8, IDEALLY 7, SLATED 6
MANOMETER 9, MEMENTO 7, MOMENT 6
ARYTENOID 9, RATIONED 8, DETRAIN 7
HAMPERED 8, EARTHED 7, PARTED 6
$25 + (5 \times 3) = 40$; $(40 + 2) \times 8 = 336$; $336 + 3 = 339$
$100 + (10 \times 10) = 200$; $200 + 9 + 7 = 216$
TRANSPORT

Round 11
LANKIEST 8, PANTILE 7, INLETS 6
BENTWOOD 8, BOOTED 6, TOWED 5
PICKETED 8, DEPICT 6, ADEPT 5
OBSCURANT 9, ROBUSTA 7, CARBON 6
$9 \times (8 + 4) = 108$; $(108 + 3) \times 8 = 888$
$(5 \times 75) - 5 = 370$; $(50/25) \times 370 = 740$
FESTOONED

Round 12
HARDWARE 8, HARRIED 7, DRAWER 6
SAMPHIRE 8, HAMPERS 7, PHRASE 6
VOLLEYING 9, LOVINGLY 8, YELLING 7
YARDBIRD 8, BRIARY 6, RABID 5
$(25 - 4) \times 8 = 168$; $168 + (50/10) = 173$
$(9 - 2) \times (100 - 4) = 672$; $672 - 1 = 671$
LADDERING

Round 13
CADENZA 7, FAÇADE 6, NAKED 5
RACKETING 9, REACTING 8, TRACING 7
KILOBYTE 8, LIBERTY 7, LOITER 6
WOMANIZED 9, WOMANIZE 8, MIAOWED 7
$(3 \times 10) + (6/3) = 32$; $75 + 32 = 107$; $107 \times 8 = 856$
$6 \times 75 = 450$; $9 + (100/50) = 11$; $450 + 11 = 461$
ISOLATION

Round 14
POLISHED 8, SPLODGE 7, SLEIGH 6
DAREDEVIL 9, DEADLIER 8, DELIVER 7
PILLOWED 8, WILLED 6, PLIED 5
BAILMENT 8, TIMBALE 7, NIMBLE 6
$100 + 25 + 1 = 126$; $126 \times (6/2) = 378$
$4 \times 9 \times 25 = 900$; $900 - (10 + 7) = 883$
REPUTABLE

Round 15

UNRELATED 9, UNDERATE 8, ALTERED 7
DEPARTING 9, GRADIENT 8, PAINTED 7
CALAMITY 8, ACTUAL 6, CLAIM 5
BUNFIGHT 8, FOUGHT 6, THING 5
$100 + 75$ (2×5) = 165; (165×4) + 2 = 662
$3 \times 4 \times 75 = 900$; $900 - 100 = 800$; $800 + 25 - 2 = 823$
FLICKERED

Round 16

RADIATOR 7, ADROIT 6, TARDY 5
SIxPENCE 8, SINCERE 7, ExPIRE 6
ENCAGES 7, ESCAPE 6, PECAN 5
FACSIMILE 9, FAMILIES 8, LAICISE 7
$(8 \times 75) - 50 = 550$; $550 + 6 + 1 = 557$
$5 \times (7 + 1) = 40$; $40 \times 25 = 1000$; $1000 - (6 + 3) = 991$
TATTOOING

Round 17

PAGODAS 7, SEADOG 6, SPEAK 5
MACHISMO 8, CHAMOIS 7, MOSAIC 6
SURROGATE 9, OUTRAGES 8, TROUSER 7
CALUMNIES 9, MUSICALE 8, CAESIUM 7
$75 + 2 + 1 = 78$; $78 \times 8 = 624$; $624 + 50 = 674$
$(5 + 2) \times 2 = 14$; $100 - 14 = 86$; $86 \times 10 = 860$; $860 - 3 = 857$
MOUTHWASH

Round 18

DARTBOARD 9, BARRATOR 8, ABROAD 6
YIELDING 8, DINGILY 7, INDIGO 6
EMIGRATED 9, DIAMETER 8, EMIRATE 7
VIRGATES 8, THRIVES 7, VISAGE 6
$(9 \times 7) - 3 = 60$; $(9 \times 60) - 4 = 536$
$(2 + 1) \times 25 = 75$; $(75 + 2) \times 10 = 770$; $770 + 9 = 779$
AFTERLIFE

Round 19

WORRISOME 9, ROOMIER 7, SORROW 6
JAILBREAK 9, BALKIER 7, AERIAL 6
WARDROBE 8, BOARDER 7, ROARED 6
LISTABLE 8, LOBELIA 7, BALLOT 6
$(3 - 1) \times 50 = 100$; $(100 + 7) \times (5 + 4) = 963$
$10 \times 75 = 750$; $750 - 100 - 50 = 600$; $600 + 25 - 7 = 618$
LUMBERING

Round 20

RAINCOAT 8, OCARINA 7, CARTON 6
BILINGUAL 9, BILLING 7, AILING 6
CAMSHAFT 8, MATCHES 7, ASTHMA 6
BUDGETARY 9, TRAGEDY 7, GRATED 6
$100 + 25 - 2 = 123$; $123 \times 7 = 861$; $861 - 1 = 860$
$(75 + 10) \times 10 = 850$; $6 + 5 + 3 = 14$; $850 + 14 = 864$
SHRINKAGE

Round 21

BOLDFACE 8, LOAFED 6, FLOOD 5
STEPSONS 8, PISTONS 7, STONES 6
OVERAWED 8, WATERED 7, TOWARD 6
POOLSIDE 8, SPOILED 7, POODLE 6
$75 - (9/9) = 74$; $6 \times 74 = 444$; $444 - 100 - 7 = 337$
$2 \times (8 - 1) = 14$; $14 \times 50 = 700$; $700 - (9 + 8) = 683$
CORRODING

Round 22

CRABBY 6, CUBBY 5, ARIA 4
DATABASE 8, BASTARD 7, TREADS 6
YOUNGEST 8, IGNEOUS 7, GENIUS 6
BALLPOINT 9, PINBALL 7, OBTAIN 6
$100 + 25 - (50/5) = 115$; $115 \times 8 = 920$; $920 - 4 = 916$
$(2 \times 75) - 6 = 144$; $144 \times 4 = 576$; $576 - (2 + 1) = 573$
TACKINESS

Round 23

EMBRYONIC 9, COMBINE 7, BONIER 6
UNCARING 8, RUINING 7, CURING 6
CANKEROUS 9, NACREOUS 8, CONKERS 7
TARGETING 9, TREATING 8, NITRATE 7
$75 + 50 + 2 = 127$; $127 \times 7 = 889$; $889 - (3 - 2) = 888$
$100 + 75 + 25 = 200$; $9 - (50/10) = 4$; $200 + 4 = 204$
DETERGENT

Round 24

MACKEREL 8, MIRACLE 7, MALICE 6
FAMISHED 8, FISHED 6, SHEAF 5
LACEWORK 8, WARLOCK 7, CLERKS 6
LAMPOONED 9, LAMPOON 7, PLANED 6
$(6 \times 5) + 1 = 31$; $31 \times 25 = 775$; $775 + 1 = 776$
$3 \times 4 \times 10 = 120$; $(120 + 7) \times 5 = 635$
RASPBERRY

Round 25

UNSALTED 8, SALUTED 7, JAUNTS 6
SCAVENGE 8, ENCAGES 7, AGENCY 6
CANTABILE 9, BALANCE 7, CLIENT 6
ANGLIEST 9, STEALING 8, GENITAL 7
$75 - (4 + 2) = 69$; $25 - (7 + 4) = 14$; $69 \times 14 = 966$
$8 \times (7 + 1) = 64$; $64 \times (5 + 5) = 640$; $640 + 2 = 642$
MOTIVATED

Round 26

PALFREYS 8, PARSLEY 7, FLARES 6
NARCOTIC 8, ACTINIC 7, RATION 6
BALCONIES 9, SOCIABLE 8, SANICLE 7
OBSIDIAN 8, IONISED 7, ANODES 6
$10 \times 9 \times 7 = 630$; $630 + 100 + 10 + 1 = 741$
$9 + (8/2) = 13$; $13 \times 50 = 650$; $650 + 6 = 656$
PREACHING

Round 27

BROTHER 7, AUTHOR 6, BERTH 5
VINTAGERS 9, ANGRIEST 8, STRIVEN 7
CAPSIZED 8, SPICED 6, SEPIA 5
SIZEABLE 8, BALDIES 7, SEALED 6
$(9 \times 50) + 75 = 525$; $(100/25) - 1 = 3$; $525 - 3 = 522$
$8 \times 5 = 40$; $40 \times (75/3) = 1000$; $1000 - 1 = 999$
EFFICIENT

Round 28

VINDALOO 8, OVATION 7, LOTION 6
HEADGEAR 8, DRAGEE 6, RAGED 5
ZESTIEST 8, EASIEST 7, SIESTA 6
ARROGANT 8, NARRATE 7, RANGER 6
$(10 + 5) \times 50 = 750$; $750 - (25 + 2) = 723$
$100 + 5 + 3 = 108$; $108 \times (9 - 3) = 648$
ALBATROSS

Round 29

ELOQUENT 8, TOLUENE 7, ELUENT 6
SCHIZOID 8, IODIZES 7, COSHED 6
VALENTINE 9, VENETIAN 8, ENLIVEN 7
CAPTIONED 9, PEDANTIC 8, NOTEPAD 7
$2 \times 9 \times 50 = 900$; $(9 - 4) \times 7 = 35$; $900 - 35 = 865$
$(75 + 4) \times 10 = 790$; $100/50 = 2$; $790 - (6/2) = 787$
MONKEYING

Round 30

PORTRAIT 8, AIRPORT 7, ROTTER 6
MAGAZINE 8, MANAGED 7, MAIDEN 6
STILETTO 8, THISTLE 7, TOILET 6
BRITCHES 8, BRIOCHE 7, CHORES 6
$(100/4) + 1 = 26$; $26 \times 9 = 234$
$4 \times (3 + 1) = 16$; $16 \times (25 + 2) = 432$; $432 - 1 = 431$
UNDAMAGED

Round 31

UNAWARES 8, UNSCREW 7, ANSWER 6
WATERBED 8, BERATED 7, TIRADE 6
JAVELINS 8, NAIVELY 7, SALINE 6
RATEPAYER 9, TAPERER 7, ERRATA 6
$(100 - 9) \times 8 = 728; 728 - 50 = 678; 678 - (4/4) = 677$
$75 - (8 + 4) = 63; 63 \times 3 = 189; 189 \times 5 = 945$
RECEPTION

Round 32

UNCLIMBED 9, INCLUDE 7, INDUCE 6
HERALDIC 8, RECITAL 7, TRACED 6
UNWANTED 8, TWANGED 7, GNAWED 6
DEBACLES 8, BEAGLES 7, SLEDGE 6
$100 + 7 + (6/2) = 110; 110 \times (7 + 1) = 880$
$(75 + 6) \times 9 = 729; 729 - 5 = 724$
IMPASSIVE

Round 33

NARROWEST 9, SENATOR 7, ARROWS 6
COMPENDIA 9, PANDEMIC 8, NOMADIC 7
CAPTIVATE 9, ACTIVATE 8, CAPTIVE 7
ELEPHANT 8, PLEATED 7, PEAHEN 6
$9 \times 9 = 81; (8 + 3) \times 81 = 891; 891 + 8 + 7 = 906$
$(7 + 5) \times (50 + 4) = 648; 648 - (5 + 4) = 639$
TENDERING

Round 34

BANISHED 8, BEHINDS 7, WIDENS 6
STEVEDORE 9, DEVOTEES 8, DESERVE 7
FATEFUL 7, FAULTS 6, STUFF 5
FAREWELL 8, WELFARE 7, FILLER 6
$10 + 10 + 2 = 22; 22 \times 25 = 550; 550 + (6 \times 4) = 574$
$(7 + 3) \times 100 = 1000; (75/5) \times 3 = 45; 1000 - 45 = 955$
LANDSLIDE

Round 35

SCORPION 8, OPSONIC 7, CROONS 6
BRIEFCASE 9, FREESIA 7, FIBRES 6
MAILBOXES 9, MIXABLE 7, MOBILE 6
CARDAMOM 8, COMRADE 7, ARCADE 6
$75 - 8 = 67; 67 - (50/25) = 65; 65 \times 8 = 520; 520 + 100 = 620$
$(3 \times 9) + 4 = 31; 31 \times 25 = 775; 775 + 10 = 785$
ASPARAGUS

Round 36

WAXCLOTH 8, LOCATE 6, CHEAT 5
ARCHIVED 8, RAWHIDE 7, CRAVED 6
ZOMBIFY 7, OPIUM 5, BUMP 4
MEDICATE 8, DICTATE 7, MATTED 6
$50 + 25 - (10 - 9) = 74; (9 + 2) \times 74 = 814$
$100 + 75 + 50 = 225; 9 + 9 + 6 = 24; 225 + 24 = 249$
WHOLESOME

Round 37

OBSTETRIC 9, BISECTOR 8, BITTERS 7
PANDERING 9, REAPING 7, GARDEN 6
PASTILLE 8, ESTIVAL 7, PLATES 6
TAXIDERMY 9, DAYTIME 7, DREAMY 6
$(3 \times 25) + 5 = 80; (6 \times 80) + 4 = 484$
$(8 \times 50) + 100 = 500; 25 + 7 - 2 = 30; 500 + 30 = 530$
SIMILARLY

Round 38

LARCENIES 9, SILENCER 8, CLEANSE 7
PROUDEST 8, GROUTED 7, TOURED 6
HEXASTYLE 9, EYELASH 7, EXALTS 6
SKINHEAD 8, SARDINE 7, SINKER 6
$(8 \times 10) + 6 = 86; 9 - (2 + 1) = 6; 86 \times 6 = 516$
$75 + 3 = 78; 78 \times 9 = 702$
MULTIPLEX

Round 39

BANISTER 8, REPAINT 7, BRAINS 6
UKULELE 7, CUPULE 6, PLUCK 5
VAMPIRES 8, WAIVERS 7, ASPIRE 6
WAKENING 8, DAWNING 7, WINKED 6
$100 - 2 = 98; 98 \times (4 \times 2) = 784; 784 + 75 = 859$
$6 \times 75 = 450; 25 - (100/50) = 23; 450 - 23 = 427$
RECEIVING

Round 40

CASHBACK 8, CHICKS 6, BASIC 5
NASTINESS 9, SESTINAS 8, SIESTAS 7
PASTURED 8, TRAIPSE 7, PARTED 6
BANTERING 9, REBATING 8, NEARING 7
$(6 + 4 + 3) \times 50 = 650; 650 + (9 \times 9) = 731$
$25 + 6 + 2 = 33; 33 \times 3 \times 10 = 990$
PROPRIETY

Round 41

MAKEOVER 8, REMOVED 7, MARKED 6
DECIPHER 8, PREDICT 7, RECIPE 6
SCREWBALL 9, WARBLES 7, LABELS 6
STOCKIEST 9, STOCKIST 8, TICKETS 7
$(50 + 9) \times 3 = 177; 177 - (7 - 4) = 174; 174 \times 5 = 870$
$(6 \times 50) + 100 = 400; 400 - (9 - 2) = 393$
WAISTBAND

Round 42

CEASEFIRE 9, FRICASEE 8, FIACRES 7
MUTILATE 8, GIMLET 6, AGLET 5
REALISTIC 9, ARTICLES 8, REALIST 7
ELASTOMER 9, MOLESTER 8, REMOTES 7
$4 \times 4 \times 5 = 80; 9 \times 80 = 720; 720 + (6 - 5) = 721$
$7 \times 6 \times 2 = 84; 5 \times (3 - 1) = 10; 84 \times 10 = 840$
HYPERBOLE

Round 43

VILLAGER 8, ALLEGRO 7, GRAVEL 6
BREASTFED 9, BREASTED 8, DEAREST 7
UNCOUTHLY 9, UNCOUTH 7, TOUCHY 6
HINDRANCE 9, INARCHED 8, HANDIER 7
$3 \times 8 \times 25 = 600; 2 \times 3 \times 9 = 54; 600 + 54 = 654$
$8 \times 7 = 56; 100 - (75 + 10) = 15; (56 - 15) \times 9 = 369$
LABORIOUS

Round 44

CELESTIAL 9, ELASTIC 7, CLEATS 6
PARACHUTE 9, CAPTURE 7, TEACUP 6
SURFACED 8, TRADUCE 7, CRATED 6
GRAFTING 8, RAFTING 7, FRIGHT 6
$(2 \times 50) = 99; 99 \times (7 + 3) = 990; 990 + 2 = 992$
$(100 + 25) \times 6 = 750; 8 - (4/4) = 7; 750 + 7 = 757$
AFFECTION

Round 45

OCARINAS 8, INSOFAR 7, CASINO 6
DENIGRATE 9, TREADING 8, GRENADE 7
OPERATICS 9, PRACTISE 8, SEAPORT 7
TEASPOON 8, TOECAPS 7, OCTANE 6
$10 \times (50 - 1) = 490; 490 + (75/25) = 493; 493 - 100 = 393$
$9 \times 50 = 450; 450 - (75/25) = 447; 447 \times (8/4) = 894$
LOOSENING

Round 46

JEROBOAM 8, BROMATE 7, REBOOT 6
STOMACHED 9, HEADMOST 8, CATHODE 7
CHAGRINED 9, REACHING 8, CRINGED 7
UFOLOGIST 9, OLOGIST 7, FLOUTS 6
$(2 \times 7) + 4 = 18; 18 \times 50 = 900; 900 + (8 \times 3) = 924$
$8 - (10 - 9) = 7; 7 \times 75 = 525; 525 + 4 = 529$
BRAINWAVE

Round 47

BREADLINE 9, DENIABLE 8, BRINDLE 7
HONEYDEW 8, HONEYED 7, ANYHOW 6
EMULSIFY 8, HIMSELF 7, HELIUM 6
BAREFACED 9, REFACED 7, ARCADE 6
$(5 + 6) - (1 + 1) = 9; 9 \times (100 - 7) = 837$
$4 - (2/2) = 3; 3 \times 9 \times 25 = 675; 675 - 4 = 671$
IMPERFECT

Round 48

AUSTERITY 9, ESTUARY 7, STATUE 6
BABYSIT 7, ABBOTS 6, TABBY 5
OVERPRICE 9, OVERRIPE 8, RECOVER 7
GROUPIES 8, PIROGUE 7, GROPES 6
$6 \times 5 = 30; 30 \times (25 + 1) = 780; 780 + 4 - 1 = 783$
$7 \times (100 - 8) = 644; (50/5) +10 = 20; 644 - 20 = 624$
MARKETING

Round 49

PASTRAMI 8, IMPORTS 7, RAPIST 6
PAGANISE 8, AGONISE 7, PONIES 6
STEAMROLL 9, MAESTRO 7, TALLER 6
CALIBRATE 9, BACTERIA 8, CABARET 7
$75 + 2 = 77; (6 + 1) \times 77 = 539; 539 + 9 = 548$
$100 + 75 + 25 = 200; (200 - 6) \times 4 = 776; 776 + 50 = 826$
TIGHTENED

Round 50

WESTBOUND 9, SNOUTED 7, DEBUTS 6
ZEALOTRY 8, EATERY 6, EARLY 5
EARBASHED 9, BEHEADS 7, ERASED 6
STAIRWELL 9, LITERALS 8, RETAILS 7
$(8 + 5) \times 50 = 650; (9 \times 2) - 1 = 17; 650 - 17 = 633$
$(9 + 7) \times 25 = 400; 100 - (8 \times 7) = 44; 400 + 44 = 444$
COLLECTOR

Round 51

SQUIREDOM 9, SQUIRMED 8, MOUSIER 7
CARPENTER 9, RECREANT 8, CATERER 7
YABBERING 9, BRAYING 7, REGAIN 6
YEARBOOK 8, BAKERY 6, BROKE 5
$9 \times (50 + 25) = 675; 675 + 9 + 2 = 686; 686 + 100 = 786$
$10 + 2 + 1 = 13; 13 \times (50 + 2) = 676$
BUTTONING

Round 52

DEXTERITY 9, EXITED 6, TRIED 5
AROMATIC 8, MARITAL 7, COITAL 6
PAINTWORK 9, PATRON 6, PRANK 5
SQUELCHY 8, CLIQUES 7, CHISEL 6
$7 \times 8 \times 10 = 560; 560 - (4 + 1) = 555$
$6/ (7 - 5) = 3; (9 \times 10) + 3 = 93; 93 \times 8 = 744$
DISPLACED

Round 53

FOOLHARDY 9, LOOFAH 6, FLOOD 5
CARTILAGE 9, TRAGICAL 8, ARTICLE 7
TYPEFACE 8, PREFACE 7, CARPET 6
WATERHOLE 9, WEATHER 7, LOATHE 6
$75 - (50/25) = 73; 73 \times 8 = 584; 584 + 100 + 3 = 687$
$(7 \times 5) \times 25 = 875; 875 + (9 - 8) = 876$
PURPORTED

Round 54

PALMTOPS 8, LAPTOPS 7, ALMOST 6
WINEMAKER 9, RAMEKIN 7, MARINE 6
GOSSAMER 8, MAESTRO 7, STORES 6
ARACHNID 8, RADIANT 7, RANCID 6
$(5 + 4) \times (100 + 2) = 918; 918 + 10 + 3 = 931$
$75 + (50/25) = 77; 3 \times (2 + 1) = 9; 9 \times 77 = 693$
LOITERING

Round 55

SPREADING 9, READINGS 8, PRANGED 7
HOSPITAL 8, ASPHALT 7, POSTAL 6
TRIUMPHED 9, THUMPED 7, UMPIRE 6
CARETAKER 9, RETRACE 7, CREATE 6
$(50 + 5) \times 2 = 110; (110 \times 9) - 2 = 988$
$50 + 6 + 4 = 60; (8 + 5) \times 60 = 780; 780 - 8 = 772$
LOCKSMITH

Round 56

WEBMASTER 9, BERATES 7, BEWARE 6
SPECIFIC 8, SCEPTIC 7, CITIES 6
BARNACLE 8, BALANCE 7, CLARET 6
WASSAILED 9, ASSAILED 8, ALIASES 7
$75 + 9 = 84; (6 + 4) \times 84 = 840$
$3 \times (4 + 1) = 15; 15 \times 25 = 375; 375 - (7 + 2) = 366$
TREMBLING

Round 57

GLYCERINE 9, REGENCY 7, LINGER 6
BULLETINS 9, UTENSIL 7, BLUEST 6
RULERSHIP 9, PLUSHIER 8, HURRIES 7
SPACEMAN 8, PANCAKE 7, SEAMAN 6
$7 \times 75 = 525; 9 + 8 - 3 = 14; 525 - 14 = 511$
$(4 \times 10) \times (4 \times 5) = 800; 800 + (7 \times 5) = 835$
INVISIBLE

Round 58

FLEXITIME 9, LIFETIME 8, LEFTIE 6
TREATMENT 9, ENTREAT 7, MATTER 6
MUTILATES 9, SIMULATE 8, AMULETS 7
LOWERMOST 9, TREMOLOS 8, LOOTERS 7
$75 + 9 + 8 = 92; (92 \times 10) + 9 = 929$
$8 \times (100 - 7) = 744; 75/25 = 3; 744 - (3/3) = 743$
SOLDIERED

Round 59

WARHORSE 8, SPARROW 7, PHASER 6
OVERTAXED 9, OVEREAT 7, ADVERT 6
WAREHOUSE 9, REHOUSE 7, SHOWER 6
CARDPHONE 9, ANCHORED 8, PARCHED 7
$2 \times 3 \times 6 = 36; (36 - 2) \times 25 = 850; 850 + 4 = 854$
$10 \times 10 = 100; 100 + (100/50) = 102; (75/25) \times 102 = 306$
ANIMOSITY

Round 60

MOTORCADE 9, DEMOCRAT 8, REDCOAT 7
PUCCOONS 8, COUPONS 7, CUCKOO 6
CAUTERIZE 9, AZURITE 7, CREATE 6
BALLPOINT 9, PINBALL 7, OBTAIN 6
$(8 + 5) \times 75 = 975; (8 \times 4) + 10 = 42; 975 - 42 = 933$
$9 \times (50 + 7) = 513; 513 + 8 = 521$
ORDAINING

Round 61

TRANSPIRE 9, TERRAPIN 8, PAINTER 7
AMPOULES 8, MALTOSE 7, PLATES 6
VULTURES 8, RIVULET 7, SILVER 6
DETOXIFY 8, EXOTIC 6, FIXED 5
$25 - (5 - 3) = 23; 10 + 8 = 18; 18 \times 23 = 414$
$7 \times (10 + 2) = 84; 4 + 4 = 8; 84 \times 8 = 672$
SHABBIEST

Round 62

COUPLETS 8, POSTURE 7, CLOUTS 6
BANQUETED 9, EQUATED 7, BEATEN 6
HOOLIGAN 8, HOWLING 7, LOWING 6
PARAGLIDE 9, REGALIA 7, GLIDER 6
$(2 \times 50) - 4 = 96; 96 \times 10 = 960; 960 + (5 + 2) = 967$
$100 + 7 + 5 =112; (6 + 1) \times 112 = 784; 784 + 75 = 859$
THUNDERED

Round 63

VOYAGEUR 8, FORGAVE 7, VOYEUR 6
PARBOILED 9, PIEBALD 7, PAROLE 6
LOTTERIES 9, RETITLES 8, LOITERS 7
SOMBRERO 8, ROOSTER 7, MOTORS 6
$(50 + 4) \times 2 = 108$; $(108 + 3) \times 9 = 999$
$6 + (75/25) = 9$; $9 \times 8 = 72$; $100 + 72 + 50 = 222$
CORKSCREW

Round 64

SOFTBACK 8, SETBACK 7, FACETS 6
PASTURED 8, PARQUET 7, QUARTS 6
TRADESMAN 9, MANDATES 8, MANTRAS 7
MORPHINE 8, MONIKER 7, HEROIN 6
$100 - (7 + 5) = 88$; $88 \times 7 = 616$
$(4 \times 25) + 3 = 103$; $(4 + 2) \times 103 = 618$; $618 + 1 = 619$
TIPTOEING

Round 65

SOBRIQUET 9, BRIQUETS 8, BUSTIER 7
VOICEMAIL 9, ALCOVE 6, CLAIM 5
BEARSKIN 8, ARSENIC 7, BICKER 6
FLAMINGO 8, PALMING 7, MALIGN 6
$(7 \times 5) + 3 = 38$; $(50 + 38) \times 10 = 880$; $880 - 4 = 876$
$(3 \times 4) + 1 = 13$; $13 \times (8 \times 5) = 520$; $520 + 2 = 522$
HEARTBEAT

Round 66

SNOWFALL 8, SWOLLEN 7, FALLEN 6
BARGEPOLE 9, OPERABLE 8, PERGOLA 7
CARNOTITE 9, REACTION 8, CATTIER 7
TOWELING 8, TOWLINE 7, TWINGE 6
$9 \times 75 = 675$; $675 + 100 + 6 = 781$
$100 - (9 - 2) = 93$; $93 \times 10 = 930$; $930 + 2 + 1 = 933$
SPREADING

Round 67

MOONSCAPE 9, COMPOSE 7, POMACE 6
WHORLING 8, HOWLING 7, GLORIA 6
ONLOOKERS 9, SNORKEL 7, SOONER 6
OVULATING 9, VAULTING 8, ANTILOG 7
$6 \times (5 - 3) = 12$; $12 \times (75 - 4) = 852$; $852 - 50 = 802$
$(7 + 2) \times 25 = 225$; $(225 - 10) \times 3 = 645$
MESMERISE

Round 68

TORNADOES 9, RATOONED 8, SNORTED 7
SNARLING 8, SOARING 7, ORGANS 6
CERTAINTY 9, INTERACT 8, CATTERY 7
SOLITARY 8, TAILORS 7, STRAIT 6
$75 + (100/50) = 77$; $77 \times 4 = 308$; $308 - 25 = 283$
$75 + 2 + 2 + 1 = 80$; $4 \times 3 \times 80 = 960$
PERSUADED

Round 69

PEDALOES 8, PLEASED 7, BLADES 6
SMOOCHED 8, MEDICOS 7, CHOOSE 6
BUMPINESS 9, NIMBUSES 8, MINUSES 7
ANEURYSM 8, SURNAME 7, MANURE 6
$3 \times (25 + 9) = 102$; $102 \times 6 = 612$; $612 - (6 - 5) = 611$
$(50 - 10) \times 8 = 320$; $320 + 3 - 4 = 319$
CHASTISED

Round 70

ISSUANCE 8, CRUISES 7, CRANES 6
WANDERED 8, WARDEN 6, DRAWN 5
CUSPIDATE 9, AUSPICE 7, SPACED 6
MODULATE 8, MOULTED 7, LOQUAT 6
$(8 \times 10) + 10 = 90$; $(7 \times 90) - 9 = 621$
$25 + 4 - 9 = 20$; $20 \times 50 = 1000$; $1000 - 2 = 998$
PONDEROUS

Round 71

CAPSULATE 9, PLACATES 8, TEACUPS 7
PEEKABOO 8, POOKA 5, BOOK 4
DOMINOES 8, GOODIES 7, DENIMS 6
MINEFIELD 9, INFIDEL 7, DEFINE 6
$100 + 10 + 2 = 112$; $(5 + 2) \times 112 = 784$
$(10 + 2) \times 9 = 108$; $108 + 25 = 133$; $133 \times 7 = 931$
PATTERING

Round 72

HIBERNATE 9, TRAINEE 7, BREATH 6
THUMBNAIL 9, HALIBUT 7, LABIUM 6
BARRISTER 9, BARRIERS 8, RAREBIT 7
ADOPTED 7, PADDLE 6, BLOAT 5
$(75/25) \times 3 = 9$; $100 - (1 + 1) = 98$; $98 \times 9 = 882$
$6 \times (50 + 2) = 312$; $312 + 100 + 9 = 421$
ALLOCATED

Round 73

PENALISE 8, PELICAN 7, SPLICE 6
ANYTHING 8, INANITY 7, HATING 6
CHAMPION 8, CAMPION 7, PHONIC 6
OWNERSHIP 9, WHISPER 7, HERONS 6
$8 + 6 = 14$; $14 \times (75 - 4) = 994$; $994 + (10/2) = 999$
$(3 \times 50) - 9 = 141$; $(10/2) \times 141 = 705$; $705 + 1 = 706$
BLANKETED

Round 74

ADVISOR 7, LIZARD 6, AVOID 5
METHADONE 9, ANTHEMED 8, METHANE 7
BRAINWAVE 9, WAIVER 6, BRINE 5
OPTICAL 7, POSTAL 6, CLAWS 5
$(8 + 7) \times 10 = 150$; $(150 + 1) \times 6 = 906$; $906 + 3 = 909$
$100 + 50 + 8 = 158$; $158 \times 4 = 632$; $632 + 3 - 1 = 634$
ANIMATION

Round 75

PENTHOUSE 9, ENTHUSE 7, POTEEN 6
CUFFLINK 8, UNCIAL 6, FLANK 5
BATHROOM 8, ROWBOAT 7, WOMBAT 6
URBANISED 9, BRANDIES 8, BRAINED 7
$(10 \times 10) + 9 = 109$; $(75/25) \times 109 = 327$; $327 + 50 = 377$
$9 \times 4 \times 25 = 900$; $7 \times (9 - 3) = 42$; $900 - 42 = 858$
INHABITED

Round 76

SKELETAL 8, OLEATES 7, ALLOTS 6
THINGAMY 8, ANYTIME 7, HATING 6
EROTICISM 9, MORTICES 8, MOISTER 7
BAYONETED 9, BAYONET 7, DENOTE 6
$2 \times 100 = 200$; $200 + 25 - 5 = 220$; $220 \times 4 = 880$
$10 - 2 = 8$; $8 \times 5 \times 10 = 400$; $400 + 75 - 7 = 468$
CAROUSING

Round 77

ANCHOVIES 9, EVASION 7, CHIVES 6
ELUCIDATE 9, DELICATE 8, DIALECT 7
SINCERITY 9, INCITERS 8, CISTERN 7
GINORMOUS 9, GUNROOMS 8, MOORING 7
$5 + 4 + 4 = 13$; $100 + 50 - 13 = 137$; $137 \times 5 = 685$
$5 + 7 - 3 = 9$; $9 \times (75 - 1) = 666$
ASTRONOMY

Round 78

PHILANDER 9, HELIPAD 7, HINDER 6
ROULETTE 8, LETTER 6, OUTER 5
KNOWLEDGE 9, GOLDEN 6, WEDGE 5
THEORISES 9, SHORTIES 8, STEREOS 7
$8 - (5 - 3) = 6$; $6 \times 75 = 450$; $450 - 9 = 441$
$(7 + 4) \times 25 = 275$; $(275 + 1) \times 3 = 828$; $828 + 2 = 830$
BECKONING

Round 79

BICONCAVE 9, VACCINE 7, BOVINE 6
AMETHYST 8, STEAMY 6, MATHS 5
BEANFEAST 9, ABSENT 6, FATES 5
OPTIMIZE 8, EPIZOIC 7, POETIC 6
$(4 \times 6) - (2/2) = 23$; $(8 \times 100) - 23 = 777$
$(10 \times 10) - 7 = 93$; $93 \times 9 = 837$; $837 + 5 = 842$
WEARISOME

Round 80

CANOODLE 8, CONDOLE 7, CLONED 6
INVASION 8, SAPONIN 7, PIANOS 6
PHOSPHATE 9, PATHOS 6, HATES 5
FETLOCKS 8, TICKLES 7, FLECKS 6
$(50 + 25) \times 2 = 150$; $150 - (8 + 1) = 141$; $141 \times 7 = 987$
$100 + 9 + 4 = 113$; $113 \times 6 = 678$
DELEGATED

Round 81

JINGOISM 8, AMIGOS 6, GAINS 5
TURBINES 8, BRUISED 7, RUSTED 6
BECHAMEL 8, BLEACH 6, BLAZE 5
CHELATION 9, CHATLINE 8, ETHICAL 7
$(100 + 75) \times 3 = 525$; $525 + 3 = 528$; $528 + (50/25) = 530$
$50 + 25 + 7 = 82$; $82 \times 4 = 328$; $328 + 5 = 333$
ENJOYABLE

Round 82

PIPETTES 8, SPITTLE 7, TITLES 6
HEARTSICK 9, CHARIEST 8, STICKER 7
LIMOUSINE 9, EMULSION 8, ELUSION 7
BEDSPREAD 9, SPEARED 7, SADDER 6
$75 + 25 - 5 = 95$; $95 \times 7 = 665$; $665 - (3 + 3) = 659$
$(7 + 5) \times 25 = 300$; $300 + (7 \times 6) = 342$
INTRUSION

Round 83

BELLYACHE 9, EYEBALL 7, BLEACH 6
DEFAULTED 9, DEFLATED 8, DELATED 7
SHUFFLED 8, FLUSHED 7, FLUIDS 6
NOSTALGIC 9, COASTING 8, LASTING 7
$7 + 7 + 3 = 17$; $17 \times (50 - 1) = 833$; $833 - 6 = 827$
$50 - (4 + 4) = 42$; $42 \times 8 = 336$; $336 - (6/2) = 333$
PENETRATE

Round 84

CONVULSE 8, LOUNGES 7, UNCLES 6
SWEATSHOP 9, POSHEST 7, PATHOS 6
PISCATORY 9, APRICOTS 8, PROSAIC 7
METAFILE 8, MALEATE 7, FEMALE 6
$9 \times (75 + 5) = 720$; $720 + (100/25) = 724$
$(75 - 2) \times 8 = 584$; $100 + 25 - 10 = 115$; $584 - 115 = 469$
INFESTING

Round 85

SHOEBLACK 9, BACKHOES 8, SHACKLE 7
ROLLMOP 7, IMPORT 6, TRILL 5
LIGHTENED 9, DELETING 8, DELIGHT 7
BROACHED 8, TORCHED 7, COATED 6
$(2 \times 7) + 4 = 18$; $18 \times 50 = 900$; $900 + 25 + 9 = 934$
$(9 \times 8) - 1 = 71$; $71 \times 10 = 710$; $710/2 = 355$
WORRISOME

Round 86

BROWBEAT 8, PROBATE 7, BOATER 6
JETLINER 8, THEREIN 7, ENTIRE 6
ONCOMING 8, AWAITED 7, INMATE 6
UNBEATEN 8, PENNATE 7, BUTANE 6
$(8 \times 8) - 5 = 59$; $7 + 3 + 2 = 12$; $12 \times 59 = 708$
$3 \times (7 - 1) = 18$; $18 \times 25 = 450$; $450 - (5 + 1) = 444$
GUTTERING

Round 87

RIDERSHIP 9, DISHIER 7, SPIDER 6
KNITWEAR 8, RETRAIN 7, WANKER 6
CLASSMATE 9, CALMEST 7, CAMELS 6
STATEMENT 9, TESTATE 7, ATTEST 6
$(8 \times 100) - 25 = 775$; $(2 \times 8) + 10 = 26$; $775 - 26 = 749$
$3 \times 9 \times 25 = 675$; $(8 \times 6) - 1 = 47$; $675 + 47 = 722$
CONCEITED

Round 88

OILFIELD 8, FILLED 6, PILED 5
AMBERGRIS 9, ARMIGERS 8, MARRIES 7
NOSEBAND 8, BONNIES 7, ANODES 6
SHIRTIEST 9, THIRTIES 8, HITTERS 7
$7 \times 7 = 49$; $49 - (8 - 6) = 47$; $8 \times 47 = 376$
$75 + 8 = 83$; $83 \times 6 \times 2 = 996$; $996 - 3 = 993$
CORDIALLY

Round 89

MAVERICK 8, TACKIER 7, ACTIVE 6
CINEPLEX 8, RECLINE 7, PINCER 6
AVERSION 8, INSHORE 7, HEROIN 6
PUBLICAN 8, UNCIAL 6, QUAIL 5
$(9 - 7) \times 75 = 150$; $150 + 100 - 8 = 242$
$3 \times 3 \times (2 + 1) = 27$; $27 \times (25 - 1) = 648$
BIOGRAPHY

Round 90

QUICKSTEP 9, QUICKEST 8, PIQUETS 7
SHAMROCK 8, MARCHES 7, HACKER 6
LEMONADE 8, OMENTAL 7, LAMENT 6
DYSPHORIA 9, SHIPYARD 8, HAIRDOS 7
$100 + 6 = 106$; $(7 + 1) \times 106 = 848$; $848 - 25 = 823$
$(9 \times 3) - 5 = 22$; $(10 \times 10) + 22 = 122$; $122 \times 7 = 854$
DISPERSAL

Round 91

ODOURLESS 9, SOLDERS 7, DOSSER 6
FELONIES 8, ONESELF 7, FLEETS
EUPHORIC 8, COUGHER 7, GOPHER 6
PROSTATE 8, TAMPERS 7, TEAPOT 6
$7 \times (100 + 25) = 875$; $875 + 50 = 925$; $925 - 7 = 918$
$100 + 50 + 6 = 156$; $156 \times 5 = 780$; $780 + 4 - 1 = 783$
ALLOWANCE

Round 92

BEWILDER 8, TREBLED 7, BELTER 6
CLEARWING 9, CLEARING 8, WRANGLE 7
SUCTORIAL 9, CURTAILS 8, RITUALS 7
SHAMBOLIC 9, CHOLIAMB 8, ABOLISH 7
$(9 + 1) \times 75 = 750$; $750 - (9 \times 2) = 732$
$8 \times 25 = 200$; $4 + (10/10) = 5$; $(200 + 5) \times 3 = 615$
MORTICIAN

Round 93

BOATHOUSE 9, ATHEOUS 7, BATHOS 6
RETRACING 9, CATERING 8, GRANITE 7
SINEWING 8, SEWING 6, BINGE 5
DENOUNCE 8, UNDONE 6, CONED 5
$75 + 50 + 10 + 9 = 144$; $(8 \times 100) + 144 = 944$
$25 - (7 + 4) = 14$; $14 \times 75 = 1050$; $1050 - (9 \times 8) = 978$
BICKERING

Round 94

SHABBIEST 9, TABBIES 7, BABIES 6
SPILLAGE 8, PILLAGE 7, SILAGE 6
PROPHETIC 9, CHOPPIER 8, PITCHER 7
CLAMMIEST 9, CLIMATES 8, LACIEST 7
$(75/25) + (100/50) = 5$; $5 \times 8 \times 9 = 360$
$(7 + 3) \times 10 = 100$; $(6 \times 100) - 8 = 592$
PHILANDER

Round 95

PROOFING 8, ROOFING 7, ROWING 6
BRASSERIE 9, BRASSIER 8, SIERRAS 7
TERMINUS 8, ROUTINE 7, TUNERS 6
CLUBHOUSE 9, BLOUSE 6, CLUES 5
$(2 \times 7) + 9 = 23; 23 \times 25 = 575; 575 + 10 = 585$
$(6 \times 2) - 1 = 11; 100 + 11 = 111; (3 + 2) \times 111 = 555$
DIFFICULT

Round 96

RETARDANT 9, NARRATED 8, TARTARE 7
CULMINATE 9, CLIMATE 7, MENTAL 6
MEGASTORE 9, GAMESTER 8, STEAMER 7
SENIORITY 9, TYROSINE 8, NOISIER 7
$75 - 4 = 71; (5 + 4) \times 71 = 639; 639 - (50/25) = 637$
$8 \times (75 - 4) = 568; (50/2) - 4 = 21; 568 - 21 = 547$
PARAGRAPH

Round 97

PNEUMATIC 9, PETUNIA 7, PEANUT 6
ALPENHORN 9, PLANNER 7, PAROLE 6
HARANGUED 9, UNHEARD 7, AGENDA 6
NIGHTWEAR 9, WATERING 8, RIGHTEN 7
$(9 + 4) \times 50 = 650; (7 \times 5) - 6 = 29; 650 + 29 = 679$
$3 \times 100 = 300; 9 \times 7 = 63; 300 - 63 = 237$
ROUGHNESS

Round 98

CRUSTACEA 9, ACCURATE 8, ACCUSER 7
EQUISETUM 9, MESQUITE 8, QUIETUS 7
BILLYCAN 8, LUNACY 6, BULLY 5
GABERDINE 9, BEARDING 8, BANDIER 7
$7 \times 6 \times 3 = 126; (126 - 8) \times 8 = 944; 944 - 3 = 941$
$2 \times 7 \times 50 = 700; 8 + 4 - 1 = 11; 700 - 11 = 689$
INCLUSION

Round 99

JAUNDICE 8, INJURED 7, DANCER 6
TEENAGER 8, EARTHEN 7, HANGER 6
ALLOCATED 9, COLLATED 8, LOCATED 7
BEZIQUE 7, PIQUET 6, QUIET 5
$(5 + 4) \times 75 = 675; 675 + 50 = 725; 725 + 4 - 3 = 726$
$(6 + 5) \times 75 = 825; 825 + (6 \times 4) = 849$
QUICKSAND

Round 100

MANIFOLD 8, DIAMOND 7, ALMOND 6
PODGIEST 8, TEDIOUS 7, DEPOTS 6
CONCEITED 9, NOTICED 7, COINED 6
ALGEBRAIC 9, REGALIA 7, GARLIC 6
$(75 + 50) \times 8 = 1000; 3 \times 25 = 75; 1000 - 75 + 2 = 927$
$75 - (100/50) = 77; 25 - (4 \times 4) = 9; 77 \times 9 = 693$
UNDOUBTED

Round 101

JINGLES 7, LOSING 6, GLOSS 5
VINEGARY 8, CRAVING 7, GRAINY 6
CRESCENDO 9, CONCEDES 8, ENDORSE 7
ORNATELY 8, PENALTY 7, TEAPOY 6
$100/4 = 25; 25 \times 25 = 625; 625 + 50 + 1 = 676$
$(5 + 4) \times (100 - 7) = 837; 837 + 6 + 6 = 849$
WITHERING

Round 102

MUTILATED 9, ALTITUDE 8, MUTATED 7
OSTEOPATH 9, POTATOES 8, TEAPOTS 7
BEHEADING 9, BIGHEAD 7, GAINED 6
PUSHOVER 8, SOUPIER 7, HOVERS 6
$(7 + 6) \times 10 = 130; (130 + 1) \times (2 \times 2) = 524$
$(9 \times 2) \times (50 - 1) = 882; 882 - 7 = 875$
PERSPIRED

Round 103

RAINBOW 7, JOINER 6, BROWN 5
PATRONIZE 9, ATROPINE 8, PAINTER 7
FALCONRY 8, CORNEAL 7, CRAYON 6
BANDAGE 7, AGENDA 6, BANJO 5
$(6 \times 3) \times 50 = 900; (5 + 1) \times 4 = 24; 900 - 24 = 876$
$5 + 3 + 1 = 9; 9 \times (75 - 1) = 666$
PURCHASED

Round 104

WEALTH 6, ALGAE 5, AXLE 4
VIOLENT 7, MOTIVE 6, LEMON 5
VANISHED 8, INVADES 7, ONSIDE 6
TUTENAG 7, NOUGAT 6, VAUNT 5
$(3 \times 6) \times (50 + 5) = 990; 990 - (9 - 7) = 988$
$8 \times 9 = 72; 72 \times (8 + 1) = 648; 648 + 2 = 650$
INTERVIEW

Round 105

OVERCOAT 8, OVERACT 7, VECTOR 6
BIZARRELY 9, LIBRARY 7, LAZIER 6
ETHMOID 7, METHOD 6, HOPED 5
PENTHOUSE 9, POTHEENS 8, ENTHUSE 7
$(3 \times 5) + 10 = 25; 25 \times 25 = 625; 625 + 6 - 7 = 624$
$(6 + 4) \times 75 = 750; 750 + 100 = 850; 850 - (3/3) = 849$
CULMINATE

Round 106

MOUSETRAP 9, TEMPURAS 8, PASTURE 7
LIMEADE 7, MENACE 6, DENIM 5
OUTLINED 8, QUOINED 7, DILUTE 6
NOMINATED 9, DOMINATE 8, DOMAINE 7
$(8 \times 5) = 40; 40 \times (7 + 1) = 320; 320 + 9 = 329$
$(4 \times 25) - 7 = 93; 93 \times (4 + 1) = 465$
TURNTABLE

Round 107

LOUSIEST 8, SOLUTES 7, TISSUE 6
FRIGATE 7, BOATER 6, BRIEF 5
AQUIFER 7, FIGURE 6, QUIRE 5
BOOGIES 7, IMPOSE 6, POISE 5
$(7 + 2) \times 50 = 450; 450 + 8 = 458; 458 \times (5 - 3) = 916$
$3 \times 75 = 225; 225 - 5 - 4 - 1 = 215; 215 \times 4 = 860$
TRIBUTARY

Round 108

EXAMPLE 7, FEMALE 6, EXPEL 5
CONSOLER 8, COLOGNE 7, LONGER 6
GRIMACED 8, RAGTIME 7, MIDGET 6
OPUNTIAS 8, OUTSPAN 7, PATIOS 6
$8 \times 2 \times 2 = 32; 32 \times 25 = 800; 800 - (10 + 9) = 781$
$4 \times 3 \times 3 = 36; (36 + 1) \times 25 = 925; 925 - 2 = 923$
NUMBERING

Round 109

PROGRADE 8, VAPORED 7, GROPED 6
SEDATION 8, INSTEAD 7, FASTEN 6
DILEMMAS 8, MISLEAD 7, SLIDES 6
CASCADED 8, SACCADE 7, CASHED 6
$100 - (8 + 4) = 88; 88 \times 6 = 528; 528 - (1 + 1) = 526$
$(9 + 2) \times (5 - 2) = 33; 75 + 33 = 108; 108 \times 8 = 864$
BATTERING

Round 110

TUTORAGE 8, GAROTTE 7, PUTTER 6
VANISHED 8, INVADES 7, SIENNA 6
MANICURE 8, NUMERIC 7, CRAVEN 6
RHEOSTAT 8, SHATTER 7, HORNET 6
$(7 + 5) \times (6 + 1) = 84; (84 \times 10) + 2 = 842$
$(9 + 2) \times 9 = 99; 99 \times 6 = 594; 594 - 8 = 586$
SPAGHETTI

Round 111

NOVELTY 7, YEOMAN 6, OVATE 5
LOZENGES 8, ENCLOSE 7, CLONES 6
GATEAUX 7, KARATE 6, GRATE 5
OTHERWISE 9, THEORISE 8, WITHERS 7
$(8 - 6) \times 75 = 150; 150 + 5 + 4 = 159; 159 \times 5 = 795$
$100 + 10 + 7 = 117; (8/2) \times 117 = 468$
INSINCERE

Round 112

HERNIATE 8, HAIRNET 7, RETINA 6
ALCOVES 7, COAXES 6, SLAVE 5
PILOTED 7, POLICE 6, OPTIC 5
AMNIOTIC 8, ACONITE 7, INMATE 6
$(6 \times 25) + 50 = 200; (200 + 6) \times 4 = 824; 824 - 4 = 820$
$(6 \times 25) + 3 = 153; 153 \times 2 = 306; 306 + 5 = 311$
ENDORSING

Round 113

PENTODES 8, POINTED 7, STONED 6
CORONAL 7, RACOON 6, CORAL 5
READMITS 8, WARTIME 7, MISTER 6
FETCHES 7, THEMES 6, COMET 5
$(6 + 3) \times (100 - 10) = 810; 810 - (7 - 2) = 805$
$9 \times 9 \times 3 \times 3 = 729$
QUIESCENT

Round 114

TINKLED 7, PINKED 6, UNLIT 5
FRIVOLED 8, DIVORCE 7, FOLDER 6
SHEEPDOG 8, HOOPED 6, HOODS 5
HABITAT 8, BATTER 6, HEART 5
$(9 \times 10) - 10 = 80; (80 + 1) \times 9 = 729; 729 - 100 = 629$
$6 + (100/25) = 10; 75 + 9 = 84; 84 \times 10 = 840$
LIMITLESS

Round 115

LOUNGED 7, TONGUE 6, TOLLED 6
CHARMER 7, MARROW 6, CHORE 5
STOPGAP 7, POTASH 6, HOIST 5
ESSAYING 8, SAYINGS 7, VEGANS 6
$(8 \times 3) + 1 = 25; 25 \times 25 = 625; 625 - (4 - 1) = 622$
$100 + 75 + 50 = 225; 225 \times 3 = 675; 675 - (4 \times 4) = 659$
RADIATION

Round 116

DOUBTER 7, DITHER 6, THIRD 5
PILLAGE 7, GOALIE 6, LOYAL 5
ENDOCARPS 9, OPERANDS 8, RESPOND 7
TIDEWAYS 8, WIDGETS 7, SWEATY 6
$8 \times (75 - 6) = 552; 2 + (4/4) = 3; 552 + 3 = 555$
$(8 + 2) \times 7 = 70; 70 \times 5 = 350; 350 - 7 = 343$
TOUGHENED

Round 117

PATHOGEN 8, HEXAGON 7, POTAGE 6
FORGIVEN 8, VERTIGO 7, ROVING 6
ELOQUENT 8, OPULENT 7, TOUPEE 6
DISMANTLE 9, MANLIEST 8, STAINED 7
$(9 \times 7) - 5 = 58; 58 \times 6 = 348; 348 - 100 = 248$
$10 \times (10 + 4) = 140; 140 + 6 + 2 = 148; 148 \times 5 = 740$
SATELLITE

Round 118

UPRATE 6, AVERT 5, FARE 4
TETANUS 7, FASTEN 6, TUNES 5
SEETHING 8, SHOEING 7, INGEST 6
MINIVERS 8, VERMIN 6, VIRUS 5
$(9 + 8) \times (50 - 4) = 782; 782 + 5 - 3 = 784$
$2 \times 7 \times 50 = 700; (4 \times 8) - 25 = 7; 700 - 7 = 693$
WEALTHIER

Round 119

ADMIXES 7, SHAMED 6, WAXES 5
MOONLET 7, TOWNEE 6, MELON 5
FLUIDRAM 8, MAUDLIN 7, MARLIN 6
CEREALS 7, CALLER 6, LARGE 5
$8 \times 6 = 48; 48 - (5 - 1) = 44; 44 \times 7 = 308$
$(4 \times 25) - (5 + 2) = 93; 3 \times 3 = 9; 93 \times 9 = 837$
RECOUPING

Round 120

UPENDING 8, PENGUIN 7, GUNNED 6
VITRIOL 7, FILTER 6, OLIVE 5
AEROSOL 7, SOLACE 6, GEARS 5
MISRATED 8, SIDEARM 7, MUSTER 6
$7 + 7 - 3 = 11; 50 + 11 = 61; 61 \times 4 = 264$
$(2 \times 10) + 7 = 25; (4 + 1) \times 6 = 30; 25 \times 30 = 750$
TRANSCEND

Round 121

URETHRAL 8, BLATHER 7, HERBAL 6
FOOTMARKS 9, FORMATS 7, MOTORS 6
MORGUES 7, SOURED 6, DRUMS 5
APOLUNES 8, CAPSULE 7, PLACES 6
$(6 \times 25) - 3 = 147; (5 + 1) \times 147 = 882$
$3 \times (75 - 1) = 222; 50 - 8 = 42; 222 + 42 = 264$
WHIRLPOOL

Round 122

TERRIFY 7, FILTER 6, RIFLE 5
BROACHES 8, CARBOYS 7, CHORES 6
HEXAPOD 7, HOAXED 6, APHID 5
YOUNGER 7, GRUNGE 6, PRONE 5
$6 \times (9 + 1) = 60; 60 - 2 = 58; 58 \times (5 \times 2) = 580$
$(3 \times 8) + 5 + 2 = 31; 31 \times 25 = 775; 775 + 2 = 777$
TANTALISE

Round 123

MOISTER 7, JOSTLE 6, MERIT 5
COGNATES 8, NOSEBAG 7, AGENTS 6
SITUATE 7, STATUE 6, FUMES 5
VINEGAR 7, VAGINA 6, GRAVE 5
$(10 + 9) \times 50 = 950; 950 - (6 \times 6) = 914$
$(8 \times 100) + (3 \times 7) = 821; 821 - (50/25) = 819$
GROTESQUE

Round 124

FIREDAMP 8, DEMIREP 7, FAIRED 6
DOORMATS 8, STARDOM 7, SMOOTH 6
EXORCISTS 9, COEXISTS 8, COSIEST 7
DOCKAGE 7, TACKED 6, KITED 5
$75 - (9/9) = 74; 5 + (10/10) = 6; 74 \times 6 = 444$
$(8 - 6) + 1 = 3; 3 \times 7 \times 25 = 525; 525 + 8 = 533$
BEDSPREAD

Round 125

TZIGANE 7, NEGATE 6, TINGE 5
POOREST 7, TOWERS 6, WROTE 5
FRAILTY 7, RATIFY 6, TARDY 5
QUEERLY 7, PURELY 6, EQUIP 5
$25 - 3 - 2 = 20; 4 \times 20 = 80; (7 \times 100) - 80 = 620$
$(8 \times 8) - 6 = 58; 58 + 75 = 133 \times 7 = 931$
FORSAKING

Round 126

OVERLAND 8, REMOVAL 7, RANDOM 6
INSPIRER 8, SPINIER 7, SNIPER 6
CESTODE 7, STODGE 6, BEGET 5
BARONET 7, ORANGE 6, BORNE 5
$(3 \times 50) + 10 = 160; 160 \times 4 = 640; 640 + 2 = 642$
$(7 \times 8) + 5 = 61; 61 \times 4 = 244; 244 + 9 = 253$
INCORRECT

Round 127

JITTERED 8, ERUDITE 7, JETTED 6
PREDATION 9, ORDINATE 8, PAROTID 7
FISHMEAL 8, HIMSELF 7, FLAMES 6
FRUCTOSE 8, FORGETS 7, FOSTER 6
$(5 \times 75) + 100 = 475; (2 \times 6) - 1 = 11; 475 - 11 = 464$
$10 \times (7 + 4) = 110; (110 - 1) \times 8 = 872; 872 + 3 = 875$
EVOLUTION

Round 128

LANGUISH 8, SEALING 7, SINGLE 6
SALLOWED 8, SWOLLEN 7, WALLED 6
ENGRAVED 8, ANGERED 7, GARDEN 6
GREYHOUND 9, HYDROGEN 8, YOUNGER 7
$6 \times (75 + 6) = 486; 486 - 100 = 386$
$75 + 8 + 3 = 86; 86 \times 8 = 688; 688 + 6 + 3 = 697$
LUBRICATE

Round 129

ORDAINER 8, RANDIER 7, ROARED 6
MARINERS 8, SEMINAR 7, INSURE 6
ELECTRUM 8, LECTURE 7, CUTLER 6
NOTABLE 7, COATED 6, BLADE 5
$100 - (7 + 6) = 87; 87 \times (5 + 5) = 870; 870 - 2 = 868$
$(4 + 1) \times 50 = 250; 250 + 9 + 8 + 7 = 274$
UPSETTING

Round 130

ANECDOTE 8, CLEANED 7, DECANT 6
SLOGGER 7, UGLIER 6, ROGUE 5
SNAKIER 7, SIENNA 6, INNER 5
JUKEBOX 7, JOUKED 6, BIJOU 5
$7 \times 3 \times 25 = 525; 525 - (10/5) = 523$
$9 \times 9 \times 10 = 810; 25 - (2 \times 7) = 11; 810 + 11 = 821$
PROSECUTE

Round 131

VOLTAGE 7, OCTAVE 6, COVET 5
DILUTION 8, UNTOLD 6, LIMIT 5
PRISONED 8, SOUPIER 7, POURED 6
SUAVEST 7, STAVES 6, PASTE 5
$(2 \times 50) - 6 = 94; 94 \times 4 = 376; 376 + 4 - 3 = 377$
$75 + (7 - 3) = 79; (6 + 6) \times 79 = 948$
ACCORDION

Round 132

POLECAT 7, OCTAVE 6, CLOVE 5
JETTISONS 9, STONIEST 8, NOSIEST 7
EXPENDS 7, SPONGE 6, DOPES 5
ARMISTICE 9, SCIMITAR 8, AIRTIME 7
$100 + 75 + 50 + 25 = 250; 250 - 3 = 247; 247 \times 3 = 741$
$(9 + 7) \times 9 = 144$
DIFFERING

Round 133

IGNORED 7, INDIGO 6, IRONY 5
DIAGNOSED 9, ADENOIDS 8, AGONIES 7
ROULADE 7, VALOUR 6, DROVE 5
UNDERUSED 9, SUNDERED 8, ENDURED 7
$(4 \times 10) - 3 = 37; 37 \times 25 = 925; 925 + 7 + 5 = 937$
$9 \times (100 - 9) = 819; 6 + (2/2) = 7; 819 + 7 = 826$
EXPOUNDED

Round 134

WOOLLIES 8, SWILLED 7, SLOWED 6
OVULATE 7, VOLANT 6, NAVAL 5
GREYISH 7, RUSHED 6, HIDES 5
PROFANELY 9, FOREPLAY 8, PALFREY 7
$(7 \times 25) + 7 = 182; 182 \times 5 = 910; 910 + (8/2) = 914$
$(8 \times 75) + 25 = 625; 625 - (6/3) = 623$
AUTOGRAPH

Round 135

REPLIES 7, EERILY 6, PRIZE 5
NOURISH 7, ONRUSH 6, SHORN 5
PLECTRUM 8, CRUMPET 7, TRIPLE 6
DISCOED 7, ESCUDO 6, DICED 5
$(9 - 4) \times (100 + 2) = 510; 510 + 75 = 585; 585 - 7 = 578$
$6 - (1 + 1) = 4; 4 \times (50 + 8) = 232; 232 + 7 = 239$
PROTESTED

Round 136

ALRIGHT 7, SAILOR 6, LIGHT 5
DISASTER 8, TIGRESS 7, STAIRS 6
PAIRING 7, INWARD 6, WRING 5
ESCALATED 9, ESCALADE 8, DELATES 7
$100 - (2 \times 10) = 80; 6 \times 80 = 480; 480 - 9 = 471$
$(75/25) \times 100 = 300; 300 + 50 + 2 = 352; 352 \times 2 = 704$
SUFFOCATE

Round 137

DENOTED 7, HUNTED 6, ENDED 5
FLOURISH 8, OURSELF 7, RELISH 6
FACILELY 8, IDEALLY 7, FILLED 6
DIVIDER 7, DIVERT 6, TIRED 5
$100 - (10/5) = 98; 98 \times 7 = 686; 686 - 50 + 3 = 639$
$7 \times (4 + 3) = 49; 49 \times 6 = 294$
CONSONANT

Round 138

VAPIDLY 7, DEPLOY 6, YIELD 5
FIXATED 7, FIESTA 6, TAXES 5
THUMPED 7, TEDIUM 6, THYME 5
ICEBOAT 7, COATED 6, DEBIT 5
$(25 + 2) \times 10 = 270; (270 + 4) \times 2 = 548; 548 + 7 = 555$
$9 \times 8 = 72; 10 - 2 = 8; (72 + 1) \times 8 = 584$
SMOOTHING

Round 139

ARGALIS 7, SPIRAL 6, SPRIG 5
CROAKILY 8, SCARILY 7, CLOAKS 6
RELATOR 7, ZEALOT 6, ALTER 5
UGLIER 6, GRUEL 5, RELY 4
$10 \times (9 + 8) = 170; 170 + 75 = 245; 245 - (9 - 8) = 244$
$2 \times (50 + 1) = 102; 102 + 75 + 9 = 186$
DEHYDRATE

Round 140

OBTRUSIVE 9, VITREOUS 8, BUSTIER 7
BLUSHER 7, HERBAL 6, RELAX 5
POACHED 7, COATED 6, PHAGE 5
DALLIANCE 9, ALLIANCE 8, CEDILLA 7
$4 \times (10 - 1) = 36; (36 - 1) \times 25 = 875$
$(10 + 8) \times 50 = 900; (5 \times 8) - 7 = 33; 900 + 33 = 933$
CONGEALED

Round 141

YOURSELF 8, OURSELF 7, SURELY 6
VICEROY 7, DRIVEL 6, COVER 5
CARTONED 8, REDCOAT 7, TRACED 6
CAGOULES 8, GLUCOSE 7, SOLACE 6
$9 + 6 = 15; 25 - 2 = 23; 15 \times 23 = 345; 345 + 1 + 1 = 347$
$8 \times (50 - 9) = 328; 328 - 10 - 7 = 311$
PLOUGHMAN

Round 142

SABOTEUR 8, BOATERS 7, BEAUTY 6
GRANULES 8, WRANGLE 7, LAGERS 6
BASSIST 7, BOASTS 6, AUTOS 5
BOARDING 8, ADORING 7, DRAGON 6
$(4 \times 7) + 4 = 32; 32 \times 25 = 800; 800 + 10 + 2 = 812$
$4 \times (100 + 50) = 600; 9 - (75/25) = 6; 600 + 6 = 606$
SOMETHING

Round 143
JUNKIES 7, INJURE 6, VIRUS 5
UNGLAZED 8, DANGLES 7, SLUDGE 6
BAYONET 7, GOATEE 6, AGENT 5
LIBERATE 8, BLOATER 7, REBATE 6
$(10 + 7) \times 50 = 850; (2 \times 6) + 9 = 21; 850 + 21 = 871$
$100 - 7 = 93; 93 \times 2 \times 2 = 372$
ABSCONDED

Round 144
THINNED 7, ENGINE 6, THING 5
IMPLODES 8, MILDEST 7, POSTED 6
ASTOUND 7, DIVOTS 6, VAUNT 5
PLACATE 7, PACKER 6, CREAK 5
$(2 \times 3) + 1 = 7; 7 \times 6 \times 5 \times 4 = 840$
$3 \times (2 + 1) = 9; 9 \times 4 \times 3 = 108; 108 \times 8 = 864$
MATERNITY

Round 145
GADFLIES 8, LADIES 6, FIELD 5
BOASTERS 8, BASKETS 7, SORBET 6
TETRAPOD 8, ROTATED 7, POTTER 6
BIPLANES 8, LESBIAN 7, SALINE 6
$(7 - 1) \times 100 = 600; 9 \times (4 + 1) = 45; 600 - 45 = 555$
$10 \times (9 + 7) = 160; 8 \times 7 = 56; 160 + 56 = 216; 216 + 10 = 226$
POLLUTING

Round 146
ARMIGER 7, RETAIL 6, GRIME 5
RANNIES 8, SPANNER 7, CRANES 6
LOATHING 8, SALTING 7, GLOATS 6
MONETARY 8, ANYMORE 7, ORNATE 6
$5 \times (4 + 1) = 25; 25 \times 25 = 625; 625 + 10 - 7 = 628$
$8 + 6 + 3 = 17; 50 + 1 = 51; 17 \times 51 = 867$
SPECIALTY

Round 147
FRUITAGE 8, OUTRAGE 7, FIGURE 6
CATEGORY 8, CORDAGE 7, GRACED 6
FOLKISH 7, GHOULS 6, FLOGS 5
INTERFACE 9, FRENETIC 8, FIANCEE 7
$75 + 25 + 8 - 3 = 105; 105 \times 9 = 945$
$(100 + 75) \times 5 = 875 + 10 = 885$
IRRITATED

Round 148
MINERAL 7, WAILED 6, DREAM 5
SMARTIES 8, FIRMEST 7, FIESTA 6
NOTIFYING 9, TOYING 6, INGOT 5
BRIEFEST 8, FORTIES 7, FIBRES 6
$9 \times 50 = 450; 450 + 25 - 3 = 472; 472 \times 2 = 944$
$50 - 6 = 51; 8 + 8 + 1 = 17; 17 \times 51 = 867$
COMFORTED

Round 149
DURATIVE 8, VIRTUAL 7, VALUED 6
GOLFERS 7, SLEIGH 6, RIFLE 5
GLEAMING 8, NIGGLES 7, SILAGE 6
DENSITY 7, NUDITY 6, VINES 5
$(5 + 3) \times 75 = 600; 9 \times (7 - 4) = 27; 600 - 27 = 573$
$9 - (50/25) = 7; 100 - (6/6) = 99; 7 \times 99 = 693$
DORMITORY

Round 150
OPUNTIA 7, KIDNAP 6, POINT 5
SIMILAR 7, GARISH 6, RAILS 5
UNSIZED 7, UNISEX 6, SEDAN 50
PADOUKS 7, SOAKED 6, SPOKE 5
$50 - 3 = 47; 10 + 10 + 5 - 4 = 21; 47 \times 21 = 987$
$(2 \times 5) + 3 = 13; 75 + 13 = 88; 88 \times 8 = 704$
ELEGANTLY

Round 151
AMMONIA 7, ANIMAL 6, MANIA 5
CANOEIST 8, JACONET 7, ACTION 6
SALIENCY 8, ANGELIC 7, NICELY 6
ATTEND 6, NAKED 5, DATA 4
$8 \times (100 - 10) = 720; 720 - 3 - 1 = 716$
$(2 \times 9) + 1 = 19; 19 \times 25 = 475; 475 - (10 + 3) = 462$
APPEARING

Round 152
DIALOGUE 8, PLAGUED 7, LAPDOG 6
HEADLINE 8, INHALED 7, WAILED 6
NATIVELY 8, VIOLENT 7, LITANY 6
ERUPTION 8, JUNIPER 7, PUNTER 6
$75 + 8 - 5 = 78; (78 \times 10) - 1 = 779$
$6 \times 5 \times 2 \times 2 = 120; 120 - 7 = 113; 113 \times 8 = 904$
WEAKENING

Round 153
NUTCASE 7, JAUNTS 6, SCANT 5
BEGONIA 7, OBTAIN 6, JINGO 5
RENEWING 8, WARNING 7, REGAIN 6
TARGETED 8, AVERTED 7, VETTED 6
$9 \times 7 = 63; 63 \times (10 - 2) = 504; 504 - 100 = 404$
$50 - 1 = 49; (3 \times 5) - 1 = 14; 49 \times 14 = 686$
PROTRUDED

Round 154
NIGHTWEAR 9, WATERING 8, HAIRNET 7
ARGUFY 6, RUGBY 5, BEAU 4
INFRARED 8, RANDIER 7, FRIEND 6
DISPUTES 8, STUMPED 7, UPSETS 6
$(6 \times 6) - 2 = 34; 25 - 2 = 23; 34 \times 23 = 782; 782 + 3 = 785$
$(75 - 1) \times 2 = 148; 148 \times 2 = 296; 296 - 6 = 290$
FOREFRONT

Round 155
TEACHABLE 9, HEATABLE 8, ACTABLE 7
POACHES 7, PSYCHO 6, SPACE 5
LETTERED 8, RELATED 7, DEALER 6
ECHOGRAM 8, MONARCH 7, CHROME 6
$50 + 9 - 8 = 51; 51 \times 7 = 357; 357 - (10/10) = 356$
$8 \times (9 + 2) = 88; 9 \times (88 - 5) = 747; 747 + 1 = 748$
DEVOURING

Round 156
COULISSE 8, VISCOSE 7, SLUICE 6
INDOORS 7, DISOWN 6, DROWN 5
GRAVITON 8, ADORING 7, VIRAGO 6
FAILURE 7, PURIFY 6, FLARE 5
$7 + 5 - 1 = 11; 3 \times 11 = 33; 9 \times 75 = 675; 675 - 33 = 642$
$2 \times (4 + 1) = 10; 10 \times (100 - 4) = 960$
IMBALANCE

Round 157
BOREHOLE 8, BELCHER 7, BREECH 6
PIERCER 7, CREEPY 6, PRICE 5
FOOTAGE 7, GOOFED 6, ADOPT 5
MATADOR 7, DREAMT 6, AVERT 5
$6 \times 50 = 300; 25 \times 3 = 75; 300 - (75/75) = 299$
$(9 + 4) \times 25 = 325; 325 + 6 + 2 = 333$
FLUCTUATE

Round 158
ROAMING 7, LOWING 6, GROAN 5
UPGRADE 7, LAAGER 6, PURGE 5
DISTANCE 8, CHAINED 7, HINTED 6
BROODIEST 9, STEROID 7, BOOTED 6
$10 \times (5 + 5) = 100; (100 + 7) \times (6 + 3) = 963$
$100 - 3 = 97; (8 + 2) \times 97 = 970; 970 - 4 = 966$
STIPULATE

Round 159
DRAWBACK 8, WRACKED 7, ARCADE 6
LOWLIEST 8, TOILERS 7, WRITES 6
SCRAPPED 8, SIDECAR 7, ASPIRE 6
ONESELF 7, LOWEST 6, FLEET 5
$(75 + 3) \times (5 + 4) = 702;\ 702 + 2 = 704$
$3 \times (3 + 4) = 21;\ 21 \times 25 = 525;\ 525 + 8 - 6 = 527$
ADDICTION

Round 160
SQUARELY 8, EQUABLY 7, BARLEY 6
HOLIDAYS 8, HASTILY 7, STOLID 6
DEFLATE 7, FAILED 6, HATED 5
DOGFISH 7, OXHIDE 6, HOSED 5
$25 + 6 - 1 = 30;\ 9 + 7 = 16;\ 30 \times 16 = 480;\ 480 - 2 = 478$
$(9 \times 25) + 6 + 3 = 234;\ 234 \times 4 = 936;\ 936 + 2 = 938$
CONCEALED

Round 161
DEROGATED 9, DEGRADE 7, GOATEE 6
TROPICAL 8, PARBOIL 7, COITAL 6
ORBITAL 7, ARTFUL 6, ULTRA 5
TAPESTRY 8, TEAPOTS 7, SPORTY 6
$50 + (9 \times 4) = 86;\ 86 \times 7 = 602$
$10 + 1 - 4 = 7;\ (100 + 6) \times 7 = 742;\ 742 + 5 = 747$
PRIVILEGE

Round 162
FIREDAMP8, PYRAMID 7, DREAMY 6
FINALIZED 9, INFIDEL 7, FINALE 6
VIOLATED 8, TABLOID 7, BOLTED 6
PURGATORY 9, PORTRAY 7, YOGURT 6
$6 + 5 + 4 = 15;\ 15 \times 25 = 375;\ 375 + 8 = 383$
$7 \times 7 \times 3 = 147;\ 147 + (5/5) = 148;\ 148 \times 3 = 444$
RENDITION

Round 163
MIAOWED 7, MILDEW 6, GLEAM 5
THORAXES 8, EARSHOT 7, HOAXES 6
TOASTED 7, SEADOG 6, GOATS 5
ANCESTRY 8, CRYSTAL 7, TRACES 6
$(10 + 9) \times 4 = 76;\ 76 \times (5 \times 2) = 760$
$7 \times (75 + 25) = 700;\ 50 - (9 + 6) = 35;\ 700 - 35 = 665$
DASTARDLY

Round 164
DRIFTER 7, FIDGET 6, FRUIT 5
CHAPERON 8, ANOTHER 7, TRANCE 6
OBLIVION 8, OLIVINE 7, VIOLIN 6
EPIBLAST 8, POTABLE 7, ALBEIT 6
$75 + 5 = 80;\ 80 \times (8 + 4) = 960;\ 960 - 9 = 951$
$100 - (7 \times 4) = 72;\ 72 \times 8 = 576;\ 576 - 2 = 574$
GAMBOLLED

Round 165
STUPEFY 7, PUTZES 6, PIETY 5
BROADEST 8, BOASTED 7, MASTER 6
PALACES 7, CANOES 6, PLACE 5
LACKEYED 8, TACKLED 7, TACKED 6
$5 \times (25 + 3) = 140;\ 140 \times 7 = 980$
$(5 \times 5) + 10 = 35;\ 35 \times 25 = 875;\ 875 - (10 + 1) = 864$
CIVILISED

Round 166
DILEMMAS 8, MISLEAD 7, MEDIUM 6
OVERCAST 8, AVOCETS 7, CARROT 6
MIGRATES 8, MASTERY 7, ARMIES 6
INTERPLAY 9, TRIPLANE 8, PAINTER 7
$5 \times 6 \times 3 \times 3 = 270;\ 270 + 4/4 = 271$
$(6 - 2) \times (75 + 10) = 340;\ 340 + 7 = 347$
FRUMPIEST

Round 167
SURVEYOR 8, DEVOURS 7, DROVER 6
JAWBONES 8, BANJOES 7, ABSENT 6
CHARIOTS 8, HARICOT 7, CHARTS 6
SUBLATED 8, BUSTLED 7, WASTED 6
$(6 \times 75) - (7 \times 5) = 415;\ 415 + (50/25) = 417$
$(3 \times 5) + 1 = 16;\ 16 \times 50 = 800;\ 800 + 4 - 3 = 801$
HORSEBACK

Round 168
ROWBOAT 7, BOOTER 6, ORATE 5
CURABLE 7, WARBLE 6, CRAWL 5
MIDWIFE 7, DIMWIT 6, MEDIA 5
SCENERY 7, WINERY 6, CREWS 5
$7 - (8 - 7) = 6;\ (6 \times 100) - 4 = 596$
$(10 \times 25) - 2 = 248;\ 9 - 5 = 4;\ 248 \times 4 = 992$
BREAKFAST

Round 169
FIREBUGS 8, FIGURES 7, BIGGER 6
INSULTED 8, DUSTBIN 7, BLINDS 6
WISHBONE 8, TOWNIES 7, BESTOW 6
EXOTERIC 8, COTERIE 7, EXCITE 6
$(6 + 4) \times 50 = 500;\ 500 - (9 + 8) = 483$
$(50 + 8) \times (8 + 5) = 754;\ 754 + (3 - 1) = 756$
OTHERWISE

Round 170
NAIVELY 7, MENIAL 6, ANVIL 5
EPIDURAL 8, PREVAIL 7, REPAID 6
MOONFISH 8, NOISOME 7, MONIES 6
HOTLINE 7, BOTHIE 6, THINE 5
$3 \times (75/25) = 9;\ 9 \times 50 = 450;\ 450 + 100 + 4 = 554$
$(7 - 1) \times 6 = 36;\ 36 \times 8 = 288$
JOURNEYED

Round 171
CONSUME 7, POUNCE 6, SCONE 5
FLYWEIGHT 9, WHITEFLY 8, WEIGHTY 7
ROUNDELS 8, SOUNDLY 7, YONDER 6
KEYBOARD 8, BROADEN 7, BRANDY 6
$(8 \times 100) - 75 = 725;\ 725 - 6 = 719$
$3 \times (2 + 1) = 9;\ 100 + 2 + 1 = 103;\ 9 \times 103 = 927$
BRIEFCASE

Round 172
WALTZED 7, ZEALOT 6, DELTA 5
POWERFUL 8, FLOURED 7, POURED 6
REARMOST 8, STAMPER 7, POSTER 6
MAYPOLE 7, EPONYM 6, FLAME 5
$9 + 5 = 14;\ 25 + 8 = 33;\ 14 \times 33 = 462;\ 462 + 7 = 469$
$50 + (75/25) = 53;\ 8 + 2 = 10;\ 53 \times 10 = 530$
MEDITATED

Round 173
FRIVOLED 8, FORGIVE 7, LODGER 6
GUARANTY 8, UNITARY 7, GRAINY 6
GUILDERS 8, GROUSED 7, SOURED 6
REMOVAL 7, MOTHER 6, LOVER 5
$100 - 5 = 95;\ (7 + 3) \times 95 = 950;\ 950 - 4 = 946$
$100 + 75 - 2 = 173;\ 173 \times 4 = 692$
MATCHLESS

Round 174
RAMEKIN 7, REMAIN 6, HIKER 5
CAPITOLS 8, OPTICAL 7, POLICY 6
OXYGENATE 9, GOATEE 6, TANGO 5
CENTAVOS 8, OCTAVES 7, ENCASE 6
$(10 + 8) \times 50 = 900;\ 100/4 = 25;\ 900 + 25 = 925$
$(3 \times 25) - 1 = 74;\ 74 \times 9 = 666$
AEROPLANE

Round 175

CRUDELY 7, CLOVER 6, CLOUD 5
MANIFESTO 9, AMNIOTES 8, MOISTEN 7
GLEAMING 8, NIGGLES 7, MANGLE 6
HOCUSING 8, ANGUISH 7, CHAINS 6
$5 \times (100 + 50) = 750; 4 + 2 = 6; 6/6 = 1; 750 - 1 = 749$
$6 \times (25 - 2) = 138; 138 - 4 = 134; 134 \times 5 = 670; 670 - 1 = 669$
PROCESSOR

Round 176

HUSBANDER 9, UNSHARED 8, BRUSHED 7
OBEYING 7, IGNORE 6, BEING 5
NUCELLAR 8, NUCLEAR 7, RECALL 6
CARIBOUS 8, CARIOUS 7, SOCIAL 6
$(10 - 8) \times 100 = 200; (8 \times 7) - 10 = 46; 200 + 46 = 246$
$7 + 2 + 2 = 11; 11 + (4 \times 25) = 111; 111 \times 8 = 888$
CATHEDRAL

Round 177

ADHESIVE 8, HEAVIES 7, DEVISE 6
TELEMARK 8, ETERNAL 7, MARKET 6
AMYLOID 7, CYMBAL 6, MADLY 5
FOUNTAIN 8, TONNEAU 7, INFANT 6
$(9 + 8) \times 25 = 425; 425 - 6 = 419; 419 \times (1 + 1) = 838$
$(8 \times 25) + 6 = 206; 206 \times 4 = 824$
SPARKLING

Round 178

RANDOMIZE 9, ROMANIZE 8, ANEROID 7
FROGMEN 7, WOOFER 6, FROWN 5
LOWERING 8, COWGIRL 7, WINGER 6
BAYONET 7, BANNER 6, ABORT 5
$75 + 4 + 1 = 80; 80 \times 9 = 720$
$(3 \times 3) \times (50 + 25) = 675; 675 - (6 + 2) = 667$
LEATHERED

Round 179

MACKEREL 8, FRECKLE 7, REMAKE 6
TAURINE 7, TANNER 6, ANNEX 5
ORGANDIE 8, READING 7, FRINGE 6
VISCID 6, DISCS 5, VIED 4
$3 \times 2 \times 25 = 150; 150 - (4 + 4) = 142; 142 \times 6 = 852$
$7 \times 5 = 35; 35 \times 25 = 875; 875 + 9 + 3 = 887$
PROVOKING

Round 180

FASHIONED 9, ADHESION 8, ANODISE 7
RESIDENCE 9, SCREENED 8, SINCERE 7
SECRETIVE 9, EVICTEES 8, SERVICE 7
DIMETRIC 8, TIMIDER 7, CHIMED 6
$2 \times 3 \times 5 = 30; (30 + 1) \times 25 = 775; 775 + 7 = 782$
$(100 + 2) \times 9 = 918; 918 - 75 = 843; 843 + 4 - 3 = 844$
HONOURING

Round 181

AIRMAILED 9, ALARMED 7, RADIAL 6
EMPLOYED 8, POLYMER 7, ELOPED 6
DEBRIEFS 8, SEABIRD 7, BRIDES 6
REPAIRED 8, PARRIED 7, HARPED 6
$(6 + 4) \times 75 = 750; 8 + (5 - 3) = 10; 750 + 10 = 760$
$8 \times (10 + 5) = 120; 120 \times 7 = 840; 840 + 1 = 841$
HARVESTED

Round 182

PROMOTED 8, TORPEDO 7, ROOTED 6
POLKAING 8, PARKING 7, ROPING 6
KISSOGRAM 9, ORGASMS 7, SMIRKS 6
SCREAMED 8, SECURED 7, DREAMS 6
$(100 - 25) \times 8 = 600; (7 \times 4) + 1 = 29; 600 + 29 = 629$
$(50/5) + 3 = 13; 13 \times 25 = 325; 325 - 8 = 317$
IMPLICATE

Round 183

PULSATED 8, DEFAULT 7, LAPSED 6
OBTRUSIVE 9, VITREOUS 8, BUSTIER 7
AFTERCARE 9, TERRACE 7, FERRET 6
JALAPENO 8, WEAPON 6, ALONE 5
$(50/5) \times 75 = 750; 750 + 25 + 1 = 776$
$75 + 50 + 4 = 129; 129 \times (4 + 2) = 774; 774 + 2 = 776$
PANORAMIC

Round 184

SCRAPING 8, RASPING 7, PRANGS 6
REGIONAL 8, RAILING 7, LINGER 6
BLUEGRASS 9, GARBLES 7, ABUSES 6
DYSLEXIC 8, SEXILY 6, DISCO 5
$(4 + 3) \times 75 = 525; 525 + 10 + (6/2) = 538$
$7 + 7 + 2 = 16; 16 \times 50 = 800; 800 + (5 \times 4) = 820$
INTIMATED

Round 185

POULTICE 8, COMPUTE 7, POETIC 6
QUAVERING 9, VINEGAR 7, QUIVER 6
LAPSTONE 8, POLENTA 7, PLANET 6
GUITARIST 9, GUITARS 7, ARTIST 6
$100 - 8 = 92; (75/25) \times 92 = 276; 276 - 10 = 266$
$9 \times 9 = 81; 81 \times 8 = 648; 648 - 5 = 643$
ELONGATED

Round 186

BUREAUX 7, BUREAU 6, BUYER 5
PURCHASE 8, ACCUSER 7, PUSHER 6
REFUTABLE 9, FEATURE 7, BEATER 6
KEEPABLE 8, BLEAKER 7, BEAKER 6
$8 \times 9 \times 10 = 720; (3 + 4) \times 2 = 14; 720 + 14 = 734$
$25 - (8 + 7) = 10; 10 \times (50 + 5) = 550; 550 - 7 = 543$
SENSATION

Round 187

SCIMITAR 8, SATIRIC 7, RACISM 6
REFINANCE 9, FIANCEE 7, REFACE 6
AEROBATIC 9, BACTERIA 8, AIRBOAT 7
DOGMATIC 8, AGOUTI 6, ADMIT 5
$(10 + 1) \times 75 = 825; 4 \times 4 = 16; 825 + 16 = 841$
$(9 + 5) \times 8 = 112; 112 + 2 = 114; 114 \times (9 - 4) = 570$
PRAGMATIC

Round 188

HANDSOME 8, DAEMONS 7, DOMAIN 6
SCHOONER 8, CHOOSER 7, HERONS 6
UNDERHAND 9, UNHANDED 8, HUNDRED 7
ADORNMENT 9, ORNAMENT 8, MORDENT 7
$3 \times (3 + 6) = 27; 27 \times 25 = 675; 675 - 8 = 667$
$75 + 10 + 10 + 9 = 104; 104 \times (100/25) = 416$
SOLILOQUY

Round 189

DEERSKIN 8, KINDEST 7, TINKER 6
JACONET 7, DEACON 6, CANOE 5
ENDURABLE 9, LAUNDER 7, BURNED 6
CAHOOTS 7, STARCH 6, TORSO 5
$(3 \times 3) + 2 = 11; (75 + 1) \times 11 = 836; 836 + 100 = 936$
$5 \times 75 = 375; (50/5) + 1 = 11; 375 + 11 = 386$
EXTRICATE

Round 190

BLISTERED 9, BRISTLED 8, TREBLES 7
ADAPTIVE 8, AVIATED 7, DATIVE 6
IMMATURE 8, MEATIER 7, ATRIUM 6
STABILES 8, ELASTIC 7, BEASTS 6
$10 + 10 + 7 = 27; 27 \times 9 = 243; 243 + 1 = 244$
$(100 + 50) \times 7 = 1050 ; 75 + 25 + 8 = 108; 1050 - 108 = 942$
VALIDATED

Round 191
SAVELOYS 8, SOLVATE 7, VASTLY 6
CANDLELIT 9, CEDILLA 7, CALLED 6
SLOPPIER 8, RIPPLES 7, SAILOR 6
RECEPTION 9, ERECTION 8, PIONEER 7
$3 \times 5 \times 7 = 105$; $105 + 4 + 2 = 111$; $111 \times 9 = 999$
$100 - 25 + 7 = 82$; $82 \times 7 = 574$; $574 + 4 = 578$
DOMINATED

Round 192
LANDLORD 8, ADORNED 7, LADDER 6
BONEMEAL 8, BOATMEN 7, LAMENT 6
ACOUSTIC 8, CAUSTIC 7, CACTUS 6
PRICKLIER 9, PRICKIER 8, PICKLER 7
$100 + 75 + 2 = 177$; $177 \times 4 = 708$; $708 - 25 = 683$
$100 - 10 = 90$; $(50/10) + 1 + 1 = 7$; $90 \times 7 = 630$
HORRIFIED

Round 193
PURIFIED 8, PUFFIER 7, DIFFER 6
REARWARD 8, AWARDER 7, RETARD 6
TRAGEDIAN 9, DRAINAGE 8, READING 7
CREOSOTES 9, SCOOTERS 8, STEREOS 7
$50 + 4 = 54$; $10 + 7 + 1 = 18$; $54 \times 18 = 972$
$(4 \times 25) - 5 = 95$; $9 \times 95 = 855$; $855 - (6 + 1) = 848$
PANDERING

Round 194
TANDOORI 8, OVATION 7, ORDAIN 6
REALISTIC 9, RECITALS 8, ECLAIRS 7
DESECRATE 9, DECREASE 8, CREATED 7
CAMPFIRE 8, PRIMATE 7, ARMPIT 6
$75 + 50 + 2 = 127$; $127 \times 3 = 381$; $381 + 25 + 1 = 407$
$(9 + 7) \times 50 = 800$; $25 + 5 - 2 = 28$; $800 + 28 = 828$
SUSPECTED

Round 195
HOUSEMAID 9, MADHOUSE 8, HIDEOUS 7
BOOKSHELF 9, BEFOOLS 7, BLOKES 6
ACCLIMATE 9, ACCLAIM 7, MALICE 6
TALISMAN 8, STAMINA 7, AWAITS 6
$(75/5) \times 6 = 90$; $90 \times 6 = 540$; $540 + 1 + 1 = 542$
$(3 + 4) \times (3 + 2) = 35$; $35 \times 25 = 875$; $875 + 7 = 882$
PROPOSING

Round 196
NAVIGABLE 9, GAINABLE 8, LEAVING 7
MEDICAL 7, MALICE 6, EDICT 5
LABOURED 8, BURGLED 7, ORDEAL 6
DRIVEWAY 8, WAVIER 6, JAWED 5
$4 \times 5 \times 4 = 80$; $(80 + 2) \times 8 = 656$; $656 + 1 = 657$
$(75 + 25) - (6 + 2) = 92$; $92 \times 9 = 828$; $828 + 2 = 830$
GERIATRIC

Round 197
RATEPAYER 9, TAPERER 7, RETYPE 6
SAINTDOM 8, MASTOID 7, VOMITS 6
UNDERSEA 8, WARDENS 7, WANDER 6
FALSEHOOD 9, SELFHOOD 8, SEAFOOD 7
$(8 + 6) \times 50 = 700$; $(7 \times 5) - 6 = 29$; $700 + 29 = 729$
$(50 + 7) \times 10 = 570$; $570 - (8 - 2) = 564$
MENTALITY

Round 198
TAILGATE 8, AGITATE 7, LIGATE 6
BREAKDOWN 9, BEADWORK 8, BROWNED 7
ABSINTHE 8, LESBIAN 7, LISTEN 6
ANGRIEST 8, STINGER 7, TAXING 6
$100 + 50 - 6 = 144$; $144 \times 3 = 432$; $432 - (75/25) = 429$
$(8 + 1) \times 75 = 675$; $5 \times (2 + 2) = 20$; $675 + 20 = 695$
BLACKENED

Round 199
SAILBOAT 8, SOLATIA 7, AFLOAT 6
RAINCOAT 8, OCARINA 7, RATION 6
CALIBRATE 9, BACTERIA 8, ARTICLE 7
LAKESIDE 8, LEASHED 7, LADIES 6
$(100 + 25) - (9 - 4) = 120$; $120 \times 8 = 960$; $960 - 4 = 956$
$(6 \times 6) - (10 + 1) = 25$; $25 \times 25 = 625$; $625 + 3 = 628$
INSTIGATE

Round 200
CRINOLINE 9, INCLINER 8, ONEIRIC 7
REGIONAL 8, HALOGEN 7, LONGER 6
WHITEBAIT 9, TIBIAE 6, HABIT 5
WAISTLINE 9, LITANIES 8, SALIENT 7
$8 + (3 \times 2) = 14$; $(6 \times 7) \times 14 = 588$; $588 + 3 = 591$
$(10 \times 25) - 8 = 242$; $242 \times 3 = 726$; $726 + (10/2) = 731$
PETROLEUM

Round 201
SEASHORE 8, EARSHOT 7, TOSSER 6
CHANGEFUL 9, FLANGE 6, LUNCH 5
PARASITE 8, TRAIPSE 7, PIRATE 6
READWARD 8, AWARDER 7, ERRATA 6
$50 + 1 + 1 = 52$; $8 + 5 = 13$; $13 \times 52 = 676$
$4 \times (10 - 2) = 32$; $(32 + 2) \times 25 = 850$; $850 - 9 = 841$
SATURATED

Round 202
DENTALISE 9, ENLISTED 8, LINSEED 7
NECKLACE 8, CACKLED 7, LANCED 6
SLALOMED 8, STALLED 7, MODEST 6
CHIMAERAS 9, CHARISMA 8, CASHIER 7
$(6 + 4) \times 100 = 1000$; $75 + 5 + 3 = 83$; $1000 - 83 = 917$
$(4 + 3) \times 100 = 700$; $8 + (50/25) = 10$; $700 - 10 = 690$
OBSCURING

Round 203
SUNBATHE 8, ENTHUSE 7, UNSEAT 6
LADYLIKE 8, IDEALLY 7, LATELY 6
MARATHON 8, MATRON 6, THORN 5
TWOPENNY 8, ANYONE 6, PANTO 5
$8 \times 25 = 200$; $8 + 7 + 7 = 22$; $200 + 22 = 222$
$100 - (9 + 7) = 84$; $84 \times 10 = 840$; $840 + 2 + 1 = 843$
DECORATOR

Round 204
SATIRICAL 9, ITALICS 7, RACIST 6
STOPOVER 8, RIPOSTE 7, TROOPS 6
TRADABLE 8, BRADAWL 7, WARBLE 6
SEMBLANCE 9, CLEANSE 7, CABLES 6
$(75/5) \times 50 = 750$; $5 - (100/25) = 1$; $750 - 1 = 749$
$3 \times 75 = 225$; $225 + (4 \times 4) = 241$; $241 \times (2 + 2) = 964$
ABDOMINAL

Round 205
CHIEFDOM 8, COWHIDE 7, CHIMED 6
LATECOMER 9, RELOCATE 8, TREACLE 7
OCCUPIED 8, PRODUCE 7, COPIER 6
TELEGRAM 8, RAGTIME 7, MEAGRE 6
$10 \times (8 + 2) = 100$; $(100 - 1) \times 5 = 495$
$75 - 3 = 72$; $(8 + 3) \times 72 = 792$; $792 - 6 = 786$
STAIRCASE

Round 206
FEATURING 9, REFUTING 8, TANGIER 7
REPINING 8, PEERING 7, ENGINE 6
DELUDED 7, DELUXE 6, UDDER 5
CHROMATE 8, MACHETE 7, HEATER 6
$100 - (9 - 7) = 98$; $(98 \times 10) + 8 + 7 = 995$
$(50 + 25) \times 8 = 600$; $7 + 3 + 2 = 12$; $600 - 12 = 588$
DISABLING

Round 207

GOATEE 6, GIANT 5, NOTE 4
ARCHIVE 7, THRICE 6, CRAZE 5
REBOOTING 9, ROOTING 7, BORING 6
BARLEYMOW 9, WARBLE 6, RELAY 5
$75 + 50 + 6 = 131; 131 \times 6 = 786; 786 + 100 + 1 = 887$
$10 \times (10 + 7) = 170; 8 - (2 + 1) = 5; 170 \times 5 = 850$
PERSECUTE

Round 208

HEADREST 8, DARKEST 7, SHARED 6
JETTISON 8, TOILETS 7, JOSTLE 6
UPRISING 8, GUNSHIP 7, HIRING 6
MARMOSET 8, HAMMERS 7, MOTHER 6
$(10 + 3) \times 50 = 650; 650 + (2 \times 9) = 668$
$(100 - 25) \times 4 = 300; (7 \times 5) + 4 = 39; 300 + 39 = 339$
HAVERSACK

Round 209

BOWSTRING 9, BROWSING 8, STOWING 7
VANISHED 8, ADVISED 7, HANDED 6
CHUTNEY 7, COUNTY 6, YOUTH 5
TENSIONAL 9, TOENAILS 8, ELATION 7
$9 + 9 + 2 = 20; 75 + 20 = 95; 95 \times (6 + 4) = 950$
$100/(5 - 3) = 50; (50 + 6 + 3) \times 8 = 472$
BEGUILING

Round 210

ELITISM 7, MILLET 6, STILL 5
CRIMPLENE 9, RECLINE 7, PENCIL 6
NERVOUSLY 9, VENOUSLY 8, VOYEURS 7
RACONTEUR 9, COURANTE 8, TROUNCE 7
$9 \times (7 - 3) = 36; 36 \times 25 = 900; 900 - 6 = 894$
$8 \times (7 - 1) = 48; 48 + 25 = 73; 73 \times (9 + 1) = 730$
IMMOVABLE

Round 211

ENCHILADA 9, HACIENDA 8, CHAINED 7
FERTILISE 9, FIERIEST 8, FILTERS 7
PARODIED 8, READOPT 7, RAIDED 6
CIRCULATE 9, CRUCIATE 8, ARTICLE 7
$100 + 50 + 25 = 175; 175 \times 5 = 875; 875 + 9 + 4 = 888$
$4 \times 8 \times 10 = 320; 320 + 9 = 329$
PICKETING

Round 212

BARRELLED 9, RELABEL 7, BELLED 6
STUMPIER 8, UMPIRES 7, RUSTLE 6
HORMONES 8, MOORHEN 7, SHINER 6
DEPILATE 8, LEGATED 7, PLEDGE 6
$10 + 6 + 2 = 18; 18 \times 50 = 900; 900 + 7 + 4 = 911$
$(10 \times 10) + 25 = 125; (9 - 4) \times 125 = 625; 625 + 9 = 634$
THANKLESS

Round 213

EGOMANIA 8, ANGIOMA 7, ENIGMA 6
RECEPTION 9, PRENTICE 8, POINTER 7
CITIZENS 8, SECTION 7, ICIEST 6
EARPIECE 8, RECEIPT 7, CARPET 6
$75 + 50 - 7 = 118; 118 \times 8 = 944; 944 - 25 = 919$
$100 + 25 = 125; 125 - (10 + 4) = 111; (10/5) \times 111 = 222$
TESTIFIED

Round 214

PREMIERED 9, PERIDERM 8, EPIDERM 7
BOURGEOIS 9, BOOGIES 7, BRUISE 6
SWAMPIER 8, PROMISE 7, POWERS 6
ITINERANT 9, INTRANET 8, NITRATE 7
$6 \times (50 - 7) = 258; (258 + 4) \times 3 = 786$
$(9 \times 10) - 3 = 87; 8 \times 87 = 696; 696 - 2 = 694$
ADJOINING

Round 215

TUNESMITH 9, MINUTEST 8, SMITTEN 7
CLAYMORE 8, MAJORLY 7, CREAMY 6
UNDERBID 8, RIDDEN 6, DRIVE 5
QUILTING 8, FLUTING 7, FILING 6
$(8 + 4) \times 50 = 600; 600 + (9 \times 9) = 681$
$3 \times (7 - 1) = 18; 75 + 18 = 93; 93 \times 2 = 186$
INTENSIFY

Round 216

BASEPLATE 9, EATABLES 8, PALATES 7
LINEARITY 9, INTERLAY 8, AIRLINE 7
ENACTION 8, TOENAIL 7, CANNOT 6
FINAGLING 9, ALIGNING 8, ANGLING 7
$(100 + 75) \times 2 = 350; 9 - (50/25) = 7; 350 - 7 = 343$
$7 \times (50 + 2) = 364; 364 + (7 - 3) = 368; 368 + 100 = 468$
DESPERATE

Round 217

MASTERFUL 9, REFUTALS 8, TEARFUL 7
CLIPBOARD 9, CORDIAL 7, PLACID 6
KNOTHOLE 8, HOTLINE 7, TINKLE 6
NETWORKS 8, STINKER 7, WORSEN 6
$(7 + 6) \times 8 = 104; 104 + 3 = 107; (5 + 4) \times 107 = 963$
$9 \times 9 \times 10 = 810; 8 \times 8 = 64; 810 + 64 = 874$
OPERATION

Round 218

PIRANHAS 8, MARINAS 7, SPRAIN 6
FRONTAGES 9, SEAFRONT 8, TANGOES 7
BOUNCIEST 9, COUNTIES 8, SECTION 7
CLOUDIEST 9, SOLITUDE 8, COLDEST 7
$(4 \times 25) + 8 = 108; (8 - 3) \times 108 = 540$
$(100 - 25) \times 5 = 375; 375 - 7 = 368$
PATRONAGE

Round 219

MARKINGS 8, MARGINS 7, RISING 6
LAVENDER 8, RELIVED 7, INVADE 6
SEMICOLON 9, COLONIES 8, CONSOLE 7
HOTPLATE 8, HOPLITE 7, POLITE 6
$75 - (50/25) = 73; (3 \times 73) - 4 = 215; 215 \times 3 = 645$
$6 \times (100 - 10) = 540; 540 - (6/2) = 537$
INTERFACE

Round 220

RECLUSIVE 9, VERSICLE 8, SERVICE 7
WAGONERS 8, TREASON 7, ARGENT 6
CODPIECE 8, POLICED 7, COILED 6
PROHIBIT 8, PITHIER 7, BOTHER 6
$5 \times (50 - 8) = 210; 210 + 9 = 219; 219 \times 4 = 876$
$100 + 25 + 9 = 134; (9 - 6) \times 134 = 402$
COMPILING

Round 221

ELASIPOD 8, PADDLES 7, LADIES 6
DEPRECATE 9, CARPETED 8, TAPERED 7
MATERIAL 8, PALMATE 7, LIMPET 6
NEWSAGENT 9, NEGATES 7, SENATE 6
$100 + 25 - 2 = 123; 123 \times 6 = 738; 738 + (50/2) = 763$
$75 + 1 = 76; (10 + 3) \times 76 = 988; 988 - 9 = 979$
REDUNDANT

Round 222

BATTLEAXE 9, TAXABLE 7, TABLET 6
ISOSCELES 9, OSSICLES 8, SESSILE 7
PECTORAL 8, COMPARE 7, PARCEL 6
PATENTING 9, GENTIAN 7, INTENT 6
$75 - 8 = 67; (4 + 4) \times 67 = 536$
$(7 + 5) \times 50 = 600; (7 \times 5) - 1 = 34; 600 + 34 = 634$
ALCOHOLIC

Round 223
DRYSTONE 8, DONKEYS 7, TRENDY 6
BLOWFISH 8, FOIBLES 7, BOWELS 6
QUEENFISH 9, EQUINES 7, INFUSE 6
BOUFFANT 8, BOFFIN 6, ABOUT 5
$100 + 7 + 4 = 111; (8 - 2) \times 111 = 666$
$2 \times 6 \times 7 = 84; (84 + 1) \times 10 = 850$
NOMINATED

Round 224
ODDMENTS 8, MOISTEN 7, MINTED 6
COMPUTED 8, DEMOTIC 7, DICTUM 6
SYMBOLIC 8, CYMBALS 7, MISLAY 6
TENTACLE 8, MANTLET 7, CEMENT 6
$100 + 75 = 175; 175 - (8 - 5) = 172; (50/25) \times 172 = 344$
$(4 \times 25) - 7 = 93; (93 \times 10) - 8 = 922$
QUIRKIEST

Round 225
HUNGRIEST 9, USHERING 8, REUSING 7
SURICATE 8, ERRATIC 7, CITRUS 6
EAVESDROP 9, DEPRAVES 8, ADVERSE 7
MAZURKA 7, MAZIER 6, AMAZE 5
$50 + 25 + 8 = 83; 83 + 7/7 = 84; 84 \times 8 = 672$
$9 \times 100 = 900; (25 + 3) \times 4 = 112; 900 - 112 = 788$
RUMMAGING

Round 226
RAPESEED 8, SPEARED 7, FADERS 6
FIXTURES 8, SURFEIT 7, FASTER 6
SNAPSHOT 8, PHAETON 7, POTASH 6
CONDUITS 8, SUCTION 7, FUSION 6
$100 + 75 - 2 = 173; 173 \times 3 = 519$
$(9 \times 7) + 6 = 69; 69 \times 5 = 345; 345 + 1 = 346$
CHARACTER

Round 227
BAVAROIS 8, AIRBOAT 7, ISOBAR 6
IRONCLAD 8, CLARION 7, LARDON 6
DREAMFUL 8, DEFAULT 7, MATURE 6
RAMPAGED 8, REGMATA 7, PARADE 6
$(75 + 2) \times 9 = 693; 693 - 100 = 593$
$10 \times 25 = 250; 250 - (7 - 5) = 248; (3 + 1) \times 248 = 992$
BLEMISHED

Round 228
EGGPLANT 8, TANGELO 7, TOGGLE 6
NIMBUSES 8, SUBSIDE 7, MISUSE 6
SERVIETTE 9, EERIEST 7, STRIVE 6
BOOKREST 8, BOOSTER 7, RETOOK 6
$(5 \times 50) - 3 = 247; 247 \times 3 = 741; 741 - (5 \times 2) = 731$
$100 + (9 \times 7) = 163; 8 + 7 = 15; 163 + 15 = 178$
SUCCULENT

Round 229
PATCHIER 8, HEPATIC 7, RECITE 6
OUTFACED 8, CONFUTE 7, DONATE 6
PROTEGES 8, GOPHERS 7, THREES 6
HYPOCRITE 9, PITCHER 7, POETIC 6
$75 + (9 \times 4) = 111; (4 + 3) \times 111 = 777$
$(100 + 75) \times 2 = 350; 350 - (6 + 5) = 339$
KISSOGRAM

Round 230
OFFBEAT 7, BAFFLE 6, FLOAT 5
FLASHCUBE 9, CHASUBLE 8, BASHFUL 7
STANDPIPE 9, PEDANTS 7, SIPPED 6
REFINANCE 9, FIANCEE 7, CANINE 6
$10 \times 75 = 750; 50 + 25 + 9 = 84; 750 + 84 = 834$
$50 + (8 - 5) = 53; 8 + (6/6) = 9; 53 \times 9 = 477$
FASTENING

Round 231
CONGRUENT 9, NOCTURNE 8, TROUNCE 7
TRIPWIRE 8, PITHIER 7, WRITHE 6
JODPHURS 8, PUSHROD 7, SHROUD 6
STUPIDEST 9, DUSTIEST 8, STUDIES 7
$(5 \times 10) + 1 = 51; (10 + 8) \times 51 = 918; 918 + 7 = 925$
$6 \times 5 \times 25 = 750; 2 \times (5 + 3) = 16; 750 + 16 = 766$
EVERYBODY

Round 232
DOWNPOUR 8, DROPOUT 7, ROTUND 6
TEXTILES 8, EPISTLE 7, SEXTET 6
BEACHWEAR 9, EARACHE 7, BREACH 6
SNIFFLED 8, DENIALS 7, ISLAND 6
$100 - (50/10) - 1 = 94; 94 \times 4 = 376$
$(75 + 9) \times 6 = 504; 25 - 9 = 16; 504 + 16 = 520$
PAINFULLY

Round 233
ECLAMPSIA 9, MISPLACE 8, MALAISE 7
PARADIGM 8, DIAGRAM 7, DIAPER 6
BONHOMIE 8, EMOTION 7, BOOTIE 6
MEATBALL 8, LABIATE 7, MALLET 6
$6 \times (100 + 50) = 900; 25 - (9/9) = 24; 900 - 24 = 876$
$10 \times (50 + 10) = 600; 600 + 75 - 1 = 674$
BUFFETING

Round 234
LEFTOVER 8, FERTILE 7, VIOLET 6
PEDIGREE 8, WEEDIER 7, DEEPER 6
FLIPPANT 8, FANTAIL 7, PINATA 6
INTIMATE 8, MINARET 7, MATTER 6
$100 - 3 = 97; (5 + 2) \times 97 = 679; 679 - 1 = 678$
$(75 - 4) \times 7 = 497; 497 - (4 - 1) = 494$
OVENPROOF

Round 235
CONJURER 8, CHURNER 7, JOUNCE 6
OUTBIDS 7, BROILS 6, BURST 5
OBLIGES 7, GOBLIN 6, SLING 5
DERISORY 8, DOSSIER 7, DOSSER 6
$(4 \times 7) - 5 = 23; 23 \times 5 = 115; 115 \times 8 = 920$
$3 \times 10 = 30; 30 + (10/1+1) = 35; 35 \times 25 = 875$
CHARLATAN

Round 236
DIVERSITY 9, REVISIT 7, DIVERS 6
ENORMITY 8, WINTERY 7, MOIETY 6
REFUTABLE 9, FEATURE 7, RELATE 6
NIRVANA 7, VANITY 6, TINNY 5
$(9 \times 50) + 100 = 550; 8 - (75/25) = 5; 550 + 5 = 555$
$7 \times (100 + 25) = 875; (6 \times 6) - 5 = 31; 875 - 31 = 844$
LESSENING

Round 237
DIAZOS 6, PODIA 5, SOFA 4
SNOOZED 7, DOZENS 6, SANDY 5
CONSIDER 8, SYNODIC 7, CRONES 6
PROXIMATE 9, EXPIATOR 8, EMPORIA 7
$(7 \times 25) - 9 = 166; 5 \times 166 = 830; 830 + (10 - 3) = 837$
$50 - 1 = 49; (8 + 2) \times 49 = 490; 490 - 6 = 484$
PARAMOUNT

Round 238
JONGLEUR 8, GRUNTLE 7, TONGUE 6
BEARSKIN 8, INTAKES 7, BRAINS 6
BOMBASTIC 9, COMBATS 7, ATOMIC 6
THEREUNTO 9, HEREUNTO 8, THEREON 7
$5 \times (10 + 3) = 65; 65 + 4 = 69; 69 \times 9 = 621$
$100 + 75 + 4 = 179; (7 - 2) \times 179 = 895; 895 + 50 = 945$
ABDUCTION

Round 239

MELODICA 8, MEDICAL 7, TAILED 6
FRUMPIEST 9, STUMPIER 8, IMPUTES 7
PEGBOARD 8, PAGEBOY 7, GROPED 6
SUBSIDED 8, BUDDIES 7, ISSUED 6
100 − 8 = 92; (7 − 4) × 92 = 276
7 × (2 + 1) = 21; 21 × 25 = 525; 525 + 4 = 529
DEPLOYING

Round 240

CONSTABLE 9, OBSTACLE 8, LOCATES 7
RAVISHED 8, RAWHIDE 7, WASHED 6
IMBALANCE 9, CALAMINE 8, AMIABLE 7
RELIGION 8, ROLLING 7, LONGER 6
100 + 50 + 7 + 6 = 163; 163 × 6 = 978; 978 − 8 = 970
75 + 8 + 7 = 90; 90 × 9 = 810; 810 + (25 − 6) = 829
UNDAUNTED

Round 241

ECSTATIC 8, TACTICS 7, CYSTIC 6
RACONTEUR 9, COURANTE 8, CENTAUR 7
CONTENDED 9, ENCODED 7, CONNED 6
DOMINANCE 9, COMEDIAN 8, NOMADIC 7
(5 + 4) × (3 × 3) = 81; (81 + 2) × 5 = 415
75 + 50 = 125; 100/25 = 4; 10 − 9 = 1; 125 + 4 − 1 = 128
PLAINTIFF

Round 242

QUIPSTER 8, PUNIEST 7, PRUNES 6
NOCTURNAL 9, CALUTRON 8, COURANT 7
FUSELAGE 8, LEAGUES 7, EAGLES 6
BEAVERING 9, VERBIAGE 8, ENGRAVE 7
100 + 10 + 5 = 115; 115 × (10/5) = 230
8 × 75 = 600; 25 + 9 + 2 = 36; 600 + 36 = 636
WELLBEING

Round 243

STEADIES 8, SEASIDE 7, SEDATE 6
BOBSLEIGH 9, GOBBLES 7, HOBBLE 6
MESTIZAS 8, MAZIEST 7, SIESTA 6
CONVERGE 8, ENFORCE 7, GOVERN 6
8 × (50 + 8) = 464; 464 − (75 − 25) = 414
9 × 6 = 54; 54 − (3 + 1) = 50; 50 × 10 = 500
LIBRARIAN

Round 244

PENINSULA 9, PINNULES 8, SPANIEL 7
SHARPENED 9, RESHAPED 8, PANDERS 7
SQUATTER 8, QUARTET 7, TRUSTY 6
ENTRECOTE 9, TRECENTO 8, CORNET 6
(50 + 25) × (3 × 4) = 900; 900 + (7 × 4) = 928
75 + 4 = 79; (9 + 2) 79 = 869; 869 + (5 × 2) = 879
EXHORTING

Round 245

PUBERTY 7, RUGBY 5, TUBE 4
SNOWSHOE 8, WOOSHES 7, SHINES 6
JOYRIDING 9, INDIGO 6, GRIND 5
COOKWARE 8, WRACKED 7, ROCKED 6
9 + 5 + 4 = 18; 18 × 50 = 900; 900 − (7 + 7) = 886
100 + 50 = 150; 150 + (9 × 8) = 222
WATERFALL

Round 246

LIFEBOAT 8, FOLIATE 7, OBLATE 6
RELOCATED 9, DECORATE 8, TREADLE 7
BRUISED 7, RIDGES 6, RIDER 5
EDITORIAL 9, IDOLATER 8, LEOTARD 7
6 × 5 = 30; 30 × (25 − 4) = 630; 630 + 8 + 5 = 643
75 + 50 + 1 = 126; 126 × (3 + 4) = 882
QUALIFIED

Round 247

STARLIKE 8, BRISTLE 7, TRIKES 6
BECLOUDED 9, DOUBLED 7, DEDUCE 6
NOISETTE 8, HISTONE 7, TENTHS 6
MIDWICKET 9, DIMWIT 6, TIMID 5
4 × 100 = 400; 2 × 5 × 6 = 60; 400 − 60 = 340
(10 + 7) × 50 = 850; 850 − (10 − 4) = 844
PERISHING

Round 248

COOLTH 6, THICK 5, LOOT 4
PERIDERM 8, DEMIREP 7, PRIMED 6
PLAYMATE 8, PALMATE 7, TAMELY 6
DREAMIEST 9, DIAMETER 8, SMARTED 7
100 +25 + 7 = 132; 132 × 7 = 924; 924 + 75 = 999
(2 ×8) + 6 = 22; (4 × 22) − 1 = 87; 87 × 5 = 435
DISAGREED

Round 249

DIPLOMATE 9, DIPLOMAT 8, OPTIMAL 7
IMPEDANCE 9, ENCAMPED 8, MENACED 7
DESPERATE 9, REPEATED 8, SPEARED 7
COQUETRY 8, CROQUET 7, QUARTO 6
9 + 9 + 7 = 25; (100 - 25) × 7 = 525; 525 + 8 = 533
(7 + 5) = 12; (50 + 25) × 12 = 900; 900 − (2 × 3) = 894
CHEEKIEST

Round 250

ANTIQUES 8, URINATE 7, SQUINT 6
SOAPBOX 7, SPOOF 5, COPS 4
CUTAWAY 7, CATNAP 6, PANTY 5
FRACTALS 8, FACIALS 7, TRIALS 6
100 + 75 + 2 = 177; 177 × 3 = 531; 531 + 50 + 1 = 582
(9 × 25) − 10 = 215; 215 × 3 = 645
PARTNERED

Round 251

REPAIRED 8, HARRIED 7, PAIRED 6
FERROUS 7, ROUSED 6, FRIED 5
BEDRIDDEN 9, INBREED 7, BINDER 6
PUSHBIKE 8, TUPIKS 6, SPIKE 5
(4 × 75) + 50 = 350; 350 − (8 + 4) = 338
100 + 50 + 6 = 156; 156 × 5 = 780; 780 − (9 − 6) = 777
MONOLOGUE

Round 252

CORNBREAD 9, BROADEN 7, BARRED 6
NOSEDIVE 8, ENDWISE 7, ENDOWS 6
CRANKY 6, RAINY 5, TANK 4
MILITANCY 9, INTIMACY 8, INTIMAL 7
(7 + 2) × 75 = 675; 100/25 = 4; 675 − 4 = 671
75 + 6 = 81; 81 × 7 = 567
ALLEVIATE

Round 253

INCLOSED 8, LECTION 7, CLOSET 6
RUSTICATE 9, SCATTIER 8, SAUCIER 7
SHEEPSKIN 9, HIPNESS 7, SNIPES 6
CORNERING 9, ENCORING 8, CORNIER 7
(5 + 3) × 25 = 200; (200 + 3) × 4 = 812; 812 − 1 = 811
(9 × 75) + 100 = 775; 775 + 6 + 4 = 785
MARAUDING

Round 254

STAINLESS 9, SALIENTS 8, LISTENS 7
OFFSTAGE 8, SAFETY 6, GOATS 5
EPHEMERAL 9, EPHEMERA 8, HAMPER 6
GARDENED 8, LEARNED 7, DANGLE 6
(3 − 1) × 50 = 100; (100 − 8) × 10 = 920
10 + (5/5) = 11; 11 × 75 = 825; 825 − 1 = 824
VESTIBULE

Round 255

PHEASANT 8, PEASANT 7, SEXTAN 6
CORPULENT 9, TROUNCE 7, PUNTER 6
MEDALIST 8, MILDEST 7, MAILED 6
BEEFEATER 9, REBATE 6, EATER 5
$(8 + 5) \times 10 = 130; 130 \times 6 = 780; 780 - (9 - 7) = 778$
$5 \times (6 + 1) = 35; 35 \times (25 - 1) = 840; 840 + 6 = 846$
BULLDOZER

Round 256

REANIMATE 9, MARINATE 8, TRAINEE 7
UNCEASING 9, NUISANCE 8, GUINEAS 7
INFECTED 8, DESCENT 7, FISTED 6
SUBTITLE 8, BUTTIES 7, SETTLE 6
$50 + (8 - 2) = 56; 56 \times 9 = 504; 504 - 1 = 503$
$(10 \times 50) - 75 = 425; 10 - (100/25) = 6; 425 + 6 = 431$
UNFURLING

Round 257

BLUEPRINT 9, TURBINE 7, TURNIP 6
ESOTERIC 8, GORIEST 7, EROTIC 6
THREESOME 9, THEOREMS 8, SMOTHER 7
CADETSHIP 9, PASTICHE 8, APHIDES 7
$(8 - 5) \times 3 \times 100 = 900; 900 + (7 \times 6) = 942$
$75 + 4 + 1 = 80; 80 \times 7 = 560; 560 - (100/50) = 558$
LACTATING

Round 258

MINIDISC 8, INDICIA 7, MANICS 6
RECASTING 9, CATERING 8, STINGER 7
UNETHICAL 9, ETHNICAL 8, LUNATIC 7
GARRISON 8, ROARING 7, GROANS 6
$3 \times (25 + 3) = 84; 2 \times (4 + 1) = 10; 84 \times 10 = 840$
$(6 \times 100) + 75 = 675; 675 - (5 \times 4) = 655$
PUBLISHED

Round 259

DESORBING 9, SONGBIRD 8, BRIDGES 7
COUNSELED 9, ENCLOSED 8, NODULES 7
PHOENIX 7, HORNET 6, POINT 5
QUADRATE 8, RADIATE 7, TIRADE 6
$(4 + 3) \times 50 = 350; (350 + 8) \times 2 = 716$
$6 \times 75 = 450; 450 - (100/5) = 430; 430 - (8 - 7) = 429$
TOOTHACHE

Round 260

INSCRIBE 8, ARSENIC 7, RABIES 6
RUDIMENT 8, UNTRIED 7, UNITED 6
COVALENT 8, CENTAVO 7, AVOCET 6
BEMOANED 8, ABDOMEN 7, DEBONE 6
$(75 + 25) \times 9 = 900; 50 - (2 \times 6) = 38; 900 - 38 = 862$
$(4 + 5) \times 100 = 900; 6 \times (7 + 7) = 84; 900 + 84 = 984$
THREADING

Round 261

VEHICULAR 9, CHERVIL 7, ÉCLAIR 6
EMPATHISE 9, SHIPMATE 8, EMPTIES 7
MOISTURE 8, TOURIST 7, TIMERS 6
REBATING 8, GRANITE 7, RETAIN 6
$50 + (10/5) = 52; (10 + 4) \times 52 = 728; 728 - 5 = 723$
$75 + 9 = 84; (10 - 6) \times 84 = 336; 336 - (9 + 6) = 321$
WITTERING

Round 262

OUTHOUSE 8, BOOTHS 6, THOSE 5
COVERAGE 8, CORSAGE 7, CREASE 6
OINTMENT 8, MENTION 7, NOTICE 6
SOPPIEST 8, SOPHIST 7, HIPPOS 6
$8 \times (100 - 8) = 736; 736 + (75/25) = 739$
$75 + (5 \times 4) = 95; 95 \times 7 = 665; 665 + 1 = 666$
LEISURELY

Round 263

GEARSTICK 9, AGRESTIC 8, STICKER 7
FATIGUED 8, DEFIANT 7, GIFTED 6
DESTITUTE 9, DUETTIST 8, STETTED 7
MONARCHY 8, HARMONY 7, CHROME 6
$3 \times (6 + 1) = 21; 21 \times 4 = 84; (2 \times 5) \times 84 = 840$
$75 - (100/50) = 73; (7 - 4) \times 73 = 219$
PTARMIGAN

Round 264

RAVISHED 8, DERVISH 7, VARIED 6
COWHIDES 8, WHISKED 7, SOCKED 6
COHABITEE 9, BIOTECH 7, TECHIE 6
DECODABLE 9, DEBACLE 7, CODDLE 6
$25 - (1 + 1) = 23; 9 \times 23 = 207; 207 + 100 = 307$
$75 - 8 = 67; 5 \times 67 = 335; 335 - 9 = 326$
DETESTING

Round 265

LACEWING 8, ANGELIC 7, LIGATE 6
EMOLLIENT 9, MELILOT 7, LENTIL 6
DEPRAVITY 9, VARIETY 7, DIVERT 6
BESOTTED 8, STROBED 7, BETTER 6
$(100 + 25) \times 7 = 875; 10 + 3 + 1 = 14; 875 + 14 = 889$
$(4 + 5) \times 25 = 225; 225 - 4 = 221; 221 \times 3 = 663$
SPLENDOUR

Round 266

EVAPORATE 9, OVEREAT 7, REPEAT 6
WEAKLING 8, LAPWING 7, WANGLE 6
BACKLINE 8, BLACKEN 7, BICKER 6
BLOWHOLE 8, HOLLOW 6, LIBEL 5
$75 - 6 = 69; 7 \times 69 = 483; 483 + (50/25) = 485$
$100 - (10 + 9) = 81; 81 \times 9 = 729; 729 + 50 = 779$
HANDBRAKE

Round 267

PIGTAILED 9, DIPLEGIA 8, DIGITAL 7
RECKONER 8, ENFORCE 7, CONKER 6
HORTATIVE 9, ROTATIVE 8, ATTIRE 6
SOURPUSS 8, SPROUTS 7, USURPS 6
$8 + 7 + 3 + 1 = 19; 19 \times 50 = 950; 950 - 3 = 947$
$(100 + 25) \times (6 - 2) = 500; 500 + (3 \times 8) = 524$
MEMORISED

Round 268

DETAINED 8, IDEATED 7, DEADEN 6
CRAYONED 8, DECAGON 7, GARDEN 6
SHOPLIFT 8, LOUTISH 7, FLOUTS 6
SQUABBLER 9, BARBULES 8, BARBELS 7
$(7 + 5) \times 8 = 96; (96 \times 10) - 3 = 957$
$(5 + 1) \times 4 = 24; 24 \times 25 = 600; 600 + 7 + 1 = 608$
TARANTULA

Round 269

WEEPIEST 8, SWEETIE 7, WHITES 6
GIFTWARE 8, FRAGILE 7, FILTER 6
OMNIVORE 8, EMOTION 7, INVERT 6
THROSTLE 8, HOLSTER 7, TOILET 6
$(6 + 6) \times 75 = 900; 900 - 50 + 8 = 858$
$75 + 50 = 125; (4 + 3) \times 125 = 875; 875 - (9 + 6) = 860$
SUPPLYING

Round 270

BETRAYAL 8, PARABLE 7, PLATER 6
PLECTRUM 8, CRUMPET 7, PUMICE 6
MORGANITE 9, EMIGRANT 8, TANGIER 7
RESISTANT 9, NASTIEST 8, STRAINS 7
$100 + (5 \times 7) = 135; 135 \times 7 = 945; 945 + 2 + 1 = 948$
$7 \times 8 \times 10 = 560; 25 - 9 = 16; 16/8 = 2; 560 + 2 = 562$
PROFITEER

Round 271
CALORIES 8, RISSOLE 7, SAILOR 6
KEELBOAT 8, OBLATE 6, BLEAT 5
COHERENT 8, THEREON 7, HORNET 6
LIFETIME 8, HELMET 6, LIMIT 5
$5 \times (100 + 50) = 750; 25 - (8 + 3) = 14; 750 + 14 = 764$
$75 + 10 + 6 = 91; 91 \times 7 = 637$
GRAPEVINE

Round 272
SOVEREIGN 9, SEVERING 8, REGIONS 7
GIVEAWAY 8, WEAVING 7, VAGINA 6
PINNACLE 8, ANCIENT 7, PENCIL 6
TRANSDUCE 9, UNDERACT 8, CRUSTED 7
$3 \times 4 \times 75 = 900; 50 + (3 \times 2) = 56; 900 + 56 = 956$
$(4 \times 25) - 7 = 93; 93 \times 9 = 837; 837 - 2 = 835$
DRAINPIPE

Round 273
DETHRONED 9, DEHORNED 8, TRODDEN 7
ORIENTED 8, HEROINE 7, RODENT 6
ROOSTING 8, GORIEST 7, TIGERS 6
UNHEATED 8, HAUNTED 7, HANDLE 6
$(7 \times 8) + 10 = 66; (10 \times 66) - 9 = 651$
$9 + 4 + 2 = 15; 50 + 1 = 51; 15 \times 51 = 765$
MACHINERY

Round 274
VERBOSITY 9, SOBRIETY 8, OBESITY 7
GLOBALISE 9, LOBELIAS 8, GOALIES 7
OPTIONAL 8, PLATOON 7, LOTION 6
HARVESTER 9, TRAVERSE 8, HEATERS 7
$100 + 3 = 103; 103 \times (4 + 4) = 824; 824 + (75/3) = 849$
$(75 - 5) \times 4 = 280; (2 + 1) \times 2 = 6; 280 - 6 = 274$
IMPLORING

Round 275
REDBREAST 9, ARRESTED 8, DEBATES 7
BARGAIN 7, AIRBAG 6, BRING 5
SHOULDER 8, LODGERS 7, RESOLD 6
TRADABLE 8, FLATBED 7, TABLED 6
$(8 + 6) \times 50 = 700; (7 \times 10) + 9 = 79; 700 + 79 = 779$
$(9 \times 75) - 50 = 625; (100/25) - 3 = 1; 625 - 1 = 624$
UNSIGHTLY

Round 276
GINGERING 9, REIGNING 8, RINGING 7
GRANIVORE 9, VINEGAR 7, GORIER 6
OPERATIVE 9, PRIVATE 7, PIRATE 6
SPERMATID 9, PRIMATES 8, SIDEARM 7
$6 \times 25 = 150; 150 - (3 \times 3) = 141; 141 \times 7 = 987$
$75 - (10 - 2) = 67; (6 + 2) \times 67 = 536$
PROCESSED

Round 277
ASPERITY 8, PASTURE 7, UPRATE 6
DEVISABLE 9, ABSEILED 8, BALDIES 7
TIDEMARK 8, TRACKED 7, MARKET 6
WELCOMING 9, GENOMIC 7, MINGLE 6
$25 \times (100 - 75) = 625; (50/5) + 9 = 19; 625 + 19 = 644$
$(8 + 3) \times 75 = 825; 825 - 9 = 816$
RELIGIOUS

Round 278
MUJAHIDIN 9, INDIUM 6, HUMAN 5
PIROZHKI 8, THRIP 5, PORK 4
GODPARENT 9, PRONATED 8, DRAGNET 7
DIABETES 8, DEAREST 7, TRIBES 6
$8 - 2 = 6; 6 \times (5 + 5) = 60; (8 + 7) \times 60 = 900$
$(100/25) \times 50 = 200; 200 \times 4 = 800; 800 - (3 \times 6) = 782$
WOMANHOOD

Round 279
ROCKSLIDE 9, DOCKERS 7, LOCKED 6
BIATHLON 8, HOBNAIL 7, INHALE 6
TRIBUNAL 8, ORBITAL 7, URINAL 6
VESTIBULE 9, ELUSIVE 7, SUBLET 6
$2 \times 3 \times 3 = 18; (18 - 1) \times 25 = 425; 425 + 4 = 429$
$100 + 9 = 109; 109 \times (7 - 4) = 327; 327 + 6 + 5 = 338$
LIMBERING

Round 280
TYPEFACE 8, HEPCAT 6, HEFTY 5
TRIPLEXES 9, REPTILES 8, STERILE 7
MIDSTREAM 9, MERMAIDS 8, SMARTED 7
DEWDROPS 8, PERIODS 7, SWIPED 6
$(6 \times 4) + 1 = 25; (75 - 50) \times 25 = 625; 625 - 6 = 619$
$9 \times 100 = 900; 8 \times 8 = 64; 900 + 64 + 25 = 989$
JAUNDICED

Round 281
NEGOTIANT 9, NOTATING 8, TANGENT 7
MYTHICAL 8, ALCHEMY 7, MALICE 6
SKINHEAD 8, SARDINE 7, SINKER 6
SHURIKEN 8, HUNKIER 7, SHRUNK 6
$(75 + 7) \times 10 = 820; 4 \times (100/50) = 8; 820 - 8 = 812$
$(4 + 2) \times 5 = 30; 30 \times 25 = 750; 750 + 4 - 3 = 751$
LIVESTOCK

Round 282
GROCERIES 9, CORRIES 7, ROSIER 6
SPATULA 7, FAULTS 6, SPLAT 5
WHACKIEST 9, WICKETS 7, SWITCH 6
BIFURCATE 9, FACTURE 7, FABRIC 6
$8 \times (50 + 6) = 448; 448 - (9 - 8) = 447$
$100 + 75 - 2 = 173; 173 \times 5 = 865; 865 - 50 = 815$
HILARIOUS

Round 283
TIRAMISU 8, ARMPITS 7, SPIRIT 6
LIKEABLE 8, EYEBALL 7, LIKELY 6
PANATELLA 9, PATELLA 7, PLANET 6
EXCLAIMED 9, CLIMAXED 8, DECIMAL 7
$(4 \times 10) - 10 = 30; 30 \times 25 = 750; 750 - 5 = 745$
$7 \times 100 = 700; 25 + 3 - 8 = 20; 700 - 20 = 680$
RELENTING

Round 284
PITTANCE 8, PATIENT 7, PECTIN 6
OPTICIAN 8, CAPTION 7, CATION 6
GRAPHIC 7, CHARGE 6, GRIPE 5
UNIRONED 8, ROUNDEL 7, DINNER 6
$(7 + 2) \times 5 = 45; 75 + 45 - 2 = 118; 118 \times 8 = 944$
$75 - (5 - 2) = 72; 72 \times 10 = 720; 720 + (6 - 5) = 721$
PUNCTUATE

Round 285
PRESEASON 9, RESPONSE 8, REPOSES 7
DEXTROSE 8, EXISTED 7, STORED 6
REFORMAT 8, FORMATE 7, MORTAR 6
VEXATION 8, EXOTICA 7, ACTIVE 6
$(8 + 3) \times 7 = 77; (5 + 4) \times 77 = 693$
$8 \times (8 + 3) = 88; (88 + 6) \times 10 = 940$
ANSWERING

Round 286
BILATERAL 9, ARILLATE 8, LABIATE 7
REANIMATE 9, MANATEE 7, RENAME 6
SPEEDIEST 9, SIDESTEP 8, DESPITE 7
REMARRIED 9, DREAMIER 8, ADMIRER 7
$9 - (100/25) = 5; 5 \times 50 = 250; 250 + (9 \times 4) = 286$
$50 \times 4 = 200; (9 - 6) \times 200 = 600; 600 - (1 + 1) = 598$
UNDERTAKE

Round 287

ESCAPADE 8, ESCAPED 7, ASPECT 6
SEMILUNAR 9, MINERALS 8, REALISM 7
OSTRACISE 9, SCARIEST 8, CORSETS 7
SINECURES 9, INSECURE 8, SUNRISE 7
$6 \times (50 + 25) = 450$; $7 + 4 + 4 = 15$; $450 + 15 = 465$
$(8 + 3) \times 10 = 110$; $110 + 1 = 111$; $111 \times (5 + 4) = 999$
INDIGNITY

Round 288

GUILLEMOT 9, MELILOT 7, GULLET 6
REVISABLE 9, VERBALS 7, BRAVES 6
WHISPERED 9, PERISHED 8, SPHERED 7
TRANSPIRE 9, PRINTERS 8, PARRIES 7
$(5 + 3) \times 75 = 600$; $600 + 25 = 625$; $625 + (100/50) = 627$
$75 + 9 = 84$; $84 \times 8 = 672$; $672 + 100 = 772$; $772 + (9 \times 8) = 844$
PRACTICAL

Round 289

RELEGATE 8, LEGATEE 7, REGGAE 6
DIALECTAL 9, CEDILLA 7, TAILED 6
VICTORIES 9, VORTICES 8, COVERTS 7
WATCHFIRE 9, FITCHEW 7, WAITER 6
$75 + 7 + 5 = 87$; $87 \times 10 = 870$; $870 + 9 = 879$
$(50 - 2) \times (7 + 3) = 480$; $480 - 5 = 475$
SQUEAMISH

Round 290

BLINDEST 8, ENTAILS 7, BANDIT 6
ORDERING 8, IGNORED 7, RIOTED 6
PLAINING 8, NAILING 7, PINING 6
DESCRIBE 8, SICKBED 7, BRIDES 6
$100 - (10 + 10) = 80$; $80 \times 9 = 720$; $720 + 25 = 745$
$100 + 5 + 1 = 106$; $(5 + 3) \times 106 = 848$; $848 - 2 = 846$
GIBBERING

Round 291

SPENDABLE 9, ENABLED 7, LAPSED 6
GUMSHIELD 9, HELIUM 6, SLIDE 5
TOUCHLINE 9, UNCLOTHE 8, OUTLINE 7
DOORNAILS 9, ORDINALS 8, LARDONS 7
$8 \times 75 = 600$; $25 + (9 \times 2) = 43$; $600 - 43 = 557$
$6 + 6 + 4 = 16$; $7 \times 16 = 112$; $(112 + 3) \times 7 = 805$
ENERGISED

Round 292

ABANDONED 9, ABANDON 7, BONDED 6
LEITMOTIF 9, TOILET 6, MOTEL 5
HORMONE 7, MONGER 6, GNOME 5
FALCONRY 8, CLARION 7, FROLIC 6
$6 + 6 + 4 = 16$; $(75 + 16) \times 8 = 728$; $728 + 3 = 731$
$(9 \times 5) - 7 = 38$; $38 \times 25 = 950$; $950 - 10 = 940$
FORGOTTEN

Round 293

METRICAL 8, TACKIER 7, CALMER 6
PROGESTIN 9, POINTERS 8, STINGER 7
CATENOID 8, NOTICED 7, DONATE 6
REFERABLE 9, FEEBLER 7, BARREL 6
$(5 - 4) + 1 = 2$; $100 + 50 - 2 = 148$; $148 \times 6 = 888$
$75 + (8/4) = 77$; $77 \times 9 = 693$; $693 - (100/25) = 689$
COMPUTING

Round 294

DIASTOLE 8, VIOLATE 7, OLIVES 6
BIOGRAPH 8, AIRBAG 6, ORIBI 5
CIRCULATE 9, CRUCIATE 8, ARTICLE 7
OBEDIENT 8, DENOTES 7, STONED 6
$8 \times (8 + 1) = 72$; $(72 + 3) \times 7 = 525$; $525 + 2 = 527$
$(50 + 4) \times (8 + 4) = 648$; $648 - 9 = 639$
REGULARLY

Round 295

NECKLACE 8, LICENCE 7, CACKLE 6
HOMOPHOBE 9, HOOPOE 6, OOMPH 5
POIGNANT 8, PLATING 7, TAPING 6
VENTILATE 9, LEVITATE 8, ENTITLE 7
$(5 \times 100) + 75 + 7 = 582$; $50/25 = 2$; $582/2 = 291$
$(6 \times 4) + 7 = 31$; $31 \times 25 = 775$; $775 - 3 = 772$
SWALLOWED

Round 296

AIRFIELDS 9, AIRFIELD 8, DERAILS 7
SNITCHED 8, SECTION 7, TONICS 6
TAILSPIN 8, PLANETS 7, ALPINE 6
TOUCHLINE 9, UNCLOTHE 8, HOTLINE 7
$8 \times 8 \times 10 = 640$; $9 - 5 = 4$; $640 + 4 = 644$
$7 \times 100 = 700$; $6 \times (5 - 1) = 24$; $700 - 24 = 676$
TELEPATHY

Round 297

WINDPIPE 8, PAWNED 6, WIDEN 5
FATHOMED 8, METHOD 6, FATED 5
CLAVIERS 8, REVISAL 7, SCALED 6
REGIONALS 9, SERAGLIO 8, LINGERS 7
$75 + 25 - (5/5) = 99$; $99 \times 6 = 594$; $594 - 6 = 588$
$(9 \times 3) + 1 = 28$; $28 \times 25 = 700$; $700 + 2 + 1 = 703$
INCLUDING

Round 298

PROPERTY 8, PORTRAY 7, TAPPER 6
WHITENER 8, THEREIN 7, WINTER 6
FACTOTUM 8, ATOMIC 6, ATTIC 5
TAPROOMS 8, SEAPORT 7, POSTER 6
$(50 + 2) \times (6 + 4) = 520$; $520 + 75 = 595$
$(2 \times 7) + 5 = 19$; $19 \times 50 = 950$; $950 - 8 = 942$
FLIMSIEST

Round 299

WOBBLIER 8, BLOWIER 7, BOILER 6
SOFTWARE 8, FROSTED 7, WATERS 6
DELEGACY 8, ELEGIAC 7, EYELID 6
WHETSTONE 9, TOWNEES 7, HONEST 6
$4 + 4 + 2 = 10$; $(75 + 3) \times 10 = 780$; $780 - 1 = 779$
$10 - (100/25) = 6$; $6 \times 75 = 450$; $450 + (50/10) = 455$
EAGERNESS

Round 300

AORISTIC 8, OSTRICH 7, CHARTS 6
TORTURED 8, OBTRUDE 7, TOURED 6
ABATEMENT 9, ENTAMEBA 8, EMANATE 7
BATTIEST 8, TATTIER 7, STRAIT 6
$25 + 9 + 9 = 43$; $100 - 43 = 57$; $(8 + 1) \times 57 = 513$
$(3 \times 6) - 5 = 13$; $13 \times 10 \times 6 = 780$; $780 + 7 = 787$
CONFESSED

Round 301

PARAFFIN 8, AFFAIR 6, PIANO 5
CLEAVAGE 8, LAVAGE 6, EAGLE 5
SMUGNESS 8, MESSING 7, GENIUS 6
MICROWAVE 9, WAVIER 6, CRAVE 5
$2 \times (7 - 1) = 12$; $12 \times (50 + 2) = 624$
$75 + 1 = 76$; $(9 + 4) \times 76 = 988$; $988 + 5 = 993$
CAVORTING

Round 302

GLITTERY 8, UTTERLY 7, TURTLE 6
WHALEBONE 9, OWNABLE 7, ENABLE 6
ACQUAINT 8, AQUATIC 7, ACQUIT 6
FEMINIST 8, FIGMENT 7, TINGES 6
$9 \times 9 = 81$; $81 \times 8 = 648$; $648 - (10 \times 10) = 548$
$75 \times 10 = 750$; $(8 - 5) \times 6 = 18$; $750 + 18 = 768$
HOUSEMAID

Round 303
REMARKED 8, MARRIED 7, REMADE 6
TORTILLA 8, PATRIOT 7, PILLAR 6
EYEBROWS 8, BESTREW 7, OYSTER 6
TEETOTAL 8, LOCATE 6, OCTET 5
$(8 - 3) \times 100 = 500; 7 + (50/25) = 9; 500 - 9 = 491$
$3 \times (7 - 1) = 18; 18 \times 6 = 108; (108 - 1) \times 5 = 535$
NONENTITY

Round 304
HINDERED 8, INDEXED 7, HIDDEN 6
BLINKERED 9, REKINDLE 8, BRINDLE 7
VAPORISED 9, OVERPAID 8, ROADIES 7
NEGATIVES 9, VINTAGES 8, SEATING 7
$100 + (50/2) = 125; 125 - 2 = 123; 123 \times (75/25) = 369$
$(4 + 4) \times 75 = 600; (3 \times 9) - 7 = 20; 600 - 20 = 580$
PRECISION

Round 305
DENDRITE 8, TRODDEN 7, TENDER 6
WEEKENDER 9, RENEWED 7, KEENER 6
URANIUM 7, RUMINA 6, PRIMA 5
ALGICIDE 8, CAVILED 7, ADVICE 6
$5 \times 100 = 500; 500 - (3 \times 25) = 425; 425 - (3 - 2) = 424$
$100 - (3 + 1) = 96; (6 + 3) \times 96 = 864; 864 + 1 = 865$
SCRAMBLED

Round 306
PASSWORD 8, RIPSAWS 7, RADIOS 6
FETLOCKS 8, TICKLES 7, STIFLE 6
WOLFSBANE 9, OWNABLE 7, FABLES 6
COACHWORK 9, WHACKO 6, CROAK 5
$(2 + 8) \times 6 = 60; (5 \times 60) + 7 = 307; 307 \times 3 = 921$
$(7 - 5) \times 9 = 18; 18 \times 25 = 450; 450 - 1 = 449$
BROACHING

Round 307
RIPOSTES 8, STOPPER 7, STORES 6
DEPRECATE 9, REPEATED 8, CATERED 7
ALERTNESS 9, LATENESS 8, TEASERS 7
TORNADOES 9, TANDOORS 8, ROASTED 7
$3 - (50/25) = 1; 3 + 1 = 4; (100 - 4) \times 8 = 768$
$100 + (50/25) = 102; 102 \times 8 = 816; 816 + 8 + 75 = 899$
ADVERSITY

Round 308
BLUEBERRY 9, RUBBERY 7, BLURRY 6
TELEPATH 8, ATHLETE 7, LEGATE 6
HESITATE 8, JETTIES 7, ESTATE 6
OCCLUDED 8, CLOUDED 7, CUDDLE 6
$100 + 50 + (2 \times 5) = 160; 160 \times 6 = 960; 960 + 7 = 967$
$8 \times 7 \times 4 = 224; 224 + 2 = 226; (7 - 3) \times 226 = 904$
DRUMSTICK

Round 309
SMALLPOX 8, SLALOM 6, SMELL 5
ABDICATE 8, BITCHED 7, BATHED 6
EXPRESSO 8, EXPIRES 7, SPORES 6
PUBLICAN 8, CLUBMAN 7, ALUMNI 6
$(25 + 3) \times 8 = 224; (224 + 5) \times 3 = 687; 687 - 1 = 686$
$(4 + 4) \times 75 = 600; (9 \times 7) - 10 = 53; 600 + 53 = 653$
EXTREMIST

Round 310
DESSICATE 9, ACCEDES 7, EDICTS 6
MILLIONTH 9, MILLION 7, LIMIT 5
EXACTION 8, EXOTICA 7, CATION 6
PATCHOULI 9, OPTICAL 7, COITAL 6
$9 \times 9 \times 10 = 810; 810 + 50 + 4 = 864$
$(7 + 6) \times 75 = 975; 8 \times (4 + 3) = 56; 975 - 56 = 919$
KIDNAPPER

Round 311
HOUSEMAID 9, MADHOUSE 8, HIDEOUS 7
DUNGEONS 8, IGNEOUS 7, SIGNED 6
TRACERIED 9, TERRACED 8, TARRIED 7
COCKEREL 8, CLOCKER 7, COERCE 6
$75 + 50 + 4 = 129; 129 \times 5 = 645; 645 + 8 = 653$
$(8 \times 7) - 6 = 50; 50 \times 5 \times 4 = 1000; 1000 - 4 = 996$
REVOLTING

Round 312
TANGIBLE 8, BEATING 7, LAMENT 6
NEIGHBOUR 9, ROUGHEN 7, BORING 6
BODYLINE 8, BALONEY 7, LOANED 6
UPGRADED 8, GUARDED 7, RIDGED 6
$(2 \times 7) + 8 = 22; 22 \times 25 = 550; 550 + 6 - 1 = 555$
$(100 + 8) \times 3 = 324; 324 - 4 = 320; 320 \times (75/25) = 960$
MISERABLE

Round 313
HEMIOLAS 8, IMPALES 7, POLISH 6
BASSINET 8, AMBIENT 7, INMATE 6
DESOLATE 8, LOATHED 7, LASTED 6
UNWELCOME 9, WELCOME 7, COLUMN
$50 - (10 - 8) = 48; 48 \times 6 = 288; 288 - 10 = 278$
$3 \times 4 \times 75 = 900; (7 \times 5) - 2 = 33; 900 - 33 = 867$
SCAPEGOAT

Round 314
WRENCHED 8, CHEWIER 7, HINDER 6
TETHERED 8, GREETED 7, DEGREE 6
COLDNESS 8, SECONDS 7, COILED 6
SPARROWS 8, PROWESS 7, POWERS 6
$(50/25) \times 10 = 20; 20 + 75 + 100 = 195; 195 \times 4 = 780$
$9 \times (50 + 9) = 531; 531 - 4 = 527$
SNOOKERED

Round 315
REPUBLIC 8, REPLICA 7, PLAICE 6
BOOTLACE 8, COBALT 6, ELBOW 5
PULMONARY 9, PARONYM 7, RUMPLY 6
PAYMASTER 9, STAMPER 7, STEAMY 6
$7 + 7 + 3 = 17; 5 \times 17 = 85; (85 \times 8) - 2 = 678$
$75 + 25 + 6 = 106; 9 - (3 - 2) = 8; 106 \times 8 = 848$
TARDINESS

Round 316
COALPITS 8, TOPICAL 7, OPTICS 6
ACETIFY 7, WICKET 6, TWEAK 5
SHIPLOADS 9, SLIPSHOD 8, HAPLOID 7
MISDOUBT 8, OUTBIDS 7, QUOITS 6
$(75 + 50) \times 7 = 875; (8 - 6) \times 5 = 10; 875 + 10 = 885$
$(100/2) + 1 + 1 = 52; (10 + 2) \times 52 = 624$
UNEARTHLY

Round 317
HUNGERED 8, REIGNED 7, HINDER 6
PIEDMONTS 9, NEPOTISM 8, POINTED 7
EXHUMING 8, ENOUGH 6, HINGE 5
BATTERED 8, BETTERS 7, BREAST 6
$(9 \times 75) - 3 = 672; 672 + 100 = 772$
$50 + 25 - 8 = 67; 67 \times 10 = 670; 670 - (5 - 2) = 667$
UPPERMOST

Round 318
HAYSTACK 8, KITSCHY 7, STICKY 6
COLLATING 9, LOCATING 8, CALLING 7
SPEEDWAY 8, WAYSIDE 7, SPEWED 6
RESEMBLE 8, EMERGES 7, GREBES 6
$5 \times 25 = 125; 125 - (7 - 6) = 124; 124 \times (4 + 4) = 992$
$10 + 3 = 13; 13 \times (50 - 1) = 637; 637 + 9 + 1 = 647$
ABSEILING

Round 319

ARRESTIVE 9, TRAVERSE 8, ARRIVES 7
UNSTEADY 8, DESTINY 7, DETAIN 6
WYVERNS 7, ANSWER 6, RAVEN 5
TEXTURED 8, EXTRUDE 7, RATTED 6
$(75 - 6) \times 8 = 552; 552 - (100/25) = 548$
$2 \times 5 \times 10 = 100; (100 + 4) \times 8 = 832; 832 + 3 = 835$
EQUIVOCAL

Round 320

BOTANICAL 9, ANABOLIC 8, BOTANIC 7
UNRULIEST 9, INSULTER 8, UTENSIL 7
HYSTERIA 8, THERAPY 7, STRIPE 6
SPITEFUL 8, SPICULE 7, SPLICE 6
$(4 \times 6) - 5 = 19; 19 \times (50 - 1) = 931; 931 + 8 = 939$
$8 + 6 - 4 = 10; 75 - 2 = 73; (73 \times 10) - 25 = 705$
FLAGSTAFF

Round 321

FIGURINE 8, GUNFIRE 7, FRIEND 6
PAROTITIS 9, PATRIOTS 8, PROTIST 7
WASHIEST 8, WHITEST 7, SWATHE 6
SKYDIVER 8, VISORED 7, SKIVED 6
$100 + 75 = 175; 9 \times 9 = 81; 175 + 81 - 10 = 246$
$(9 \times 4) + 3 = 39; 39 \times 25 = 975; 975 - (8 + 3) = 964$
HURRIEDLY

Round 322

CASELOAD 8, SOLACED 7, SCALED 6
RETRIEVED 9, REVERTED 8, RETIRED 7
PENALIZED 9, PENALIZE 8, DEPLANE 7
COMPERED 8, COMPARE 7, POMACE 6
$(2 \times 3) + 7 = 13; 13 \times 8 = 104; 104 \times 6 = 624$
$75 - (10 - 9) = 74; 74 \times 3 = 222; 222 \times 4 = 888$
SQUEAKING

Round 323

GLISTENED 9, SEEDLING 8, TINGLES 7
BRASSIER 8, HARRIES 7, SHARES 6
PURSUITS 8, PURISTS 7, STRIPS 6
DIAMANTE 8, TEAMING 7, TINGED 6
$100/4 = 25; (25 + 4) \times 25 = 725; 725 + 9 + 1 = 735$
$(75 - 50) \times 25 = 625; 625 + 5 = 630; 630 - (100/5) = 610$
STRICTURE

Round 324

RESIDENT 8, TENDERS 7, JESTER 6
MISQUOTED 9, MISQUOTE 8, OUTSIDE 7
EVENTFUL 8, FLUENT 6, BLUNT 5
HARMONICA 9, CHAIRMAN 8, MONARCH 7
$(8 \times 25) = 200; 200 - (8 + 7) = 185; 185 \times (6 - 2) = 740$
$(75 - 1) \times 8 = 592; 592 - 9 = 583$
RECOGNIZE

Round 325

OINTMENT 8, TONTINE 7, TOILET 6
FILTERED 8, DEFLATE 7, TRIFLE 6
UNPLAYED 8, POUNDAL 7, UPLOAD 6
CONCERTO 8, CORNICE 7, NOTICE 6
$100 + 25 = 125; 125 - (3 \times 3) = 116; 116 \times 7 = 812$
$9 + 9 = 18; (50 + 2) \times 18 = 936; 936 - 6 = 930$
LONGITUDE

Round 326

SPOKESMAN 9, SMOKES 6, SPANK 5
ASTERISK 8, STREAKS 7, SKATES 6
THEATRIC 8, CHATTER 7, HEROIC 6
TOOTSIES 8, STETSON 7, INSETS 6
$75 + 50 + 6 = 131; 131 \times 7 = 917; 917 + 10 = 927$
$(6 + 2) \times 25 = 200; (200 + 1) \times (3 + 1) = 804$
PREFACING

Round 327

SKIMPIER 8, SPIKIER 7, PERILS 6
BEEHIVES 8, SHEBEEN 7, ENVIES 6
PENLIGHT 8, HELPING 7, PLIGHT 6
XENOGAMY 8, EXOGAMY 7, OXYGEN 6
$100 + 8 + 3 = 111; 8 - (75/25) = 5; 111 \times 5 = 555$
$(10 + 1) \times (4 \times 3) = 132; 132 \times 7 = 924; 924 + 2 = 926$
IRRITABLE

Round 328

FLAMINGO 8, FOULING 7, FUMING 6
LOBELIAS 8, ABSOLVE 7, VILLAS 6
BRIMSTONE 9, BROMINES 8, MONSTER 7
OPERATIC 8, PYRETIC 7, TROPIC 6
$(10 - 4) \times 4 = 24; 24 \times 25 = 600; 600 - (9 - 7) = 598$
$(8 \times 50) + 25 = 425; 425 + (6 \times 2) = 437$
LUDICROUS

Round 329

REVISION 8, VIRGINS 7, SINGER 6
IDIOCY 6, ICILY 5, FOLD 4
UNLOADED 8, DUODENA 7, DELUDE 6
TOUGHIES 8, HOSTILE 7, LIGHTS 6
$(100 + 75) \times 5 = 875; 875 + 9 + 5 = 889$
$(9 - 5) \times 50 = 200; (200 + 7) \times 3 = 621; 621 + 7 = 628$
DIMENSION

Round 330

CONQUERED 9, ENCODER 7, ENDURE 6
ACCEPTIVE 9, PECCAVI 7, ICECAP 6
TOOTHACHE 9, HATCHET 7, CAHOOT 6
HANDBAGS 8, BASHING 7, BASING 6
$25 + 6 - 1 = 30; 3 \times 6 \times 30 = 540$
$9 - (10/10) = 8; 8 \times 100 = 800; 800 - (3 \times 4) = 788$
BARTERING

Round 331

MNEMONIC 8, INCOMER 7, MINCER 6
BURSARIES 9, BRUISERS 8, ABUSERS 7
SPONGIER 8, SPOKING 7, GRIPES 6
NETWORKED 9, KNOTWEED 8, TOWERED 7
$(100 + 75) \times 5 = 875; (50/5) + 1 = 11; 875 + 11 = 886$
$75 - 7 = 68 ; 68 \times 7 = 476; 476 + 8 = 484$
AMBULANCE

Round 332

AUDITIONS 9, ASTOUND 7, NUDIST 6
THERAPIST 9, HIPSTER 7, THIRST 6
FLATIRON 8, FRONTAL 7, FLORIN 6
UNFURLED 8, UNFIRED 7, REFUND 6
$7 \times (50 + 8) = 406; 406 - 10 = 396$
$(3 \times 25) + 9 = 84; 84 \times 8 = 672; 672 - (4 + 2) = 666$
PROMOTING

Round 333

SIXPENCE 8, EXPANSE 7, ENCASE 6
PERKIEST 8, PEEWITS 7, TWIRPS 6
DILIGENCE 9, CEILING 7, LEGEND 6
BULLFROG 8, GLOBULE 7, ROUBLE 6
$(75 + 50) \times 8 = 1000; 4 \times (100/25) = 16; 1000 - 16 = 984$
$(6 + 2) \times 75 = 600; 600 - (7 + 4) = 589$
RACONTEUR

Round 334

XENOLITH 8, PHOENIX 7, PLINTH 6
HABITUAL 8, HALIBUT 7, ALBEIT 6
TOMBSTONE 9, MOONSET 7, TOTEMS 6
ENORMOUS 8, CONSUME 7, MOROSE 6
$(8 + 2) \times 5 = 50; (9 \times 50) + 6 + 1 = 457$
$(9 \times 75) - 100 = 575; 10 - (50/25) = 8; 575 - 8 = 567$
UNWRITTEN

Round 335

DIREFUL 7, REFUND 6, FIRED 5
RHUBARB 7, RUBBER 6, RAVER 5
QUADRUPLE 9, PLAQUE 6, EQUAL 5
BUNKERED 8, BLUNDER 7, LENDER 6
$6 \times 2 = 12$; $12 \times (75 + 3) = 936$; $936 + (9 - 5) = 940$
$(2 \times 100) - 3 = 197$; $197 \times 4 = 788$; $788 + 50 + 7 = 845$
TORMENTED

Round 336

HOURLONG 8, HONOUR 6, ROUGH 5
ONWARD 6, WADER 5, YEAR 4
FLIPPANT 8, PANTILE 7, TIPPLE 6
DIAGNOSE 8, BEGONIA 7, SINGED 6
$(3 \times 25) + 5 = 80$; $9 \times 80 = 720$; $720 + (7 - 5) = 722$
$8 \times 8 \times 10 = 640$; $640 - (10 + 9) = 621$; $621 - 100 = 521$
WALLOPING

Round 337

ESPLANADE 9, SEAPLANE 8, ELAPSED 7
PERSONIFY 9, OSPREY 6, FIRES 5
MENTHOL 7, HELIUM 6, THINE 5
DISBURSE 8, SUBSIDE 7, BURIES 6
$(100 + 25) \times 7 = 875$; $(75/3) - 1 = 24$; $875 - 24 = 851$
$8 \times (100 - 4) = 768$; $768 + 6 + 3 = 777$
BODYGUARD

Round 338

NEWCOMER 8, ROMANCE 7, MENACE 6
ACADEMICS 9, CASCADE 7, MEDICS 6
GYROSCOPE 9, SCOOPER 7, CORPSE 6
SIMULCAST 9, MUSICALS 8, CULTISM 7
$6 + (6 - 4) = 8$; $8 \times (5 + 3) = 64$; $64 \times 9 = 576$
$75 + (7 \times 6) = 117$; $117 \times (100/50) = 234$
BOTHERING

Round 339

SLEUTHING 9, SUNLIGHT 8, LENGTHS 7
BUTCHERY 8, CAUTERY 7, CHERUB 6
SQUEAKIER 9, QUEASIER 8, ESQUIRE 7
THINKERS 8, THINNER 7, SHRINK 6
$(7 + 6) \times 75 = 975$; $(100/5) + 8 = 28$; $975 - 28 = 947$
$(25 + 1) \times 5 \times 4 = 520$; $520 - (2 + 2) = 516$
DEADLIEST

Round 340

AUTHORED 8, KATHODE 7, THREAD 6
FOCUSING 8, CONGIUS 7, FUSING 6
UNDERBID 8, INBRED 6, BRIDE 5
WETLANDS 8, SWEATED 7, WANTED 6
$(7 \times 9) - 9 = 54$; $54 \times 8 = 432$; $432 + 10/10 = 433$
$7 - (50/25) = 5$; $100 + 75 - 6 = 169$; $169 \times 5 = 845$
MORTALITY

Round 341

DRACONIC 8, CORNICE 7, CANCER 6
WARDROBE 8, ABORTED 7, BOATER 6
BYSTANDER 9, STANDBY 7, BETRAY 6
RIDICULE 8, LURCHED 7, HURDLE 6
$(9 \times 10) + 1 = 91$; $91 \times 8 = 728$; $728 - 2 = 726$
$100 - 75 = 25$; $8 \times 5 \times 25 = 1000$; $1000 - 7 = 993$
ATROPHIED

Round 342

QUICKIES 8, SICKIE 6, COKES 5
ALONGSIDE 9, GASOLINE 8, LEADING 7
OPERATIVE 9, OVEREAT 7, REPEAT 6
GUNFIGHT 8, HEFTING 7, NUGGET 6
$8 \times 25 = 200$; $200 - (7 + 2) = 191$; $191 \times 5 = 955$
$(100 + 7) \times (3 + 1) = 428$; $428 + 6/6 = 429$
FISHERMAN

Round 343

PHOSPHATE 9, TEASHOP 7, POTASH 6
DISEMBODY 9, DISOBEY 7, BODIES 6
STAMPEDE 8, MEDIATE 7, PASTED 6
SIDEWALK 8, WARLIKE 7, WADERS 6
$4 \times 4 \times 50 = 800$; $25 + (3 \times 5) = 40$; $800 - 40 = 760$
$75 - (100/25) = 71$; $9 \times 71 = 639$; $639 - (2 + 1) = 636$
EXAMINING

Round 344

MONSTERA 8, ALMONER 7, LAMENT 6
CACODEMON 9, CONDOM 6, NAMED 5
HOTHEADS 8, SHORTED 7, HOSTED 6
HYPERBOLE 9, OBEYER 6, PROBE 5
$(10 \times 10) - 5 = 95$; $95 \times 8 = 760$; $760 - 4 = 756$
$(6 + 5) \times 25 = 275$; $(275 - 1) \times 3 = 822$
PREJUDICE

Round 345

NEWSGIRL 8, WINGERS 7, RULING 6
EQUERRIES 9, REQUIRES 8, QUERIES 7
UNCHANGED 9, HANDGUN 7, CANNED 6
CORPORATE 9, OPERATOR 8, TROOPER 7
$9 \times (6 + 1) = 63$; $(8 \times 100) - 63 = 737$
$(10 \times 100) - 75 = 925$; $(50/5) + 8 = 18$; $925 + 18 = 943$
BILLIARDS

Round 346

WAFFLING 8, FINAGLE 7, FLANGE 6
FOOTBALL 8, FLOATEL 7, BALLOT 6
KEELHAUL 8, HECKLE 6, LEECH 5
VULGARITY 9, GRAVITY 7, GUILTY 6
$100 + (50/25) = 102$; $102 \times 6 = 612$; $612 + 75 + 5 = 692$
$(10 - 6) \times (100 + 9) = 436$; $436 - 9 = 427$
HEXAGONAL

Round 347

DISPENSED 9, DESPISED 8, PENISES 7
GUIDELINE 9, ELUDING 7, LUNGED 6
SUITABLE 8, GIBLETS 7, STABLE 6
ABSORBED 8, ROASTED 7, DOBBER 6
$10 \times (75 + 10) = 850$; $(2 + 1) \times 2 = 6$; $850 - 6 = 844$
$4 \times (8 + 4) = 48$; $48 + 3 - 1 = 50$; $50 \times 7 = 350$
UNTIDIEST

Round 348

STEADFAST 9, FEASTED 7, STATED 6
SHRIEKED 8, SHAKIER 7, HARKED 6
LOVEBIRD 8, BROILED 7, BODILY 6
SIDEWARD 8, WEIRDOS 7, SADDER 6
$7 \times (100 + 8) = 756$; $756 - 75 = 681$
$100 + 25 + 8 = 133$; $133 \times 7 = 931$; $931 + 50 - 4 = 977$
APPLIANCE

Round 349

IGNOMINY 8, MIXING 6, MINGY 5
THRILLED 8, RALLIED 7, TALLER 6
PICKETED 8, EXCITED 7, TICKED 6
COUNTRIES 9, COUNTIES 8, SECTION 7
$(8 - 6) \times 50 = 100$; $100 + (6 \times 3) = 118$; $118 \times 7 = 826$
$(8 + 1) \times 75 = 675$; $(4 \times 3) + 5 = 17$; $675 + 17 = 692$
BURDENING

Round 350

QUIXOTIC 8, TOXIC 5, QUIT 4
ORDINANCE 9, ORDNANCE 8, ANEROID 7
CONIFERS 8, INFUSER 7, CRONES 6
NIGHTWEAR 9, WATERING 8, WEARING 7
$2 \times (2 + 1) = 6$; $6 \times (75 - 1) = 444$; $444 + 100 = 544$
$8 \times 7 \times 2 = 112$; $112 - (6 - 5) = 111$; $111 \times 9 = 999$
DICHOTOMY

Round 351
CALAMARI 8, MALARIA 7, RACIAL 6
GROCERIES 9, CORRIES 7, CORGIS 6
HAILSTORM 9, MAILSHOT 8, MORTALS 7
EPITHET 7, PETITE 6, TEETH 5
$(75 + 1) \times (7 + 5) = 912; 912 - 100 = 812$
$(8 - 2) \times 75 = 450; 10 + 9 - 2 = 17; 450 - 17 = 433$
THRUSTING

Round 352
AVOUCHES 8, VOUCHER 7, CRAVES 6
DIURETIC 8, TRADUCE 7, DICIER 6
PYRAMID 7, IMAGED 6, PRIDE 5
TYPECAST 8, PATTIES 7, STATIC 6
$(4 \times 25) + 6 = 106; 106 \times (6 + 3) = 954; 954 - 1 = 953$
$(5 \times 50) + 100 = 350; (2 \times 10) - 1 = 19; 350 + 19 = 369$
DIFFIDENT

Round 353
ROISTERED 9, RESTORED 8, EDITORS 7
SHORELINE 9, HEROINES 8, INSHORE 7
SEDITION 8, NOSIEST 7, STONED 6
COMPANIES 9, CAMPIONS 8, MANIOCS 7
$9 \times (7 - 4) = 27; 27 \times 25 = 675; 675 + 7 + 5 = 687$
$75 + 6 = 81; 81 \times 4 \times 3 = 972; 972 + (3 \times 5) = 987$
FELONIOUS

Round 354
STICKLER 8, LICKERS 7, TICKLE 6
COVERTLY 8, OVERACT 7, CAVORT 6
KANGAROO 8, OREGANO 7, ANORAK 6
FOSTERING 9, FROSTING 8, FRINGES 7
$10 - (50/25) = 8; (8 \times 100) + (2 \times 9) = 818$
$3 \times 6 \times 50 = 900; 900 - 75 = 825; 825 + (4 \times 2) = 833$
CROISSANT

Round 355
PIPEWORK 8, WHOPPER 7, KIPPER 6
UNICORN 7, TURNIP 6, COUNT 5
ABSEILED 8, DISABLE 7, BLEEDS 6
DOCUMENT 8, MOUNTED 7, COATED 6
$(75 + 8) \times 9 = 747; 3 + (100/50) = 5; 747 - 5 = 742$
$(4 \times 25) - 5 = 95; 95 \times 10 = 950; 950 - (6/3) = 948$
POSTULATE

Round 356
GRIMALKIN 9, MAILING 7, LIKING 6
PLATINUM 8, SUNLAMP 7, PLANTS 6
MORTUARY 8, ARMOURY 7, YOGURT 6
LUMPIEST 8, PULSATE 7, IMPUTE 6
$(75 + 50) \times 5 = 625; 8 + (100/25) = 12; 625 + 12 = 637$
$5 \times (6 + 4) = 50; 2 \times 3 \times 50 = 300; 300 - 3 = 297$
FILLETING

Round 357
CAPONIZED 9, CANOPIED 8, ANODIZE 7
ROUGHAGE 8, GOPHER 6, GRAPE 5
DONATION 8, ANOINT 6, NINTH 5
STIGMATA 8, MATTING 7, SATING 6
$50 - 6 - 4 = 52; (10 + 5) \times 52 = 780; 780 + 1 = 781$
$(7 \times 25) + 2 + 1 = 178; 178 \times (2 + 1) = 534$
PAGEANTRY

Round 358
TUTORING 8, TOUTING 7, RATING 6
TINCTURE 8, CURTAIN 7, CUTTER 6
OUTCLASS 8, LOCUSTS 7, CLOUTS 6
CREATURES 9, TERRACES 8, RESCUER 7
$75 + 3 = 78; (7 + 5) \times 78 = 936; 936 + 8 - 1 = 943$
$100 + 5 + 4 - 1 = 108; 108 \times 8 = 864; 864 + 75 = 939$
GERMINATE

Round 359
SHINBONE 8, HONKIES 7, BONNIE 6
CARPAL 6, PLACE 5, FLAP 4
ENTIRETY 8, NATTIER 7, YTTRIA 6,
IMPURITY 8, IMPUTER 7, PUTTER 6
$7 \times 25 = 175; 5 - (9 - 7) = 3; (175 - 3) \times 5 = 860$
$(75 + 8) \times 4 = 332; (50/25) + 7 = 9; 332 + 9 = 341$
MANHANDLE

Round 360
ACQUIRED 8, QUADRIC 7, CIRQUE 6
VISITED 7, DIVEST 6, TIDES 5
FRACTURE 8, REFUTAL 7, CRATER 6
STOPPAGE 8, STOPGAP 7, POSTAGE 6
$3 - (9 - 8) = 2; (50 - 2) \times 4 = 192; 192 \times 4 = 768$
$100 + 25 - 8 = 117; 117 \times 5 = 585; 585 - (2 \times 7) = 571$
SLITHERED

Round 361
WORDIEST 8, TWIRLED 7, STORED 6
CARDIGAN 8, CARPING 7, PACING 6
GRANIVORE 9, AVERRING 8, VINEGAR 7
TUMBLERS 8, BOLSTER 7, ROUBLE 6
$(75 + 25) \times 8 = 800; 800 + 50 + 1 = 851$
$2 \times (75 + 6) = 162; (162 + 2) \times 6 = 984; 984 + 5 = 989$
EARNESTLY

Round 362
UNIFORM 7, FLORIN 6, FLOOR 5
ABROGATE 8, ALGEBRA 7, BORAGE 6
LYRICAL 7, PIRACY 6, CURLY 5
NOBLEMAN 8, NOMINAL 7, OILMAN 6
$9 + 9 + 3 = 21; 21 \times 5 = 105; (105 \times 7) - 1 = 734$
$(5 \times 6) + 10 = 40; (40 - 3) \times 25 = 925; 925 + 8 = 933$
GIBBERISH

Round 363
OUTDOING 8, HOOTING 7, OUTING 6
INDULGENT 9, UNTINGED 8, TINGLED 7
AMORTISED 9, READMITS 8, MISREAD 7
SHELTERED 9, STREELED 8, SHEETED 7
$(8 + 6) \times 50 = 700; 700 + 2 = 702; 702 + (100/4) = 727$
$75 + 5 + 4 = 84; (100/25) \times 84 = 336; 336 + 50 = 386$
TORTURING

Round 364
FRIGIDITY 9, RIGIDITY 8, DRIFTY 6
SATIRICAL 9, LARIATS 7, RACIST 6
CREVICES 8, DEVICES 7, DIVERS 6
PLAYGIRL 8, GORILLA 7, PILLAR 6
$3 \times 50 = 150; 150 + 5 + 1 + 1 = 157; 157 \times 6 = 942$
$3 \times (100 + 9) = 327; (75/25) \times 327 = 981; 981 + 6 = 987$
SLIPPIEST

Round 365
OUTERMOST 9, MUTTERS 7, TOTEMS 6
CARNIVORE 9, VERONICA 8, CORVINE 7
ENSURING 8, SNORING 7, REGION 6
GOURMAND 8, MAUNDER 7, MANGER 6
$(6 \times 10) - 1 = 59; 59 \times 7 = 413; 413 - 5 = 408$
$25 + 5 + 7 = 37; 37 \times 3 = 111; 111 \times 8 = 888$
TAWDRIEST

Round 366
MERINGUE 8, REEDING 7, NUDGER 6
RAMBLING 8, LAMBING 7, MARGIN 6
NONPAREIL 9, PRALINE 7, ALPINE 6
FROLICKED 9, FIRELOCK 8, FLOCKED 7
$(7 \times 7) + 6 = 55; 55 + 50 = 105; 105 \times 5 = 525$
$4 \times 10 \times 25 = 1000; 1000 - 75 + 3 = 928$
CULTIVATE

Round 367

DREAMIEST 9, DIAMETER 8, EMIRATE 7
INFLATED 8, FLATBED 7, FINALE 6
DOWNPOUR 8, REWOUND 7, PONDER 6
LISTENERS 9, TIRELESS 8, STERILE 7
$100 - (2 + 2) = 96$; $96 \times 9 = 864$; $864 - 25 = 839$
$(50/5) - 7 = 3$; $100 + 25 - 3 = 122$; $122 \times 8 = 976$
ENGRAVING

Round 368

AWARENESS 9, ANSWERS 7, SNARES 6
MULLIGAN 8, LUMPING 7, IMPUGN 6
MAELSTROM 9, MARMOSET 8, STAMMER 7
CRUMBIEST 9, RESUBMIT 8, TIMBERS 7
$8 \times 9 = 72$; $720 - 100 = 620$; $620 + (9 - 8) = 621$
$75 - (25 + 7) = 43$; $43 \times 10 = 430$; $430 + 9 + 3 = 442$
GODPARENT

Round 369

SHALLOTS 8, ASSHOLE 7, SLATES 6
ANARCHIST 9, ARTISAN 7, CHANTS 6
STUNTMAN 8, MUTANTS 7, ASTUTE 6
INJURIES 8, INJURES 7, SQUIRE 6
$100 - (75 + 6) = 19$; $19 \times 50 = 950$; $950 - (8 + 7) = 935$
$(4 \times 25) - 6 = 94$; $94 \times 9 = 846$; $846 + 3 = 849$
SEXUALITY

Round 370

RAINCOAT 8, OCARINA 7, TARMAC 6
PLUMPEST 8, UPTEMPO 7, SUPPLE 6
CASTIGATE 9, AGITATES 8, CAGIEST 7
ACTUALISE 9, ELASTIC 7, CASTLE 6
$9 \times (100 - 8) = 828$; $828 - 50 = 778$; $778 - 2 = 776$
$7 \times 25 = 175$; $(175 - 8) \times 4 = 668$; $668 + 1 = 669$
DISMEMBER

Round 371

RYEBREAD 8, BARRED 6, RAZED 5
KIDOLOGY 8, LOOKING 7, KINDLY 6
ENERGETIC 9, ERECTING 8, GENERIC 7
TITILLATE 9, TILLITE 7, TATTLE 6
$(75 + 5) \times 8 = 640$; $640 + (50/25) = 642$
$(6 \times 75) + 8 + 2 = 460$; $(9 - 7) \times 460 = 920$
MAGNETISM

Round 372

NOSEGAYS 8, COYNESS 7, CONGAS 6
TOBOGGAN 8, BOOTING 7, OBTAIN 6
OUTSPREAD 9, POSTURED 8, SPORTED 7
BACTERIUM 9, MURICATE 8, TERBIUM 7
$6 \times 8 = 48$; $48 - (7 + 3) = 38$; $38 \times 25 = 950$
$9 \times 100 = 900$; $75 - (6/2) = 72$; $900 - 72 = 828$
TECHNIQUE

Round 373

MAKESHIFT 9, MISTAKE 7, FETISH 6
GOLDFISH 8, DOGFISH 7, FOLIOS 6
PALTERING 9, TRIANGLE 8, REAPING 7
ADVERSARY 9, ARRAYED 7, RADARS 6
$50 + 25 - 7 = 68$; $68 \times 10 = 680$; $680 - (5 + 4) = 671$
$75 \times 10 = 750$; $(100/25) + (50/10) = 9$; $750 - 9 = 741$
CURRENTLY

Round 374

MUTINEER 8, REUNITE 7, MINUET 6
CAVALIER 8, ARCHIVE 7, ACHIER 6
CULMINATE 9, CLIMATE 7, MANTLE 6
SEVERITY 8, RESPITE 7, PRIEST 6
$7 \times 7 \times 2 = 98$; $98 \times 6 = 588$; $588 + 3/3 = 589$
$75 - 2 = 73$; $(8 + 3) \times 73 = 803$; $803 - 3 - 1 = 799$
FORGIVING

Round 375

SUBFRAME 8, IMBRUES 7, FRAMES 6
DREARIER 8, RANDIER 7, ERRAND 6
STATICES 8, COSTATE 7, ATTICS 6
PRONATING 9, POIGNANT 8, PANTING 7
$(8 - (10/2) = 3$; $100 + 6 + 5 = 111$; $3 \times 111 = 333$
$(9 \times 100) - 50 = 850$; $7 + 4 + 1 = 12$; $850 + 12 = 862$
EBULLIENT

Round 376

INTERPLAY 9, INTERLAY 8, PENALTY 7
BEAVERED 8, BEHAVED 7, ADVERB 6
SACRIFICE 9, FAIRIES 7, SCARES 6
FURNISHED 9, HINDERS 7, REFUND 6
$7 + (6/6) = 8$; $8 \times (100 + 5) = 840$; $840 + 75 = 915$
$9 + 3 = 12$; $12 \times (50 + 1) = 612$; $612 - 1 = 611$
SMARMIEST

Round 377

SLINKIER 8, REDSKIN 7, KINDER 6
ABDOMINAL 9, BIMODAL 7, DOMIAN 6
ENCRUSTED 9, CENSURED 8, REDUCES 7
WOMANISE 8, WINSOME 7, MIAOWS 6
$100 + 50 - 10 = 140$; $140 \times 4 = 560$; $560 - (25 - 7) = 542$
$(9 \times 25) - 3 = 222$; $222 \times 4 = 888$; $888 - 1 = 887$
DISPORTED

Round 378

LUCIFERS 8, TRIFLES 7, ULCERS 6
SUBSIDES 8, BLISSED 7, BUSSED 6
CELLULOSE 9, COULEES 7, CELLOS 6
MELANOID 8, ABDOMEN 7, MOANED 6
$7 \times (50 - 6) = 308$; $308 + 4 = 312$; $312 \times (8 - 5) = 936$
$(10 \times 25) + 100 = 350$; $(5 \times 7) - 9 = 26$; $350 - 26 = 324$
COMBATING

Round 379

RAPTURED 8, UPRATED 7, REPAID 6
DROPPING 8, POURING 8, DOPING 6
NOTEPAPER 9, PROPANE 7, TOPPER 6
BALCONIES 9, SOCIABLE 8, BEACONS 7
$6 \times (8 + 1) = 54$; $(2 \times 54) + 3 = 111$; $111 \times 7 = 777$
$8 \times (100 + 5) = 840$; $(50/25) \times 3 = 6$; $840 + 6 = 846$
VICIOUSLY

Round 380

MYSTIQUE 8, MISTYPE 7, STUMPY 6
GOATHERD 8, THRONED 7, HANGER 6
IRRIGATE 8, FRIGATE 7, RAFTER 6
ABHORRENT 9, BROTHER 7, BANTER 6
$75 - 2 = 73$; $9 \times 73 = 657$; $657 - 1 = 656$
$(7 \times 25) - 10 = 165$; $165 \times 5 = 825$; $825 + 7 + 2 = 834$
DIVERTING

Round 381

OVERCAST 8, CAVORTS 7, CRAVES 6
SUFFOCATE 9, OUTFACES 8, OFFCUTS 7
POLLINATE 9, POLENTA 7, PLIANT 6
ANNOYING 8, BANNING 7, BONING 6
$(9 - 6) \times 7 = 21$; $21 + 10 = 31$; $31 \times 8 = 248$
$3 \times 100 = 300$; $75 - (5 - 2) = 72$; $300 + (72 \times 2) = 444$
FORTUNATE

Round 382

SAINTHOOD 9, TOADISH 7, DHOTIS 6
SEMANTIC 8, AMNESIC 7, MINCES 6
CUSTODIAN 9, DISCOUNT 8, ACTIONS 7
KNOWLEDGE 9, LEGEND 6, WOKEN 5
$(9 \times 10) - 10 = 80$; $80 - 75 = 5$; $9 \times 8 \times 5 = 360$
$3 \times (7 + 2) = 27$; $27 \times 25 = 675$; $675 + 4 = 679$
SCATTERED